Autodesk® Revit® 2021 Fundamentals for MEP

Learning Guide
Imperial Units - 1st Edition

AUTODESK.
Authorized Publisher

ASCENT - Center for Technical Knowledge®
Autodesk® Revit® 2021
Fundamentals for MEP
Imperial Units - 1ˢᵗ Edition

Prepared and produced by:

ASCENT Center for Technical Knowledge
630 Peter Jefferson Parkway, Suite 175
Charlottesville, VA 22911

866-527-2368
www.ASCENTed.com

Lead Contributor: Cherisse Biddulph

ASCENT - Center for Technical Knowledge (a division of Rand Worldwide Inc.) is a leading developer of professional learning materials and knowledge products for engineering software applications. ASCENT specializes in designing targeted content that facilitates application-based learning with hands-on software experience. For over 25 years, ASCENT has helped users become more productive through tailored custom learning solutions.

We welcome any comments you may have regarding this guide, or any of our products. To contact us please email: feedback@ASCENTed.com.

Contents

Preface

To take full advantage of Building Information Modeling, the *Autodesk® Revit® 2021: Fundamentals for MEP* guide has been designed to teach the concepts and principles of creating 3D parametric models of MEP system from engineering design through construction documentation.

This guide is intended to introduce users to the software's user interface and the basic HVAC, electrical, and piping/plumbing components that make the Autodesk Revit software a powerful and flexible engineering modeling tool. The guide will also familiarize users with the tools required to create, document, and print the parametric model. The examples and practices are designed to take the users through the basics of a full MEP project from linking in an architectural model to construction documents.

Topics Covered

- Working with the Autodesk Revit software's basic viewing, drawing, and editing commands.
- Inserting and connecting MEP components and using the System Browser.
- Review Revit file worksharing, terminology, and workflow.
- Working with linked Revit files and CAD files.
- Creating spaces and zones so that you can analyze heating and cooling loads.
- Creating HVAC networks with air terminals, mechanical equipment, ducts, and pipes.
- Creating plumbing networks with plumbing fixtures and pipes.
- Creating electrical circuits with electrical equipment, devices, and lighting fixtures and adding cable trays and conduits.
- Creating HVAC and plumbing systems with automatic duct and piping layouts.
- Testing duct, piping and electrical systems.
- Creating and annotating construction documents.
- Adding tags and creating schedules.
- Detailing in the Autodesk Revit software.

Prerequisites

- Access to the 2021.0 version of the software, to ensure compatibility with this guide. Future software updates that are released by Autodesk may include changes that are not reflected in this guide. The practices and files included with this guide might not be compatible with prior versions (e.g., 2020).

- This guide introduces the fundamental skills you need to learn the Autodesk Revit MEP software. It is highly recommended that users have experience and knowledge in MEP engineering and its terminology.

Note on Software Setup

This guide assumes a standard installation of the software using the default preferences during installation. Lectures and practices use the standard software templates and default options for the Content Libraries.

Students and Educators Can Access Free Autodesk Software and Resources

Autodesk challenges you to get started with free educational licenses for professional software and creativity apps used by millions of architects, engineers, designers, and hobbyists today. Bring Autodesk software into your classroom, studio, or workshop to learn, teach, and explore real-world design challenges the way professionals do.

Get started today - register at the Autodesk Education Community and download one of the many Autodesk software applications available.

Visit www.autodesk.com/education/home/

Note: Free products are subject to the terms and conditions of the end-user license and services agreement that accompanies the software. The software is for personal use for education purposes and is not intended for classroom or lab use.

Lead Contributor: Cherisse Biddulph

Cherisse is an Autodesk Certified Professional for Revit as well as an Autodesk Certified Instructor. She brings 15 years of industry, teaching and technical support experience to her role as a Learning Content Developer with ASCENT. With a passion for design and architecture, she received her Associate of Applied Science in Drafting and Design and worked in the industry assisting several firms with CAD Manager needs and getting others up to speed on the latest software. In 2004 she joined IMAGINiT as an Application Engineer (AE), where she developed custom training and provided support for customers. She transitioned from her work as an AE to the IMAGINIT Solution Center as a Senior Technical Support Specialist where she became proficient in AutoCAD, BIM 360, Navisworks, and Revit. Today, Cherisse continues to expand her knowledge in the ever-evolving AEC industry and the software used to support it.

Cherisse Biddulph has been the Lead Contributor for *Autodesk Revit: Fundamentals for MEP* since 2020.

In This Guide

The following highlights the key features of this guide.

Feature	Description
Practice Files	The Practice Files page includes a link to the practice files and instructions on how to download and install them. The practice files are required to complete the practices in this guide.
Chapters	A chapter consists of the following - Learning Objectives, Instructional Content, Practices, Chapter Review Questions, and Command Summary. • **Learning Objectives** define the skills you can acquire by learning the content provided in the chapter. • **Instructional Content**, which begins right after Learning Objectives, refers to the descriptive and procedural information related to various topics. Each main topic introduces a product feature, discusses various aspects of that feature, and provides step-by-step procedures on how to use that feature. Where relevant, examples, figures, helpful hints, and notes are provided. • **Practice** for a topic follows the instructional content. Practices enable you to use the software to perform a hands-on review of a topic. It is required that you download the practice files (using the link found on the Practice Files page) prior to starting the first practice. • **Chapter Review Questions**, located close to the end of a chapter, enable you to test your knowledge of the key concepts discussed in the chapter. • **Command Summary** concludes a chapter. It contains a list of the software commands that are used throughout the chapter and provides information on where the command can be found in the software.
Appendices	Appendices provide additional information to the main course content. It could be in the form of instructional content, practices, tables, projects, or skills assessment.

Practice Files

To download the practice files for this guide, use the following steps:

1. Type the URL *exactly as shown below* into the address bar of your Internet browser, to access the Course File Download page.

   Note: If you are using the ebook, you do not have to type the URL. Instead, you can access the page simply by clicking the URL below.

   ## https://www.ascented.com/getfile/id/ochlodes

2. On the Course File Download page, click the **DOWNLOAD NOW** button, as shown below, to download the .ZIP file that contains the practice files.

   DOWNLOAD NOW ▶

3. Once the download is complete, unzip the file and extract its contents.

   The recommended practice files folder location is:
   C:\Revit 2021 Fundamentals for MEP Practice Files

   Note: It is recommended that you do not change the location of the practice files folder. Doing so may cause errors when completing the practices.

Stay Informed!
To receive information about upcoming events, promotional offers, and complimentary webcasts, visit:
www.ASCENTed.com/updates

Chapter 1

Introduction to BIM and Autodesk Revit

Building Information Modeling (BIM) and the Autodesk® Revit® software work hand in hand to help you create smart, 3D models that are useful at all stages in the building process. Understanding the software interface and terminology enhances your ability to create powerful models and move around in the various views of the model.

Learning Objectives in This Chapter

- Describe the concept and workflow of Building Information Modeling in relation to the Autodesk Revit software.
- Navigate the graphic user interface, including the ribbon (where most of the tools are found), the Properties palette (where you make modifications to element information), and the Project Browser (where you can open various views of the model).
- Open existing projects and start new projects using templates.
- Use viewing commands to move around the model in 2D and 3D views.

1.1 BIM and Autodesk Revit

Building Information Modeling (BIM) is an approach to the entire building life cycle, including design, construction, and facilities management. The BIM process supports the ability to coordinate, update, and share design data with team members across disciplines.

The Autodesk Revit software is a true BIM product. It enables you to create complete 3D building models (as shown on the left in Figure 1–1) that provide considerable information reported through construction documents, and enables you to share these models with other programs for more extensive analysis.

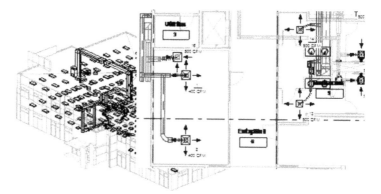

Figure 1–1

The Autodesk Revit software is considered a Parametric Building Modeler:

- *Parametric:* A relationship is established between building elements: when one element changes, other related elements change as well. For example, if you add an element in a plan view, it also displays in all of the other views.

- *Building:* The software is designed for working with buildings and the surrounding landscape, as opposed to gears or highways.

- *Modeler:* A project is built in a single file based on the 3D building model, as shown on the left in Figure 1–1. All views, such as plans (as shown on the right in Figure 1–1), elevations, sections, details, construction documents, and reports are generated based on the model.

- It is important that everyone who is collaborating on a project works in the same version and build of the software.

Workflow and BIM

BIM has changed the process of how a building is planned, budgeted, designed, constructed, and (in some cases) operated and maintained.

In the traditional design process, construction documents are created independently, typically including plans, sections, elevations, details, and notes. Sometimes, a separate 3D model is created in addition to these documents. Changes made in one document, such as the addition of a light fixture in a plan, have to be coordinated with the rest of the documents and schedules in the set, as shown in Figure 1–2.

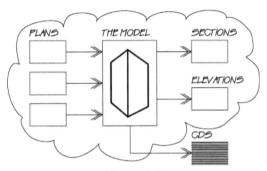

Figure 1–2

In BIM, the design process revolves around the model, as shown in Figure 1–3. Plans, elevations, and sections are simply 2D versions of the 3D model, while schedules are a report of the information stored in the model. Changes made in one view automatically update in all views and related schedules. Even Construction Documents update automatically with callout tags in sync with the sheet numbers. This is called bidirectional associativity.

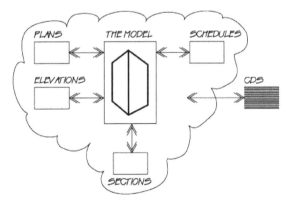

Figure 1–3

By creating complete models and associated views of those models, the Autodesk Revit software takes much of the tediousness out of producing a building design.

Revit Terms

When working in the Autodesk Revit software, it is important to know the typical terms used to describe items. Views and reports display information about the elements that form a project. There are three types of elements: Model, Datum, and View-specific, as shown in Figure 1–4 and described below:

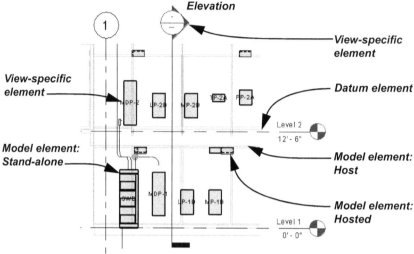

Figure 1–4

Views	Enable you to display and manipulate the model. For example, you can view and work in floor plans, ceiling plans, elevations, sections, schedules, and 3D views. You can change a design from any view. All views are stored in the project.
Reports	Reports, including schedules, gather information from the building model element that can be presented in the construction documents or used for analysis.
Model Elements	Include all parts of a building such as walls, floors, roofs, ceilings, doors, windows, plumbing fixtures, lighting fixtures, mechanical equipment, columns, beams, furniture, plants and many more. • Host elements support other categories of elements. • Hosted elements must be attached to a host element. • Standalone elements do not require hosts.
Datum Elements	Define the project context such as the levels for the floors and other vertical distances, column grids, and reference planes.
View-specific Elements	Only display in the view in which they are placed. The view scale controls their size. These include annotation elements such as dimensions, text, tags, and symbols as well as detail elements such as detail lines, filled regions, and 2D detail components.

- Autodesk Revit elements are "smart": the software recognizes them as walls, columns, plants, ducts, or lighting fixtures. This means that the information stored in their properties automatically updates in schedules, which ensures that views and reports are coordinated across an entire project, and are generated from a single model.

Revit and Construction Documents

In the traditional workflow, the most time-consuming part of the project is the construction documents. With BIM, the base views of those documents (i.e., plans, elevations, sections, and schedules) are produced automatically and update as the model is updated, saving hours of work. The views are then placed on sheets that form the construction document set.

For example, a floor plan is duplicated. Then, in the new view, all but the required categories of elements are hidden or set to halftone and annotations are added. The plan is then placed on a sheet, as shown in Figure 1–5.

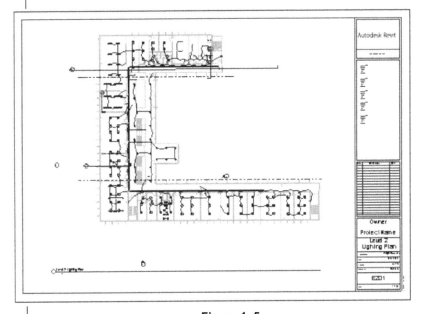

Figure 1–5

- Work can continue on a view and is automatically updated on the sheet.

- Annotating views in the preliminary design phase is often not required. You might be able to wait until you are further along in the project.

1.2 Overview of the Interface

The Autodesk Revit interface is designed for intuitive and efficient access to commands and views. It includes the ribbon, Quick Access Toolbar, Navigation Bar, and Status Bar, which are common to most of the Autodesk® software. It also includes tools that are specific to the Autodesk Revit software, including the Properties palette, Project Browser, and View Control Bar. Revit includes access to tools for architectural, mechanical, electrical, plumbing, and structural design but can be altered by utilizing the Customized Workspace. Setting up a Customized Workspace tailors your Revit environment to your specific discipline. A breakdown of the Revit interface is shown in Figure 1–6.

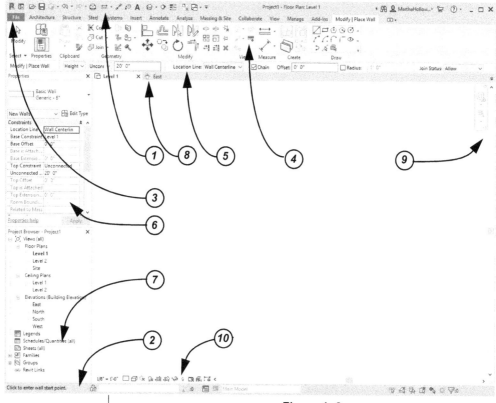

Figure 1–6

1. Quick Access Toolbar	6. Properties Palette
2. Status Bar	7. Project Browser
3. File tab	8. View Tabs
4. Ribbon	9. Navigation Bar
5. Options Bar	10. View Control Bar

For more information on how to use BIM 360 inside Revit, refer to the ASCENT guide Autodesk BIM 360: Fundamentals.

The Home Screen

When you first open the Autodesk Revit software, the **Home** screen displays, showing recently used projects and families, as well as links to BIM 360 files, as shown in Figure 1–7.

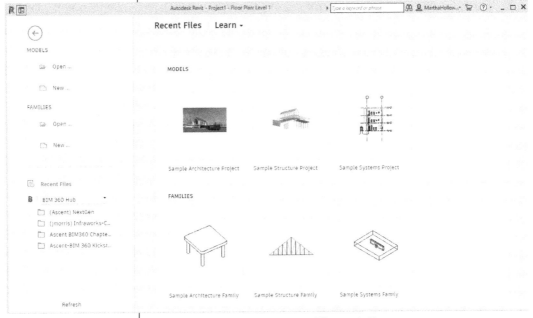

Figure 1–7

- Click on the picture to open a recent project. Hover over the name of the file, to display additional information.

- In the Quick Access Toolbar, click ▥ (Home) to return to the screen.

- In the Home screen, click ⟲ (Back) to return to the active model.

- Press **<Ctrl>+<D>** to toggle between the Home screen and active model.

1. Quick Access Toolbar

The Quick Access Toolbar (shown in Figure 1–8) includes commonly used commands, such as **Home, Open**, **Save**, **Undo**, **Redo,** and **Print**. It also includes frequently used annotation tools, including Measuring tools, **Aligned Dimension**, **Tag by Category**, and **Text**. Viewing tools, including several different 3D Views and **Sections**, are also easily accessed here.

Figure 1–8

Hint: Customizing the Quick Access Toolbar

Right-click on the Quick Access Toolbar to change the docked location of the toolbar to be above or below the ribbon, or to add, relocate, or remove tools on the toolbar. You can also right-click on a tool in the ribbon and select **Add to Quick Access Toolbar**, as shown in Figure 1–9.

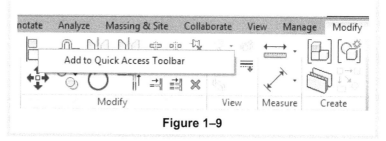

Figure 1–9

The top toolbar also hosts the InfoCenter (as shown in Figure 1–10), which includes the Autodesk sign-in, access to the Autodesk App Store, and Help options. A search field, as shown in Figure 1–11, is also available to find help on the web

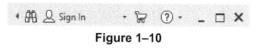

Figure 1–10

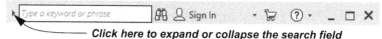

Click here to expand or collapse the search field

Figure 1–11

2. Status Bar

The Status Bar provides information about the current process, such as the next step for a command, as shown in Figure 1–12.

Click to enter wall start point.

Enter wall end point. (SZ) to close loop. Space flips orientation.

Figure 1–12

- Other options in the Status Bar are related to Worksets and Design Options (advanced tools), as well as selection methods and filters.

Hint: Shortcut Menus

Shortcut menus help you to work smoothly and efficiently by enabling you to quickly access required commands. These menus provide access to basic viewing commands, recently used commands, and the available Browsers, as shown in Figure 1–13. Additional options vary depending on the element or command that you are using.

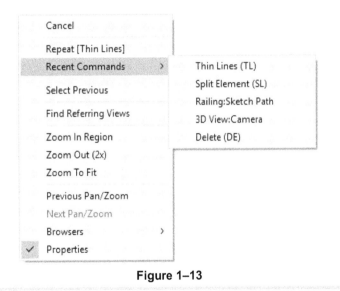

Figure 1–13

For more information on how to use Cloud Model inside Revit, refer to the ASCENT guide Autodesk BIM 360: Fundamentals.

If you click the primary icon rather than the arrow, it starts the default command.

3.File Tab

The *File* tab of the ribbon provides access to file commands, settings, and documents, as shown in Figure 1–14. Hover the cursor over a command to display a list of additional tools.

Figure 1–14

- To display a list of recently used documents, click

  (Recent Documents). The documents can be reordered as shown in Figure 1–15.

Click (Pin) next to a document name to keep it available.

Figure 1–15

- To display a list of open documents and views, click
  (Open Documents). The list displays the documents and views that are open, as shown in Figure 1–16.

You can use the Open Documents list to change between views.

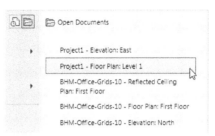

Figure 1–16

- Click (Close) to close the current project.

- At the bottom of the menu, click **Options** to open the Options dialog box or click **Exit Revit** to exit the software.

4. Ribbon

The ribbon contains tools in a series of tabs and panels as shown in Figure 1–17. Selecting a tab displays a group of related panels. The panels contain a variety of tools, grouped by task.

Figure 1–17

When you start a command that creates new elements or you select an element, the ribbon displays the *Modify | contextual* tab. This contains general editing commands and command specific tools, as shown in Figure 1–18.

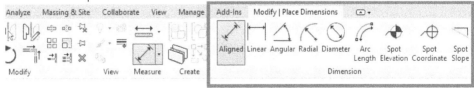

Contextual tab

Figure 1–18

- When you hover over a tool on the ribbon, tooltips display the tool's name and a short description. If you continue hovering over the tool, a graphic displays (and sometimes a video), as shown in Figure 1–19.

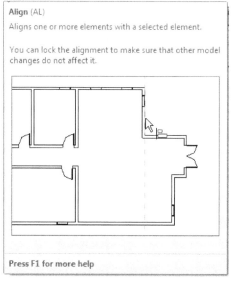

Figure 1–19

- Many commands have shortcut keys. For example, type **AL** for **Align** or **MV** for **Move**. They are listed next to the name of the command in the tooltips. Do not press <Enter> when typing shortcuts.

- To arrange the order in which the ribbon tabs are displayed, select the tab, hold <Ctrl>, and drag it to a new location. The location is remembered when you restart the software.

- Any panel can be dragged by its title into the view window to become a floating panel. Click the **Return Panels to Ribbon** button (as shown in Figure 1–20) to reposition the panel in the ribbon.

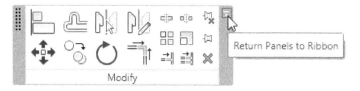

Figure 1–20

Hint: You are always in a command when using the Autodesk Revit software

When you are finished working with a tool, you typically default back to the **Modify** command. To end a command, use one of the following methods:

- In any tab on the ribbon, click ⬚ (Modify).
- Press <Esc> once or twice to revert to **Modify**.
- Right-click and select **Cancel...** once or twice.
- Start another command.

5. Options Bar

The Options Bar displays options that are related to the selected command or element. For example, when the **Rotate** command is active, the bar displays options for rotating the selected elements, as shown at the top in Figure 1–21. When the **Place Dimensions** command is active, the bar displays dimension-related options, as shown at the bottom in Figure 1–21.

Options Bar for Rotate command

Options Bar for Dimension command

Figure 1–21

6. Properties Palette

The Properties palette contains several parts, as shown in Figure 1–22. The Type Selector can be found at the top, which enables you to choose the size or style of the element you are adding or modifying. The options available on the palette enable you to make changes to information (parameters). There are two types of properties:

- **Instance Properties** are set for the individual element(s) you are creating or modifying.

- **Type Properties** control options for all elements of the same type. If you modify these parameter values, all elements of the selected type change.

The Properties palette is usually kept open while working on a project to easily permit changes at any time. If it does not display, in the Modify tab>Properties panel,

click (Properties) *or type* **PP.**

Some parameters are only available when you are editing an element. They are grayed out when unavailable.

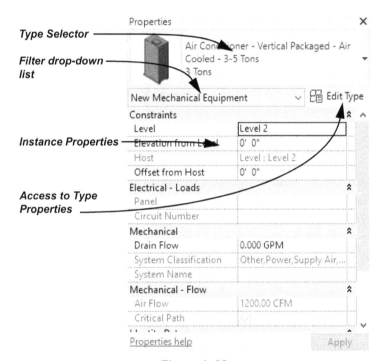

Figure 1–22

- Options for the current view display if the **Modify** command is active, but you have not selected an element.

- If a command or element is selected, the options for the associated element display.

- You can save the changes by moving the cursor off of the palette, by pressing <Enter>, or by clicking **Apply**.

- When you start a command or select an element, you can set the element type in the Type Selector, as shown in Figure 1–23.

You can limit what shows in the drop-down list by typing in the search box.

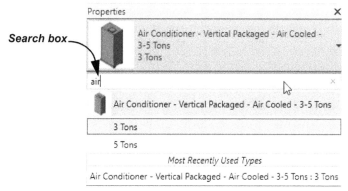

Figure 1–23

- When multiple elements are selected, you can filter the type of elements that display using the drop-down list, as shown in Figure 1–24.

The Properties palette can be placed on a second monitor, or floated, resized, and docked on top of the Project Browser or other dockable palettes, as shown in Figure 1–25. Click the tab to display its associated panel.

Figure 1–24   **Figure 1–25**

7. Project Browser

The Project Browser lists all views of the model in which you can work (as shown in Figure 1–26) and any additional views that you create, such as floor plans, ceiling plans, 3D views, elevations, sections, etc. It also includes schedules, legends, sheets (for plotting), lists of families by category, groups, and Autodesk Revit Links.

The Project Browser displays the name of the active project.

Figure 1–26

MEP projects are subdivided by discipline.

- To open a view, double-click on the view name or right-click and select **Open**.

- To rename a view, slowly double-click on the view name and the text highlights as shown in Figure 1–27. You can also right-click on a view name and select **Rename...** or press <F2>.

To display the views associated with a view type, click ⊞ (Expand) next to the section name. To hide the views in the section, click ⊟ (Collapse). You can also expand and collapse sets using the shortcut menu, as shown in Figure 1–28.

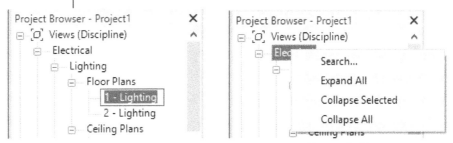

Figure 1–27   Figure 1–28

- If you no longer require a view, you can delete it. Right-click on its name in the Project Browser and select **Delete**.

- The Project Browser can be customized by changing the Browser Organization or its location within the application. The Project Browser can be floated, resized, and docked on top of the Properties palette.

How To: Search the Project Browser

1. In the Project Browser, right-click on a view and select **Search...**.
2. In the Search in Project Browser dialog box, type the words that you want to find (as shown in Figure 1–29) and click **Next**.
3. In the Project Browser, the first instance of that search displays, as shown in Figure 1–30.

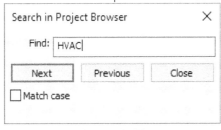

Figure 1–29

Figure 1–30

4. Continue using **Next** and **Previous** to move through the list.
5. Click **Close** when you are done.

Hint: Setting the Discipline of a View

In the default MEP templates, the Project Browser is set to display views sorted by discipline (preset) and sub-discipline (customizable). These are specified in the Properties of the view, as shown in Figure 1–31.

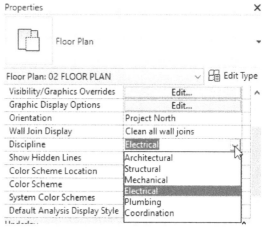

Figure 1–31

8. View Tabs

Each view of a project opens in its own tab and can be pulled out of the application window and moved to another monitor. Each view displays a Navigation Bar (for quick access to viewing tools) and the View Control Bar, as shown in Figure 1–32. You can drag tabs to other monitors.

In 3D views, you can also use the ViewCube to rotate the view.

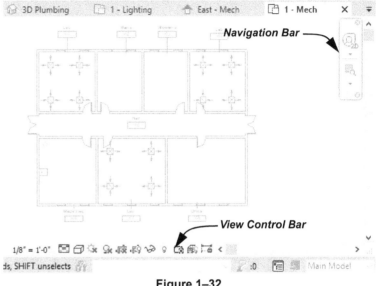

Figure 1–32

- Click on the tab to switch between views. You can also:
  - Press <Ctrl>+<Tab>.
  - Select the view in the Project Browser.
  - In the Quick Access Toolbar or *View* tab>Windows panel, expand ⬚ (Switch Windows) and select the view from the list.
  - Expand the drop-down list at the far end of the tabs, as shown in Figure 1–33.

Figure 1–33

- To close a tab, press the **X** that displays when you hover over the tab or the name in the list, as shown in Figure 1–33.

- To close all open views except the current view, in the Quick Access Toolbar or *View* tab>Windows panel, click 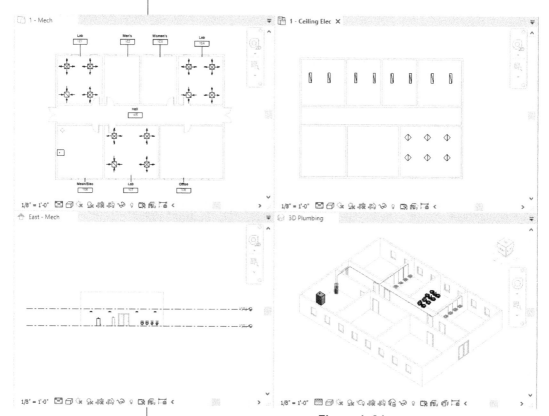 (Close Inactive Views). If you have multiple projects open, one view of each project remains open. If you have dragged a view to another monitor, that view will need to be manually closed by clicking the **X** in the upper right corner.

- You can switch between tabbed and tiled views, as shown in Figure 1–34. In the *View* tab>Windows panel, click (Tab Views) or (Tile Views).

Figure 1–34

- Drag the edge of tiled views to resize them. The other views resize to match.

9. Navigation Bar

The Navigation Bar enables you to access the 2D and Full Navigation (3D views) Wheels to navigate the view, as well as the Zoom in Region viewing commands, as shown in Figure 1–35.

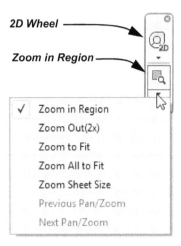

2D Wheel

Zoom in Region

Figure 1–35

10. View Control Bar

The View Control Bar (shown in Figure 1–36), displays at the bottom of each view window. It controls aspects of that view, such as the scale and detail level. It also includes tools that display parts of the view and hide or isolate elements in the view.

Figure 1–36

- The number of options in the View Control Bar change when you are in a 3D view, as shown in Figure 1–37.

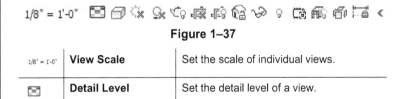

Figure 1–37

1/8" = 1'-0"	**View Scale**	Set the scale of individual views.
	Detail Level	Set the detail level of a view.
	Visual Style	Various graphic style representations.

	Sun Path On/Off	Controls the visibility of the sun's path.
	Shadows On/Off	Controls elements' shadow visibility in a view.
	Show/Hide Rendering Dialog	Available in 3D only. Shows or hides the rendering dialog box.
	Crop View	Define the crop boundaries for a view.
	Show/Hide Crop Region	Display the crop region in a view.
	Unlocked/Locked 3D Views	Lock a 3D view's orientation.
	Temporary Hide/Isolate	Temporarily isolate/hide by category or element.
	Reveal Hidden Elements	View hidden elements or unhide them in the active view.
	Worksharing Display	Available when worksharing is enabled. Controls display settings.
	Temporary View Properties	Enable, apply, or restore view properties and display recent templates and apply them.
	Show or Hide the Analytical Model	Only used for Structural and MEP to display the analytical information.
	Highlight Displacement Sets	Also known as exploded views.
	Reveal Constraints	Temporarily view the dimension and alignment constraints in the active view.
	Preview Visibility	Available in the Family Editor only. Controls the visibility of the preview.

1.3 Starting Projects

File operations to open existing files, create new files from a template, and save files in the Autodesk Revit software are found in the *File* tab, as shown in Figure 1–38.

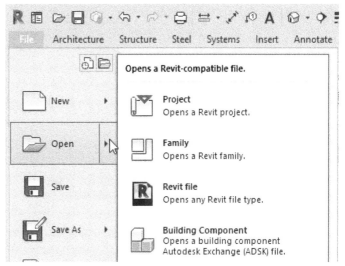

Figure 1–38

There are three main file formats:

- **Project files (.rvt):** These are where you do the majority of your work in the building model by adding elements, creating views, annotating views, and setting up printable sheets. They are initially based on template files.

- **Family files (.rfa):** These are separate components that can be inserted in a project. They include elements that can stand alone (e.g., a table or piece of mechanical equipment) or are items that are hosted in other elements (e.g., a door in a wall or a lighting fixture in a ceiling). Title block and Annotation Symbol files are special types of family files.

- **Template files (.rte and .rft):** These are the base files for any new project or family. Project templates hold standard information and settings for creating new project files. The software includes several templates for various types of projects. You can also create custom templates. Family templates include base information for creating families. Template files are usually saved as a new file.

Opening Projects

To open an existing project, in the Quick Access Toolbar or *File* tab click 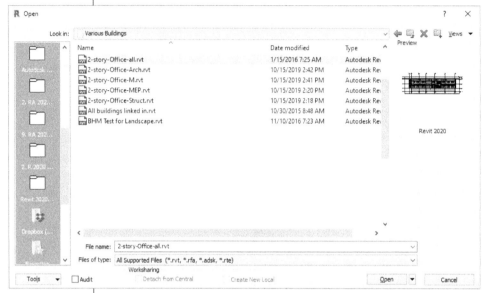 (Open), or press <Ctrl>+<O>. The Open dialog box opens (an example of the Open dialog box is shown in Figure 1–39), in which you can navigate to the required folder and select a project file.

Figure 1–39

- The software release version of the currently selected project displays below the preview. Do not open a drawing that should remain in an earlier version, as you cannot save back to previous versions.

  Note: It is important that everyone working on a project uses the same software version (e.g., 2021) and is on the same updated version (e.g., 2021.1). While your software may be able to open files created in its earlier versions, it will not be able to open files created in versions newer than the one you are using currently. For example, if you are working in Revit 2020, you cannot open a model created in Revit 2021.

- When you open a file created in an earlier version, the Model Upgrade dialog box (shown in Figure 1–40) indicates the release of a file and the release to which it will be upgraded. If needed, you can cancel the upgrade before it completes.

Figure 1–40

Hint: Opening Workset-Related Files

Worksets are used when the project becomes large enough for multiple people to work on it at the same time. At this point, a central file with multiple worksets (such as element interiors, building shell, and site) that are used by the project team members is created.

When you open a workset related file it creates a new local file on your computer as shown in Figure 1–41. Do not work in the main central file.

Figure 1–41

- For more information about opening and saving workset-related files, see *Section 3.1 Introduction to Worksets.*

- When you click on a central model showing on the Home screen, a local copy of the file is created.

- For more information on establishing and using Worksets, refer to the ASCENT guide *Autodesk Revit: Collaboration Tools.*

Starting New Projects

New projects are based on a template file. The template file includes preset levels, views, and some families, such as wall styles and text styles. Check with your BIM Manager about which template you need to use for your projects. Your company might have more than one based on the types of building that you are designing.

How To: Start a New Project

1. In the *File* tab, expand ⬜ (New) and click ⬜ (Project) (as shown in Figure 1–42), or press <Ctrl>+<N>.

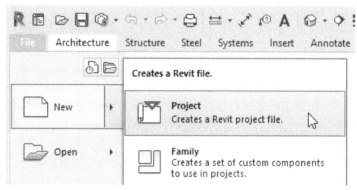

Figure 1–42

2. In the New Project dialog box (shown in Figure 1–43), select the template that you want to use and click **OK**.

The list of Template files is set in the Options dialog box in the File Locations pane. It might vary depending on the installed product and company standards.

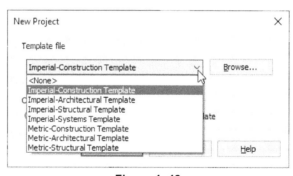

Figure 1–43

• You can select from a list of templates if they have been set up by your BIM Manager.

- You can add 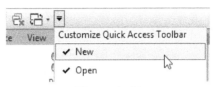 (New) to the Quick Access Toolbar. At the end of the Quick Access Toolbar, click ▼ (Customize Quick Access Toolbar) and select **New**, as shown in Figure 1–44.

Figure 1–44

Saving Projects

It is important to save your projects frequently. In the Quick Access Toolbar or *File* tab click 🖫 (Save), or press <Ctrl>+<S> to save your project. If the project has not yet been saved, the Save As dialog box opens, where you can specify a file location and name.

- To save an existing project with a new name, in the *File* tab, expand 🖫 (Save As) and click 🖺 (Project).

- If you have not saved in a certain amount of time, the software will notify you with the Project Not Saved Recently alert box, as shown in Figure 1–45. Select **Save the project**. If you want to set reminder intervals or not save at this time, select the other options.

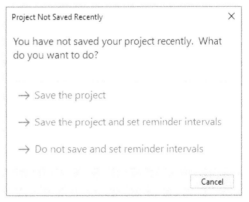

Figure 1–45

- You can set the *Save Reminder interval* to **15** or **30 minutes**, **1**, **2**, or **4 hours**, or to have **No reminders** display. In the *File* tab, click **Options** to open the Options dialog box. In the left pane, select **General** and set the interval as shown in Figure 1–46.

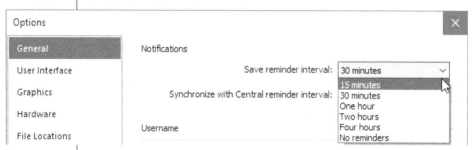

Figure 1–46

Saving Backup Copies

By default, the software saves a backup copy of a project file when you save the project. Backup copies are numbered incrementally (e.g., **My Project.0001.rvt**, **My Project.0002.rvt**, etc.) and are saved in the same folder as the original file. In the Save As dialog box, click **Options...** to control how many backup copies are saved. The default number is three backups. If you exceed this number, the software deletes the oldest backup file.

Hint: Saving Workset-Related Projects

If you use worksets in your project, you need to save the project locally and to the central file. It is recommended to save the local file frequently, just like any other file, and save to the central file every hour or so by synchronizing with the central file.

To synchronize your changes with the main file, in the Quick Access Toolbar expand 🔄 (Synchronize and Modify Settings) and click 🔄 (Synchronize Now). After you save to the central file, save the file locally again.

At the end of the day, or when you are finished with the current session, in the Quick Access Toolbar, expand 🔄 (Synchronize and Modify Settings) and click 🔄 (Synchronize and Modify Settings) to relinquish the files you have been working on to the central file.

• The maximum number of backups for workset-enabled files is set to 20 by default.

1.4 Viewing Commands

Viewing commands are crucial to working efficiently in most drawing and modeling programs and the Autodesk Revit software is no exception. Once in a view, you can use the Zoom controls to navigate in it. You can zoom in and out and pan in any view. There are also special tools for viewing in 3D.

Zooming and Panning

Using the Mouse to Zoom and Pan

Use the mouse wheel (shown in Figure 1–47) as the main method of moving around the models.

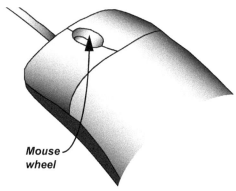

Mouse wheel

Figure 1–47

- Scroll the wheel on the mouse up to zoom in and down to zoom out.
- Hold the wheel and move the mouse to pan.
- Double-click on the wheel to zoom to the extents of the view.
- In a 3D view, hold <Shift> and the mouse wheel and move the mouse to rotate around the model.

- When you save a model and exit the software, the pan and zoom location of each view is remembered. This is especially important for complex models.

Zoom Controls

A number of additional zoom methods enable you to control the screen display. **Zoom** and **Pan** can be performed at any time while using other commands.

- You can access the **Zoom** commands in the Navigation Bar in the upper right corner of the view (as shown in Figure 1–48). You can also access them from most shortcut menus and by typing the shortcut commands.

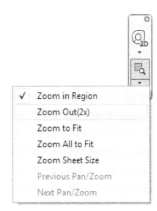 (2D Wheel) provides cursor-specific access to **Zoom** and **Pan**.

✓	Zoom in Region
	Zoom Out(2x)
	Zoom to Fit
	Zoom All to Fit
	Zoom Sheet Size
	Previous Pan/Zoom
	Next Pan/Zoom

Figure 1–48

Zoom Commands

	Zoom In Region (ZR)	Zooms into a region that you define. Drag the cursor or select two points to define the rectangular area you want to zoom into. This is the default command.
	Zoom Out(2x) (ZO)	Zooms out to half the current magnification around the center of the elements.
	Zoom To Fit (ZF or ZE)	Zooms out so that the entire contents of the project only display on the screen in the current view.
	Zoom All To Fit (ZA)	Zooms out so that the entire contents of the project display on the screen in all open views.
	Zoom Sheet Size (ZS)	Zooms in or out in relation to the sheet size.
N/A	**Previous Pan/Zoom (ZP)**	Steps back one **Zoom** command.
N/A	**Next Pan/Zoom**	Steps forward one **Zoom** command if you have done a **Previous Pan/Zoom**.

Viewing in 3D

Even if you started a project entirely in plan views, you can quickly create 3D views of the model, as shown in Figure 1–49. There are two types of 3D views: isometric views created by the **Default 3D View** command and perspective views created with the **Camera** command.

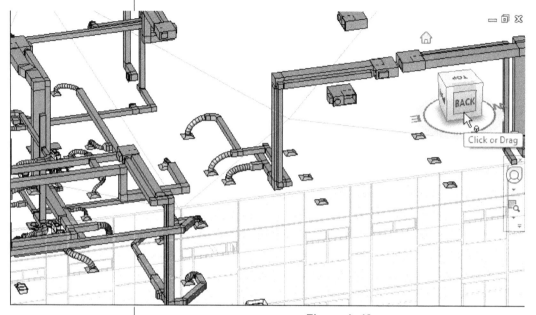

Figure 1–49

Working in 3D views helps you visualize the project and position some of the elements correctly. You can create and modify elements in both isometric and perspective 3D views, just as you can in plan views.

- Once you have created a 3D view, you can save it and easily return to it.

How To: Create and Save a 3D Isometric View

1. In the Quick Access Toolbar or *View* tab>Create panel, click
   🏠 (Default 3D View). The default 3D Southeast isometric view opens, as shown in Figure 1–50.

You can spin the view to a different angle using the mouse wheel or the middle button of a three-button mouse. Hold <Shift> as you press the wheel or middle button and drag the cursor.

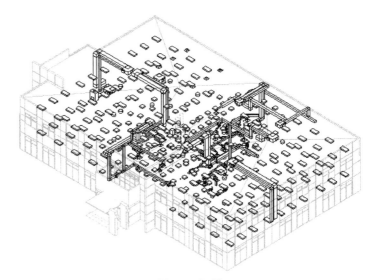

Figure 1–50

2. Modify the view to display the building from other directions.
3. In the Project Browser, double-click slowly or right-click on the {3D} view and select **Rename...**.
4. The name is placed in a text box with the original name highlighted, as shown in Figure 1–51. Type a new name in the Project Browser, as shown in Figure 1–52.

| **Figure 1–51** | **Figure 1–52** |

All types of views can be renamed.

- When changes to the default 3D view are saved and you start another default 3D view, it displays the Southeast isometric view once again. If you modified the default 3D view but did not save it to a new name, the **Default 3D View** command opens the view in the last orientation you specified.

How To: Create a Perspective View

1. Switch to a Floor Plan view.
2. In the Quick Access Toolbar or *View* tab>Create panel,

   expand 🏠 (Default 3D View) and click 📷 (Camera).
3. Place the camera on the view.
4. Click a second point to place the target in the direction in which you want it to shoot, as shown in Figure 1–53. The view displays as shown in Figure 1–54.

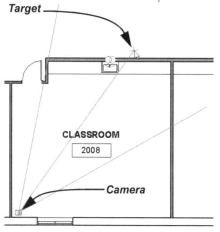

Figure 1–53

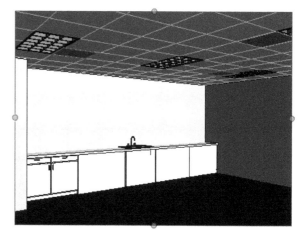

Figure 1–54

- Use the round controls to modify the display size of the view and press <Shift> + the mouse wheel to change the view.
5. In the Properties palette scroll down and adjust the *Eye Elevation* and *Target Elevation* as needed.

- If the view becomes distorted, reset the target so that it is centered in the boundary of the view (called the crop region).

  In the *Modify | Cameras* tab>Camera panel, click 🔄 (Reset Target).

Visual Styles

Any view can have a visual style applied. The **Visual Style** options found in the View Control Bar (as shown in Figure 1–55), specify the shading of the building model. These options apply to plan, elevation, section, and 3D views.

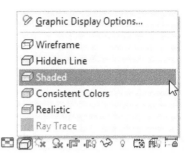

Figure 1–55

- ⬁ (Wireframe) displays the lines and edges that make up elements, but hides the surfaces. This can be useful when you are dealing with complex intersections.

- ⬁ (Hidden Line) displays the lines, edges, and surfaces of the elements, but it does not display any colors. This is the most common visual style to use while working on a design.

- ⬁ (Shaded) and ⬁ (Consistent Colors) give you a sense of the materials, including transparent glass. An example that uses Consistent Colors is shown in Figure 1–56.

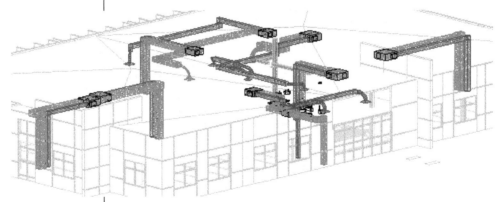

Figure 1–56

- ⬁ (Realistic) displays what is shown when you render the view, including RPC (Rich Photorealistic Content) components and artificial lights. It takes a lot of computer power to execute this visual style. Therefore, it is better to use the other visual styles most of the time as you are working.

- ⬁ (Ray Trace) is useful if you have created a 3D view that you want to render. It gradually moves from draft resolution to photorealistic. You can stop the process at any time.

Practice 1a | Open and Review a Project

Practice Objectives

- Navigate the graphic user interface.
- Manipulate 2D and 3D views by zooming and panning.
- Create 3D Isometric and Perspective views.
- Set the Visual Style of a view.

In this practice, you will open a project file, as shown in Figure 1–57, and display each of the various parts of the Autodesk Revit interface. You will open views through the Project Browser and switch between different views. You will also select elements and display the information about them in the Properties palette. Finally, you will create and save 3D views.

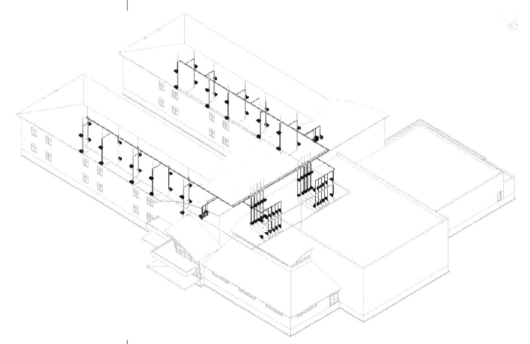

Figure 1–57

Task 1 - Open an Autodesk Revit MEP project and review it.

1. In the *File* tab, expand 📂 (Open) and click 🗔 (Project).

2. In the Open dialog box, navigate to the *Revit 2021 Fundamentals for MEP Practice Files\Introduction* folder and select **Review-School-MEP.rvt**, then click **Open**.

3. The project opens in the **3D Plumbing** view.

4. In the Project Browser, expand Mechanical>HVAC>Floor Plans, as shown in Figure 1–58.

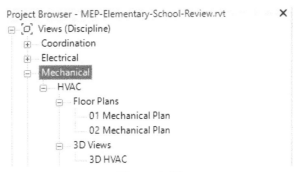

Figure 1–58

5. Double-click on **01 Mechanical Plan** to open up the floor plan view, as shown in Figure 1–59.

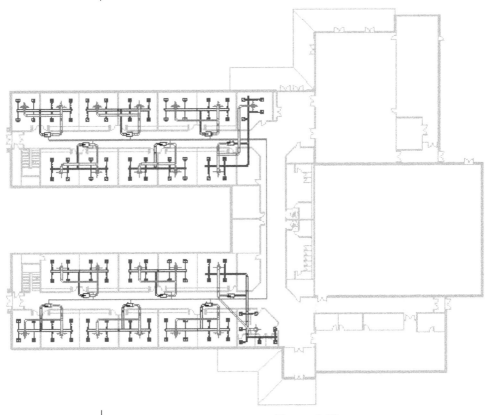

Figure 1–59

6. Use the middle mouse (scroll) wheel to zoom and pan around the view.

7. Double-click on the middle mouse (scroll) wheel or type **ZF** (Zoom to Fit) to return to the full view.

8. Expand Plumbing>Plumbing>Floor Plans and double-click on the **01 Plumbing Plan** view to open it.

9. Expand Coordination>MEP>Floor Plans and double-click on **01 Space Planning** to open this view.

10. All of the previous views are still open and can be see in the tabs, as shown in Figure 1–60.

| 3D Plumbing | 01 Mechanical Plan | 01 Plumbing Plan | 01 Space Planning ✕ |

Figure 1–60

11. In the *View* tab>Windows panel, click ⊟ (Tile Views) or type **WT** to display all of the open views on the screen at the same time.

12. Type **ZA** (Zoom All to Fit) to have the model display completely within each view window, as shown in Figure 1–61.

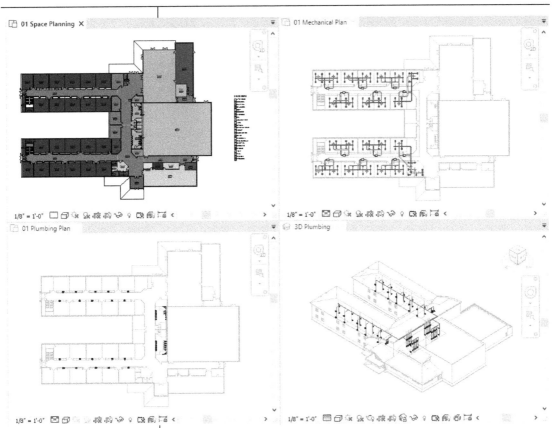

Figure 1–61

13. Click in the open **01 Mechanical Plan** view to make it active.

14. In the *View* tab>Windows panel, click ⬜ (Tab View) or type **TW**.

15. In the Quick Access Toolbar, click ▧ (Close Inactive Windows). Only the current active view is open.

Task 2 - Display the element properties.

1. In the **01 Mechanical Plan** view, hover over a duct without selecting it first. The duct highlights and a tooltip displays as shown in Figure 1–62. Information about the element also displays in the Status Bar but not in Properties.

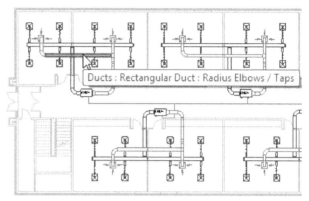

Figure 1–62

2. Click on the duct to select it. The selection color and tabs on the ribbon at the top of the screen change. Properties now displays information about this piece of ductwork, as shown in Figure 1–63.

Figure 1–63

3. Hold <Ctrl> and in the view, select another, similar Duct element, as shown in Figure 1–64. Properties now displays that two ducts (Ducts(2)) are selected with the same information.

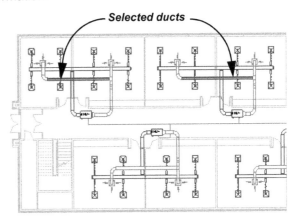

Figure 1–64

4. Hold <Ctrl> and select an air terminal. Properties now displays Common (3) in the Filter drop-down list, because the three selected elements are not of the same type. Therefore they do not share the same type of properties.

5. In Properties, expand the Filter drop-down list and select **Air Terminals**, as shown in Figure 1–65.

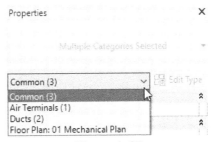

Figure 1–65

6. Only the Air Terminal properties are displayed, but the selection set has not changed. In the view they are all still selected.

7. End the command using one of the following methods:

   • In *Modify | Multi-Select* tab>Select panel, click

     ⬦ (Modify).

   • Press <Esc> twice.

   • Click in the view window (without selecting an element).

   • Right-click in the view window and select **Cancel**.

Task 3 - Create 3D views.

1. In the Quick Access Toolbar, click 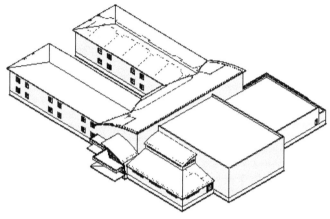 (Default 3D View).

2. A 3D Isometric view displays, as shown in Figure 1–66.

Figure 1–66

3. Press and hold <Shift> and press the middle mouse (scroll) button to orbit the view.

4. In the View Control Bar, select several different Visual Styles to see how they impact the view, as shown in Figure 1–67.

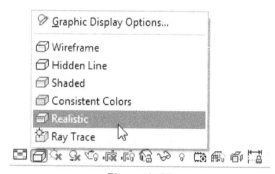

Figure 1–67

5. Select a view and visual style that you like. In the Project Browser, expand Coordination>All>**3D Views**, double-click on **{3D}** and name the view **3D Exterior** and click **OK**.

Task 4 - Create a camera view.

1. Switch back to the **01 Mechanical Plan** view.

2. In the Quick Access Toolbar, expand ⬡ (Default 3D View) and click 📷 (Camera).

3. Place the camera and select a point for the target similar to that shown in Figure 1–68.

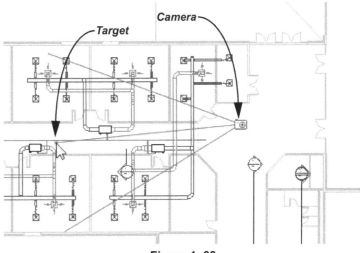

Figure 1–68

4. The new view displays. Use the controls on the outline of the view to resize the view.

5. Click inside the 3D view and use <Shift>+ mouse wheel to rotate around until you get a good view of the ductwork.

6. Set the Visual Style, as required.

7. In the Project Browser, expand Mechanical>???>3D Views and select the new **3D View 1**, as shown in Figure 1–69.

The new view displays in the ??? category because it has not been assigned a Sub-Discipline.

Figure 1–69

8. In Properties, in the *Graphics* area, expand *Sub-Discipline* and select **HVAC**, as shown in Figure 1–70.

9. Click **Apply**. The view moves to the correct sub-discipline group, as shown in Figure 1–71. Rename the view as required.

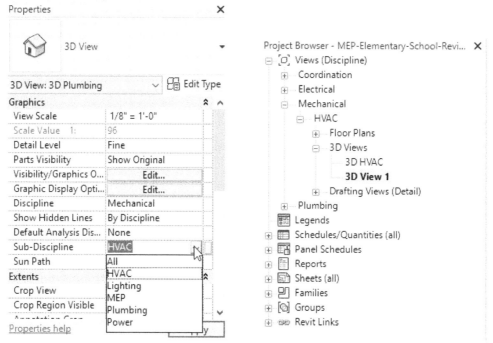

Figure 1–70	Figure 1–71

10. Save the project.

11. In the *File* tab, click ▭ (Close).

Chapter Review Questions

1. When you create a project in the Autodesk Revit software, do you work in 3D (as shown on the left in Figure 1–72) or 2D (as shown on the right in Figure 1–72)?

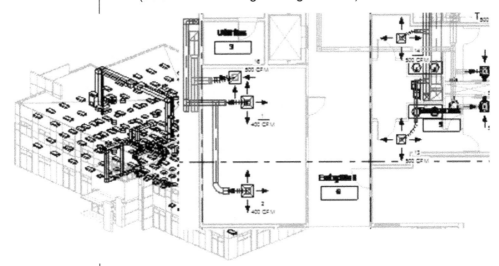

Figure 1–72

 a. You work in 2D in plan views and in 3D in non-plan views.

 b. You work in 3D almost all of the time, even when you are using what looks like a flat view.

 c. You work in 2D or 3D depending on how you toggle the 2D/3D control.

 d. You work in 2D in plan and section views and in 3D in isometric views.

2. What is the purpose of the Project Browser?

 a. It enables you to browse through the building project, similar to a walk through.

 b. It is the interface for managing all of the files that are required to create the complete architectural model of the building.

 c. It manages multiple Autodesk Revit projects as an alternative to using Windows Explorer.

 d. It is used to access and manage the views of the project.

3. Which part(s) of the interface changes when you start a command such as Wall, Beam, or Duct? (Select all that apply.)

   a. Ribbon

   b. View Control Bar

   c. Options Bar

   d. Properties Palette

4. What is the difference between Type Properties and Properties? (The ribbon location is shown in Figure 1–73.)

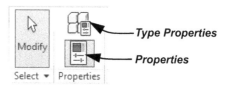

Figure 1–73

   a. Properties stores parameters that apply to the selected individual element(s). Type Properties stores parameters that impact every element of the same type in the project.

   b. Properties stores the location parameters of an element. Type Properties stores the size and identity parameters of an element.

   c. Properties only stores parameters of the view. Type Properties stores parameters of model components.

5. When you start a new project, how do you specify the base information in the new file?

   a. Transfer the base information from an existing project.

   b. Select the right template for the task.

   c. The Autodesk Revit software automatically extracts the base information from imported or linked file(s).

6. What is the main difference between a view made using

   (Default 3D View) and a view made using (Camera)?

   a. Use Default **3D View** for exterior views and **Camera** for interiors.

   b. **Default 3D View** creates a static image and a **Camera** view is live and always updated.

   c. **Default 3D View** is isometric and a **Camera** view is perspective.

   d. **Default 3D View** is used for the overall building and a **Camera** view is used for looking in tight spaces.

Command Summary

Button	Command	Location
General Tools		
	Close	• **File tab**
	Home	• Quick Access Toolbar • **Shortcut:** <Ctrl>+<D>
	Modify	• **Ribbon:** All tabs>Select panel • **Shortcut:** MD
	New	• *File* **tab** • **Shortcut:** <Ctrl>+<N>
	Open	• **Quick Access Toolbar** • *File* **tab** • **Shortcut:** <Ctrl>+<O>
	Open Documents	• *File* **tab**
	Properties	• **Ribbon:** *Modify* tab>Properties panel • **Shortcut:** PP
	Recent Documents	• *File* **tab**
	Save	• **Quick Access Toolbar** • *File* **tab** • **Shortcut:** <Ctrl>+<S>
	Save As	• *File* **tab**
	Synchronize and Modify Settings	• **Quick Access Toolbar**
	Synchronize Now	• **Quick Access Toolbar**>expand Synchronize and Modify Settings
	Type Properties	• **Ribbon:** *Modify* tab>Properties panel • **Properties palette**
Viewing Tools		
	Camera	• **Quick Access Toolbar**> Expand Default 3D View • **Ribbon:** *View* tab>Create panel> expand Default 3D View
	Close Inactive Views	• **Quick Access Toolbar** • **Ribbon:** *View* tab> Windows panel
	Default 3D View	• **Quick Access Toolbar** • **Ribbon:** *View* tab>Create panel
	Home	• **ViewCube**

N/A	Next Pan/Zoom	• **Navigation Bar** • **Shortcut Menu**
N/A	Previous Pan/Zoom	• **Navigation Bar** • **Shortcut Menu** • **Shortcut:** ZP
	Shadows On/Off	• **View Control Bar**
	Show Rendering Dialog/ Render	• **View Control Bar** • **Ribbon:** *View* tab>Graphics panel • **Shortcut:** RR
	Switch Windows	• **Quick Access Toolbar** • **Ribbon:** *View* tab> Windows panel
	Tab Views	• **Ribbon:** *View* tab> Windows panel • **Shortcut: TW**
	Tile Views	• **Ribbon:** *View* tab> Windows panel • **Shortcut: WT**
	Zoom All to Fit	• **Navigation Bar** • **Shortcut: ZA**
	Zoom in Region	• **Navigation Bar** • **Shortcut Menu** • **Shortcut:** ZR
	Zoom Out (2x)	• **Navigation Bar** • **Shortcut Menu** • **Shortcut:** ZO
	Zoom Sheet Size	• **Navigation Bar** • **Shortcut:** ZS
	Zoom to Fit	• **Navigation Bar** • **Shortcut Menu** • **Shortcut:** ZF, ZE
Visual Styles		
	Consistent Colors	• **View Control Bar:**
	Hidden Line	• **View Control Bar** • **Shortcut:** HL
	Ray Trace	• **View Control Bar:**
	Realistic	• **View Control Bar**
	Shaded	• **View Control Bar** • **Shortcut:** SD
	Wireframe	• **View Control Bar** • **Shortcut:** WF

Basic Sketching and Modify Tools

Basic sketching, selecting, and modifying tools are the foundation of working with all types of elements in the Autodesk® Revit® software, including components such as air terminals, plumbing fixtures, and electrical devices. Using these tools with drawing aids helps you to place and modify elements to create accurate building models.

Learning Objectives in This Chapter

- Learn how to place elements by incorporating drawing aids, such as alignment lines, temporary dimensions, and snaps.
- Place reference planes as temporary guide lines.
- Insert components such as mechanical equipment, plumbing fixtures, and electrical devices.
- Use techniques to select and filter groups of elements.
- Modify elements using a contextual tab, Properties, temporary dimensions, and controls.
- Move, copy, rotate, and mirror elements and create array copies in linear and radial patterns.
- Align, trim, and extend elements with the edges of other elements.
- Split linear elements anywhere along their length.
- Offset elements to create duplicates at a specific distance away from the original.

2.1 Using General Sketching Tools

When you start a command, the contextual tab on the ribbon, the Options Bar, and the Properties palette (shown in Figure 2–1) enable you to set up features for each new element you are placing in the project. As you start modeling, several features called *drawing aids* display, as shown in Figure 2–1. They help you to create designs quickly and accurately.

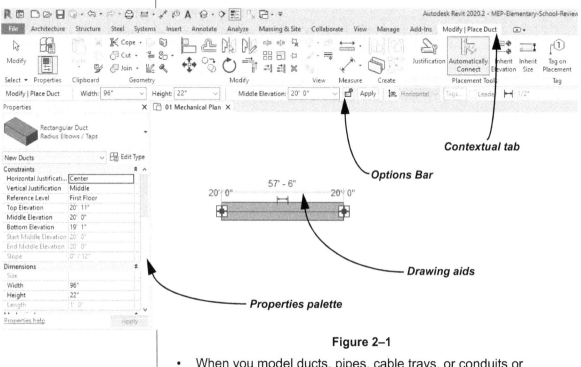

Figure 2–1

- When you model ducts, pipes, cable trays, or conduits or place elements such as air terminals, lighting fixtures or plumbing fixtures, you first need to:

  - Select a type from the Type Selector.
  - Set information in the Options Bar.
  - Check the Contextual tab for additional options.

Drawing Aids

As soon as you start sketching or placing elements, several drawing aids display, including:

- Alignment lines
- Temporary dimensions

- Snaps
- Connectors

These aids are available with most drawing and modification commands, as shown in Figure 2–2.

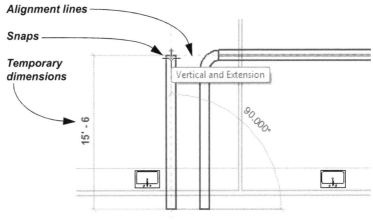

Figure 2–2

Alignment lines display as soon as you move the cursor over nearby elements. They help keep lines horizontal, vertical, or at a specified angle. They also line up with the implied intersections of walls and other elements.

- Hold <Shift> to force the alignments to be orthogonal (90 degree angles only).

Temporary dimensions display to help place elements at the correct length, angle and location.

- You can type in a value, or move the cursor until you see the dimension you want. Alternatively, you can place the element and then modify the value as needed.

- The length and angle increments shown vary depending on how far in or out the view is zoomed.

- For Imperial measurements (feet and inches), the software uses a default of feet. For example, when you type **4** and press <Enter>, it assumes 4'-0". For a distance such as 4'-6", you can type any of the following: **4'-6"**, **4'6**, **4-6**, or **4 6** (the numbers separated by a space). To indicate distances less than one foot, type the inch mark (") after the distance, or enter **0**, a space, and then the distance.

Hint: Temporary Dimensions and Permanent Dimensions

Temporary dimensions disappear as soon as you finish adding elements. If you want to make them permanent, select the

⊢ (dimension symbol) shown in Figure 2–3.

Figure 2–3

Snaps are key points that help you reference existing elements to exact points when drawing, as shown in Figure 2–4.

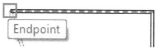

Figure 2–4

- When you move the cursor over an element, the snap symbol displays. Each snap location type displays with a different symbol.

Connectors work similar to snaps, but have more intelligence about the size, system, and flow of items (e.g., ducts, pipes, and electrical connections). For example, connectors automatically add fittings to ducts, such as the elbow, transition, and tee shown in Figure 2–5.

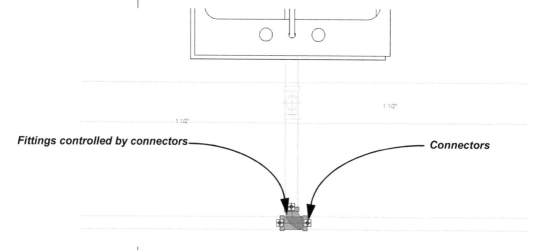

Figure 2–5

Hint: Snap Settings and Overrides

In the *Manage* tab>Settings panel, click 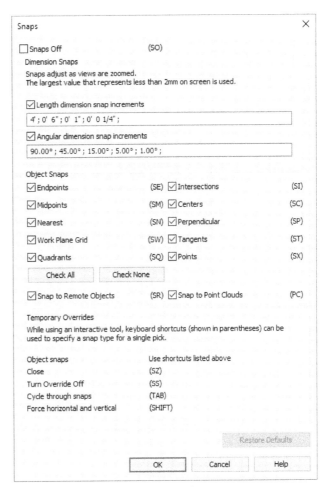 (Snaps) to open the Snaps dialog box, which is shown in Figure 2–6. The Snaps dialog box enables you to set which snap points are active, and set the dimension increments displayed for temporary dimensions (both linear and angular).

Snaps   ×

☐ Snaps Off   (SO)

Dimension Snaps

Snaps adjust as views are zoomed.
The largest value that represents less than 2mm on screen is used.

☑ Length dimension snap increments

    4' ; 0' 6" ; 0' 1" ; 0' 0 1/4" ;

☑ Angular dimension snap increments

    90.00° ; 45.00° ; 15.00° ; 5.00° ; 1.00° ;

Object Snaps

☑ Endpoints	(SE)	☑ Intersections	(SI)
☑ Midpoints	(SM)	☑ Centers	(SC)
☑ Nearest	(SN)	☑ Perpendicular	(SP)
☑ Work Plane Grid	(SW)	☑ Tangents	(ST)
☑ Quadrants	(SQ)	☑ Points	(SX)

    [Check All]   [Check None]

☑ Snap to Remote Objects   (SR) ☑ Snap to Point Clouds   (PC)

Temporary Overrides

While using an interactive tool, keyboard shortcuts (shown in parentheses) can be used to specify a snap type for a single pick.

Object snaps	Use shortcuts listed above
Close	(SZ)
Turn Override Off	(SS)
Cycle through snaps	(TAB)
Force horizontal and vertical	(SHIFT)

                                        [Restore Defaults]

            [OK]   [Cancel]   [Help]

Figure 2–6

• Keyboard shortcuts for each snap can be used to override the automatic snapping. Temporary overrides only affect a single pick, but can be very helpful when there are snaps nearby other than the one you want to use.

Reference Planes

As you develop designs in the Autodesk Revit software, there are times when you need lines to help you define certain locations. You can draw reference planes (which display as dashed green lines) and snap to them whenever you need to line up elements. For the example shown in Figure 2–7, the lighting fixtures in the reflected ceiling plan are placed using reference planes.

Reference planes do not display in 3D views.

- To insert a reference plane, in the *Systems* tab>Work Plane panel, click  (Ref Plane) or type **RP**.

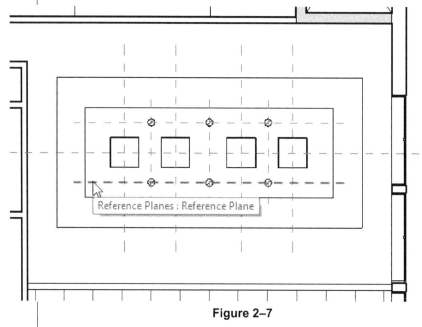

Figure 2–7

- Reference planes display in associated views because they are infinite planes, and not just lines.

- You can name Reference planes by clicking on **<Click to name>** and typing in the text box, as shown in Figure 2–8.

3D

Counter Top

<Click to name>   <Click to name>

3D

Figure 2–8

- If you sketch a reference pane in Sketch Mode (used with floors and similar elements), it does not display once the sketch is finished.

- Reference planes can have different line styles if they have been defined in the project. In Properties, select a style from the Subcategory list.

Hint: Measuring Tools

When modifying a model, it is useful to know the distance between elements. This can be done with temporary dimensions, or more frequently, by using the measuring tools found in the Quick Access Toolbar or on the *Modify* tab> Measure panel, as shown in Figure 2–9.

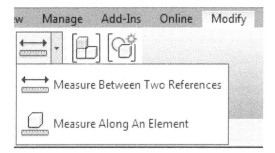

Figure 2–9

- (Measure Between Two References): Select two elements and the measurement displays.

- (Measure Along An Element): Select the edge of a linear element and the total length displays.

2.2 Inserting Components

Components (also known as families) are full 3D elements that can be placed at appropriate locations and heights, and which interact with the building elements around them. For example, a lighting fixture can be designed to be hosted by a face (such as a wall or ceiling), or to stand alone by itself, as shown in Figure 2–10. The Autodesk Revit software includes both architectural components (such as the lamp and wall sconces in Figure 2–10) and MEP components (such as the downlight fixtures) that include connectors.

*Components are located in family files with the extension .RFA. For example, a component family named **Wall Sconce.rfa** can contain several types and sizes.*

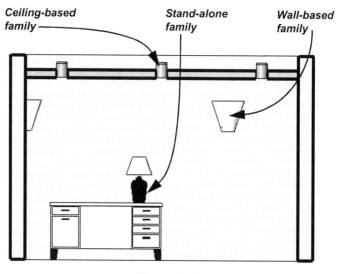

Figure 2–10

Most components are inserted using specific tools, including:

Exact steps for inserting specific components are covered later in this guide.

	Air terminal		Electrical Equipment
	Mechanical Equipment		Devices (Data, Fire Alarm, Switches, etc.)
	Plumbing Fixture		Lighting Fixtures
	Sprinkler		

- Take time to get to know the components that come with the Autodesk Revit software. Their most critical content are the connectors, as you see in for a piece of mechanical equipment in Figure 2–11.

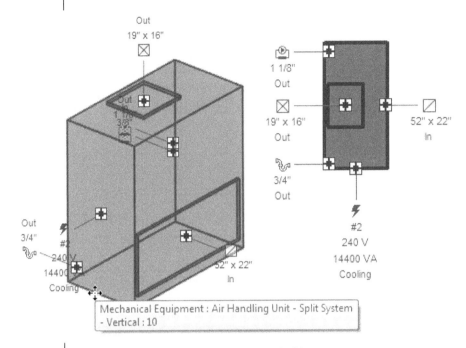

Figure 2–11

- Connectors often contain options to create systems and draw ducts and pipes when you right-click on them.

How To: Insert Components

1. Start the appropriate command.
2. In the Type Selector, select the type/size you want to use, as shown in Figure 2–12.

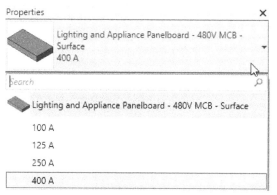

Figure 2–12

3. In the command-specific contextual tab>Tag panel, click
   ⌐① (Tag on Placement) to toggle this option on or off.
4. Proceed as follows, based on the type of component used:

If the component is...	Then...
Not hosted	Set the *Level* and *Offset from Host* in Properties, as shown in Figure 2–13.
Wall hosted	Set the *Elevation from Level* in Properties, as shown in Figure 2–14.
Face hosted	Select the appropriate method in the contextual tab>Placement panel, as shown in Figure 2–15. • Vertical Faces include walls and columns. • Faces include ceilings, beams, and roofs. • Work Planes can be set to levels, faces, and named reference planes.

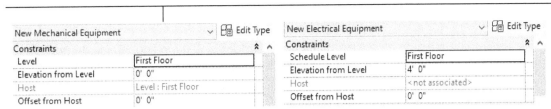

Figure 2–13   Figure 2–14

Figure 2–15

5. Place the component in the model.

•   A fast way to add components that match those already in your project is to select one, right-click on it, and select **Create Similar**, as shown in Figure 2–16. This starts the appropriate command with the same type selected.

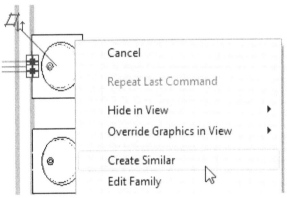

Figure 2–16

Hint: Work Planes

A work plane is the surface you sketch on or extrude from. In a plan view, the work plane is automatically parallel to the level. In an elevation or 3D view, you must specify the work plane before you start sketching.

How To: Select a Work Plane

1. Start a command that requires a work plane or, in the

   Systems tab>Work Plane panel, click ⊞ (Set).
2. In the Work Plane dialog box, select one of the following options:

   - **Name:** Select an existing level, grid, or named reference plane (as shown in Figure 2–17) and click **OK**.

Figure 2–17

   - **Pick a plane:** Click **OK** and select a plane in the view, such as a wall face. Ensure the entire plane is highlighted before you select it.
   - **Pick a line and use the work plane it was sketched in:** Click **OK** and select a model line, such as a room separation line.

   If you are in a view in which the sketch cannot be created, the Go To View dialog box opens. Select one of the views and click **Open View**.

Loading Components

You can load additional families into a project. In the related contextual tab>Mode panel, click 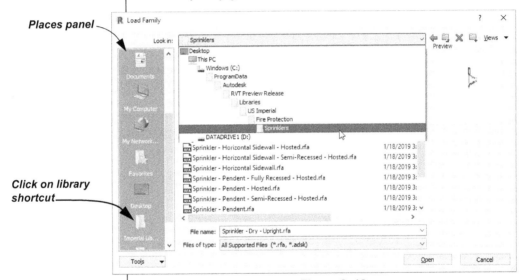 (Load Family) and then navigate to the appropriate location for your company. The Autodesk Revit library has MEP-based components available in the following folders: *Cable Tray, Conduit, Duct, Electrical, Fire Protection, Lighting, Mechanical, Pipe,* and *Plumbing.*

How To: Load a Family

1. In the related contextual tab>Mode panel or *Insert* tab>Load from Library panel, click (Load Family).
2. In the Load Family dialog box, locate the folder that contains the family or families you want to load, as shown in Figure 2–18.

   - You should default to the *Libraries* folder. If you do not, you can click **Imperial Libraries** in the Places panel to quickly get to the folder location.

Places panel

Click on library shortcut

Figure 2–18

3. Select the family or families you want to load. You can hold <Ctrl> to select multiple families.
4. Click **Open**.

Purging Unused Components

You can remove unused elements from a project, including individual component types, as shown in Figure 2–19.

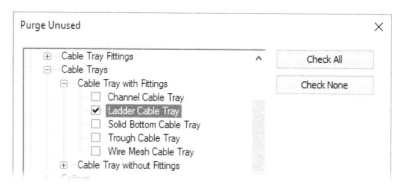

Figure 2–19

- Some elements are nested in other elements and it might require several rounds of purging the project to remove them.

How To: Purge Unused Elements

1. In the *Manage* tab>Settings panel, click (Purge Unused).
2. In the Purge unused dialog box, click **Check None** and select the elements that you want to purge.
3. Click **OK**.
4. Purging unused components not only helps simplify the component list, but more importantly, reduces the project file size.

Practice 2a | Insert Components

Practice Objectives

- Load and Insert components.
- Use drawing aids.
- Add and name a reference plan.
- Select a work plane.

In this practice, you will insert a variety of MEP fixtures, including air terminals, plumbing fixtures and lighting fixtures, as shown in Figure 2–20. You will use various drawing aids to help you place the fixtures appropriately.

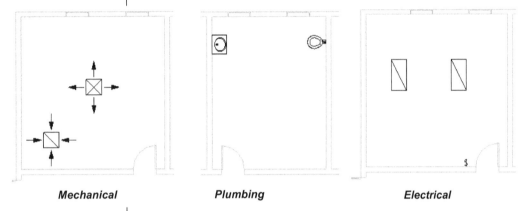

| *Mechanical* | *Plumbing* | *Electrical* |

Figure 2–20

Task 1 - Insert air terminals.

1. In the practice files *Basics* folder, open **Simple-Building-Start.rvt.**

2. In the Project Browser, expand the Mechanical>HVAC> Floor Plans node. The **1 - Mech** view is highlighted, and you are in a Mechanical floor plan.

3. In the *Systems* tab>HVAC panel, click ▣ (Air Terminal).

4. In Properties, note that the default selection is a Supply Diffuser and that the *Level* is **Level 1**. Set the *Offset from Host* to **9'-0"**.

5. Click near the center of room **Lab 101**, as shown in Figure 2–21.

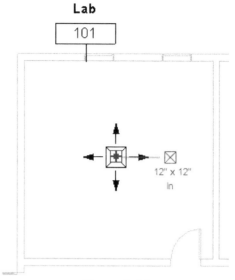

Figure 2–21

6. While still in the Air Terminal command, in the Type Selector, change the *Type* to **Return Diffuser: 24 x 24 Face 12 x 12 Connection** and set the *Offset from Host* to **9'-0"**.

7. Click to place the component in the lower left corner of room **Lab 101**.

8. In the *Systems* tab>Mechanical panel, click ⊛ (Mechanical Equipment.)

9. In the Type Selector, select **Boiler: Standard**.

10. In the **Mech/Elec Room**, move the cursor near the outside wall. Note that the boiler automatically aligns to the wall, as shown in Figure 2–22.

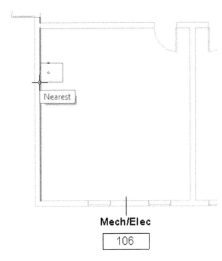

Mech/Elec
106

Figure 2–22

11. Click to place the component.

12. Save the project.

Task 2 - Load and place plumbing fixtures.

The air terminals are automatically toggled off because you are in a plumbing view, but the boiler still displays because Mechanical Equipment is typically toggled on.

1. In the Project Browser, expand the Plumbing>Plumbing> Floor Plans node and double-click to open the **1 - Plumbing** view.

2. In the *Systems* tab>Plumbing & Piping panel, click
   (Plumbing Fixture).

3. In the Type Selector, select one of the wall-mounted water closets.

4. Click along one of the walls to place the fixture, as shown in Figure 2–23.

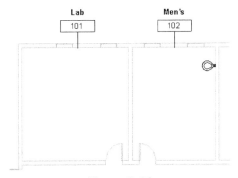

Figure 2–23

5. Return to the Type Selector and review the list. Note that there are sinks, but no lavatories.

6. In the *Modify | Place Plumbing Fixture* tab>Mode panel, click ⬇ (Load Family).

7. In the Load Family dialog box, the Autodesk Revit family library automatically displays. Navigate to the *Plumbing>MEP>Fixtures>Lavatories* folder and select **Lavatory - Oval.rfa,** as shown in Figure 2–24.

Figure 2–24

8. Click **Open**.

9. In the Type Selector, select **Lavatory - Oval: 25"x20" - Public**.

10. Place the lavatory against the wall across from the water closet.

11. Click (Modify) and select the new fixture. Drag it up or down until it meets with the alignment line of the water closet, as shown in Figure 2–25.

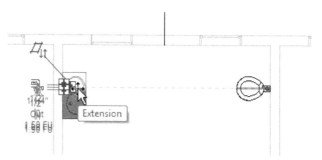

Figure 2–25

12. Click outside the building model in an empty area to release the selection.

13. Save the project.

Task 3 - Place a lighting fixture and switch.

1. In the Project Browser, expand the Electrical>Lighting>
   Ceiling Plans node and double-click on **1 - Ceiling Elec** view
   to open it.

   - Ensure that you are opening the Ceiling Plan so that the
     ceiling grids display.
   - None of the previous elements that you have added
     display.

2. In the *Systems* tab>Electrical panel, click ![icon] (Lighting
   Fixture).

3. In the Type Selector, select **Plain recessed Lighting
   Fixture: 2x4 - 277**.

4. In the *Modify | Place Fixture* tab>Placement panel, click

   ![icon] (Place on Face).

5. Go to the upper left room and hover the cursor over the grid.
   The light snaps to the grid lines, as shown in Figure 2–26.

6. Press <Spacebar> to rotate the fixture. Click to place two
   fixtures in the room, as shown in Figure 2–27.

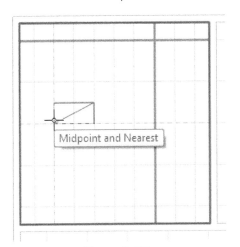

Figure 2–26

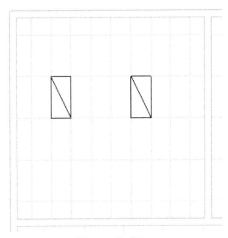

Figure 2–27

7. Open the Electrical>Lighting>Floor Plans>**1 - Lighting** view. The light fixtures display in this view although you are seeing a plan view.

8. In the *Systems* tab>Electrical panel, expand the Device drop-down list and select ▯ (Lighting).

9. In the Type Selector, select **Lighting Switches: Single Pole**.

10. In Properties, note that the *Elevation from Level* is set to **4'-0"**, a standard height for switches.

11. Place the switch to the left of the door. It displays only as a symbol.

12. Click ⌖ (Modify) to end the command.

13. Save and close the project.

2.3 Selecting and Editing Elements

Building design projects typically involve extensive changes to the model. The Autodesk Revit software was designed to make such changes quickly and efficiently. You can change an element using the methods shown in Figure 2–28, and described below:

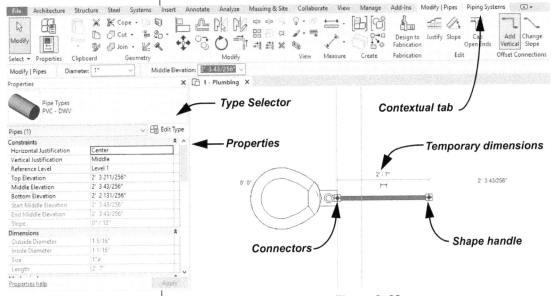

Figure 2–28

- **Type Selector:** Enables you to specify a different type of elements. This is frequently used to change the size and/or style.

- **Properties:** Enables you to modify the information (parameters) associated with the selected elements.

- **Temporary dimensions:** Enable you to change the element's dimensions or position.

- **Contextual tab:** In the ribbon. Contains the Modify commands and element-specific tools.

- **Controls:** Enable you to drag, flip, lock, and rotate the element.

- **Connectors:** Show how related elements attach to each other with intelligence about size, needed fittings, and system information.

- To delete an element, select it and press <Delete>, right-click and select **Delete**, or in the Modify panel, click ✖ (Delete).

Working with Controls and Connectors

When you select an element, various controls and connectors display depending on the element and view. Using controls, you can change an elements length or location, and flip or rotate some elements. MEP connectors also provide information about attachments and enable you to add related elements, as shown for creating pipe from a pipe accessory in Figure 2–29.

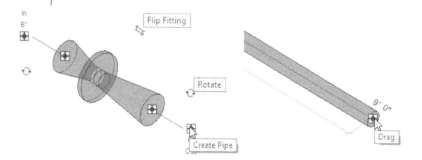

Figure 2–29

- If you hover the cursor over the control or connector, a tooltip displays showing its function.

Hint: Editing Temporary Dimensions

Temporary dimensions automatically link to the closest wall. To change the location, you can drag the *Witness Line* control, as shown in Figure 2–30, to connect to a new reference. You can also click on the control to toggle between justifications in the wall.

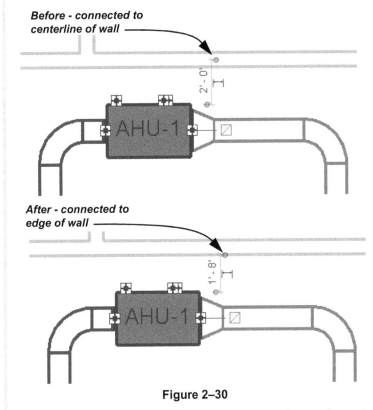

Figure 2–30

- The new location of a temporary dimension for an element is remembered as long as you are in the same session of the software.

Selecting Multiple Elements

You can select more than one element at a time. Once you have selected at least one element, hold <Ctrl> and select another item to add it to a selection set. To remove an element from a selection set, hold <Shift> and select the element.

- If you click and drag the cursor to *window* around elements, you have two selection options, as shown in Figure 2–31. If you drag from left to right, you only select the elements completely inside the window. If you drag from right to left, you select elements both inside and crossing the window.

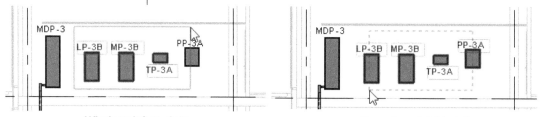

Window: left to right   *Crossing: right to left*

Figure 2–31

- If several elements are on or near each other, hover your cursor over an edge and press <Tab> to cycle through them before you click. If there are elements that might be linked to each other, such as ductwork, pressing <Tab> selects the chain of elements.

- Press <Ctrl>+<Left Arrow> to reselect the previous selection set. You can also right-click in the drawing window with nothing selected and select **Select Previous**.

- To select all elements of a specific type, right-click on an element and select **Select All Instances>Visible in View** or **In Entire Project**, as shown in Figure 2–32. For example, if you select an air terminal of a specific size and use this command, all air terminals of the same size would be selected, excluding all of the air terminals of other sizes.

You do no have to select an element; just hover over the one you want to select.

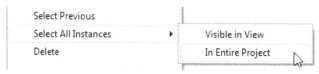

Figure 2–32

Hint: Selection Options

You can control how the software selects specific elements in a project by toggling selection options on and off on the Status Bar, as shown in Figure 2–33. Alternatively, in any tab on the ribbon that has the Modify command, expand the Select panel and select the options shown in Figure 2–34.

Figure 2–33

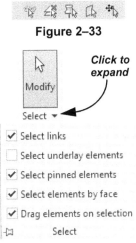

Click to expand

Figure 2–34

- <span></span> **Select links:** When toggled on, you can select linked drawings or Autodesk Revit models. When it is toggled off you cannot select them when using **Modify** or **Move**.

- <span></span> **Select underlay elements:** When toggled on, you can select underlay elements. When toggled off, you cannot select them when using **Modify** or **Move**.

- <span></span> **Select pinned elements:** When toggled on, you can selected pinned elements. When toggled off, you cannot select them when using **Modify** or **Move**.

- <span></span> **Select elements by face:** When toggled on you can select elements (such as the floors or walls in an elevation) by selecting the interior face or selecting an edge. When toggled off, you can only select elements by selecting an edge.

- <span></span> **Drag elements on selection:** When toggled on, you can hover over an element, select it, and drag it to a new location. When toggled off, the Crossing or Box select mode starts when you press and drag, even if you are on top of an element. Once elements have been selected they can still be dragged to a new location.

Filtering Selection Sets

When multiple element categories are selected, the *Multi-Select* contextual tab opens in the ribbon. This gives you access to all of the Modify tools, and the **Filter** command. The **Filter** command enables you to specify the types of elements to select. For example, you might only want to select lighting fixtures, as shown in Figure 2–35.

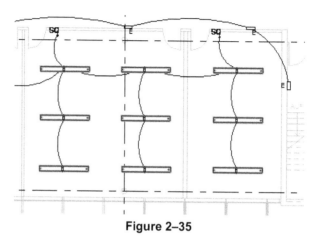

Figure 2–35

How To: Filter a Selection Set

1. Select everything in the required area.
2. in the *Modify | Multi-Select* tab>Selection panel, or in the Status Bar, click ▼ (Filter). The Filter dialog box opens, as shown in Figure 2–36.

The Filter dialog box displays all types of elements in the original selection.

Figure 2–36

3. Click **Check None** to clear all of the options or **Check All** to select all of the options. You can also select or clear individual categories as required.
4. Click **OK**. The selection set is now limited to the elements you specified.

- In the Status Bar, the number of elements selected displays beside the Filter icon, as shown in Figure 2–37. You can also see the number of selected elements in the Properties palette.

Figure 2–37

- Clicking the Filter icon in the Status Bar also opens the Filter dialog box.

Practice 2b | Select and Edit Elements

Practice Objectives

- Use a variety of selection methods.
- Use temporary dimensions and connectors to modify the location of elements.

In this practice, you will select lighting fixtures and change the type (as shown in Figure 2–38), as well as test a variety of selection methods and filters. You will then use connectors to modify the location of an air terminal and use **Create Similar** to add additional components. You will also modify the height of the air terminals in Properties.

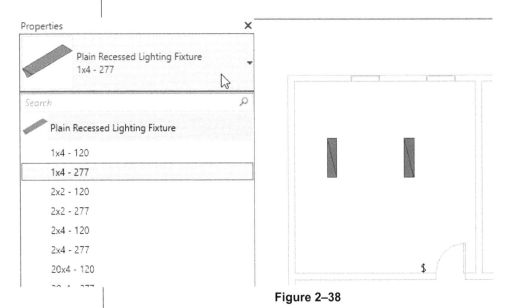

Figure 2–38

Task 1 - Use a variety of selection methods.

1. In the practice files *Basics* folder, open **Simple-Building-Edit.rvt**. It opens in the **1 - Lighting** view.

2. Select one of the light fixtures. The connectors and controls are displayed.

3. Hold <Ctrl> and select the other fixture. The connectors no longer display, but you can still modify the fixture type.

4. In the Type Selector, change the type to **Plain Recessed Lighting Fixture: 1x4 - 277**. Both fixtures change, as shown in Figure 2–39.

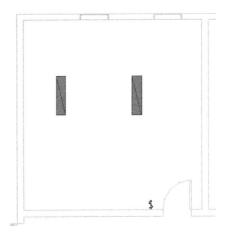

Figure 2–39

5. Click in an empty space to clear the selection.

6. Open the Mechical>HVAC>Floor Plans>**1 - Mech** view.

7. Draw a window selection from left to right around some of the elements so only those completely inside the window are selected, as shown in Figure 2–40.

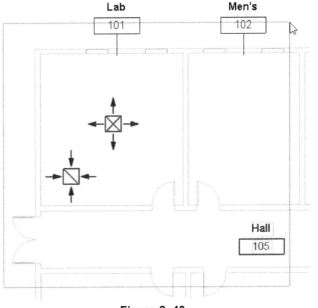

Figure 2–40

8. Click in an empty space in the view to clear the selection.

9. Draw a crossing window (i.e., from right to left) around the same area, as shown in Figure 2–41. Note that any elements that the window touches are included in the selection, including the linked architectural model.

You can toggle

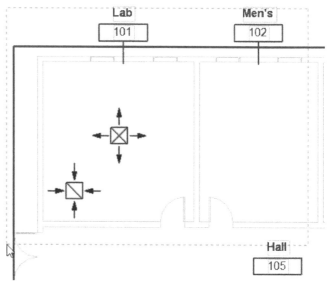 *(Select Links) in the Status Bar to keep the link from being selected.*

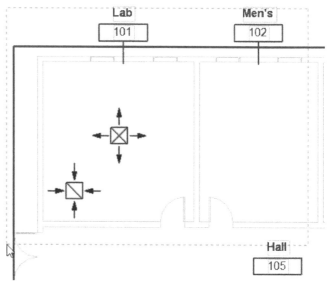

Figure 2–41

10. Hold <Shift> and select the edge of the architectural model. This removes the element from the selection set.

11. In the Status Bar, note the number of items that are selected and click (Filter).

12. In the Filter dialog box, view the categories and clear the check from **Air Terminals**.

13. Click **OK**. Only the room tags are still selected.

14. Press <Esc>. The elements are no longer selected.

15. Select one of the room tags. Right-click and select **Select All Instances>Visible in View**. All of the tags are selected.

16. Click (Modify). The elements are no longer selected.

• Remember these selection methods as you start working in the projects.

Task 2 - Modify elements using controls and properties.

1. Open the Mechical>HVAC>Floor Plans>**1 - Mech** view.

2. Select, click and drag the supply air terminal to a new location using the alignment lines referencing the return air terminal.

3. Right-click on the control and look at the variety of options you can use, as shown in Figure 2–42.

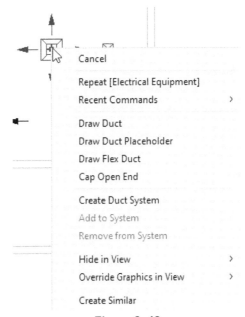

Figure 2–42

4. In the shortcut menu, select **Create Similar**. This starts the **Air Terminal** command using that type. Place two more air terminals in the same room, using alignment lines to place them.

5. Click 🔨 (Modify) and select all three of the supply air terminals. Note the information in Properties. The *Offset from Host* is set to **0'-0"** above Level 1.

6. Hold <Ctrl> and select the return air terminal. The *Level* and *Offset from Host* are available to change, although two different types of components are selected.

7. Change the *Offset from Host* to **8'-0"** and click **Apply**. The offset for all of the air terminals is updated, as shown in Figure 2–43.

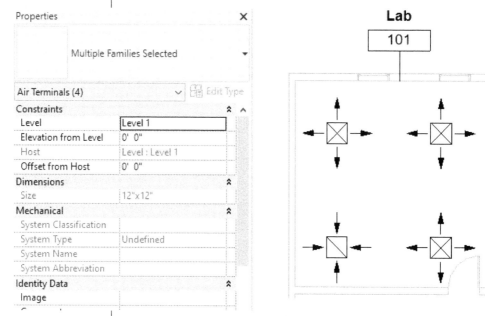

Figure 2–43

8. Click away from any elements to clear the selection.

9. Save and close the project.

2.4 Working with Basic Modify Tools

The basic modifying tools **Move**, **Copy**, **Rotate**, **Mirror**, and **Array** can be used with individual elements or any selection of elements. They are found in the Modify panel (as shown in Figure 2–44), in the *Modify* tab, and in contextual tabs.

Figure 2–44

- For these modify commands, you can either select the elements and start the command, or start the command, select the elements, and press <Enter> to finish the selection and move to the next step in the command.

Moving and Copying Elements

The **Move** and **Copy** commands enable you to select the element(s) and move or copy them from one place to another. You can use alignment lines, temporary dimensions, and snaps to help place the elements, as shown in Figure 2–45.

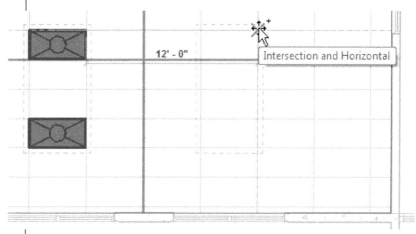

12' - 0"

Intersection and Horizontal

Figure 2–45

How To: Move or Copy Elements

1. Select the elements you want to move or copy.

2. In the Modify panel, click ✛ (Move) or ◌ (Copy).
    Alternatively, you can type **MV** for Move and **CO** for Copy. A
    dashed boundary box displays around the selected elements.
3. Select a start point on or near the element.
4. Select a second point. Use alignment lines and temporary
    dimensions to help place the elements.
5. When you are finished, you can start another modify
    command using the elements that remain selected, or select

    ⌖ (Modify) to end the command.

*   You can drag elements to new locations without starting the
    Move command. Holding <Ctrl> and dragging copies the
    element. This is quick but not very precise.

Move/Copy Elements Options

The **Move** and **Copy** commands have several options that
display in the Options Bar, as shown in Figure 2–46.

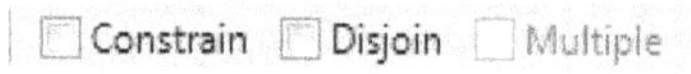

☐ Constrain ☐ Disjoin ☐ Multiple

Figure 2–46

Constrain	Restricts the movement of the cursor to horizontal or vertical, or along the axis of an item that is at an angle. This keeps you from selecting a point at an angle by mistake. **Constrain** is off by default.
Disjoin (Move only)	Breaks any connections between the elements being moved and other elements. If **Disjoin** is on, the elements move separately. If it is off, the connected elements also move or stretch. **Disjoin** is off by default.
Multiple (Copy only)	Enables you to make multiple copies of one selection. **Multiple** is off by default.

These commands only work in the current view, not between
views or projects. To copy between views or projects, in the

Modify tab>Clipboard panel, use 🗐 (Copy to Clipboard),

✂ (Cut to the Clipboard), and 🗐 (Paste from Clipboard).

- If you do not want elements to be moved, select the elements

  and in the *Modify* tab, in the Modify panel, click 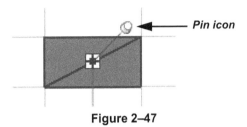 (Pin). Pinned elements can be copied, but not moved or deleted. Select the element and click the pin icon, as shown in Figure 2–47, or type the shortcut **UP** to free it.

Pin icon

Figure 2–47

Rotating Elements

The **Rotate** command enables you to rotate selected elements around a center point or origin, as shown in Figure 2–48. You can use alignment lines, temporary dimensions, and snaps to help specify the center of rotation and the angle. You can also create copies of the element as it is being rotated.

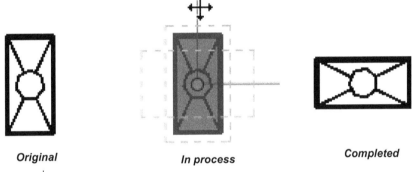

Original   *In process*   *Completed*

Figure 2–48

How To: Rotate Elements

1. Select the element(s) you want to rotate.

2. In the Modify panel, click ○ (Rotate) or type the shortcut **RO**.

3. The center of rotation is automatically set to the center of the element or group of elements, as shown in Figure 2–49. To change the center of rotation, as shown in Figure 2–50, use the following:

- Drag the ⟳ (Center of Rotation) control to a new point.
- In the Options Bar, next to **Center of rotation**, click **Place** and use snaps to move it to a new location.
- Press <Spacebar> to select the center of rotation and click to move it to a new location.

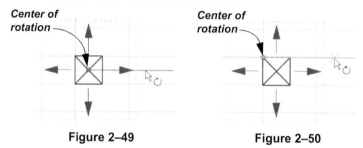

Figure 2–49   **Figure 2–50**

4. In the Options Bar, shown in Figure 2–51, specify if you want to make a copy (select **Copy**), type an angle in the *Angle* field, and press <Enter>. You can also specify the angle on screen using temporary dimensions.

Figure 2–51

5. The rotated element(s) remain highlighted, enabling you to start another command using the same selection, or click

   ⌖ (Modify) to finish.

- The **Disjoin** option breaks any connections between the elements being rotated and other elements. If **Disjoin** is on (selected), the elements rotate separately; however, with MEP elements, the connection to the system will be broken. If it is off (cleared), the connected elements also move or stretch, as shown for a wall in Figure 2–52. **Disjoin** is toggled off by default.

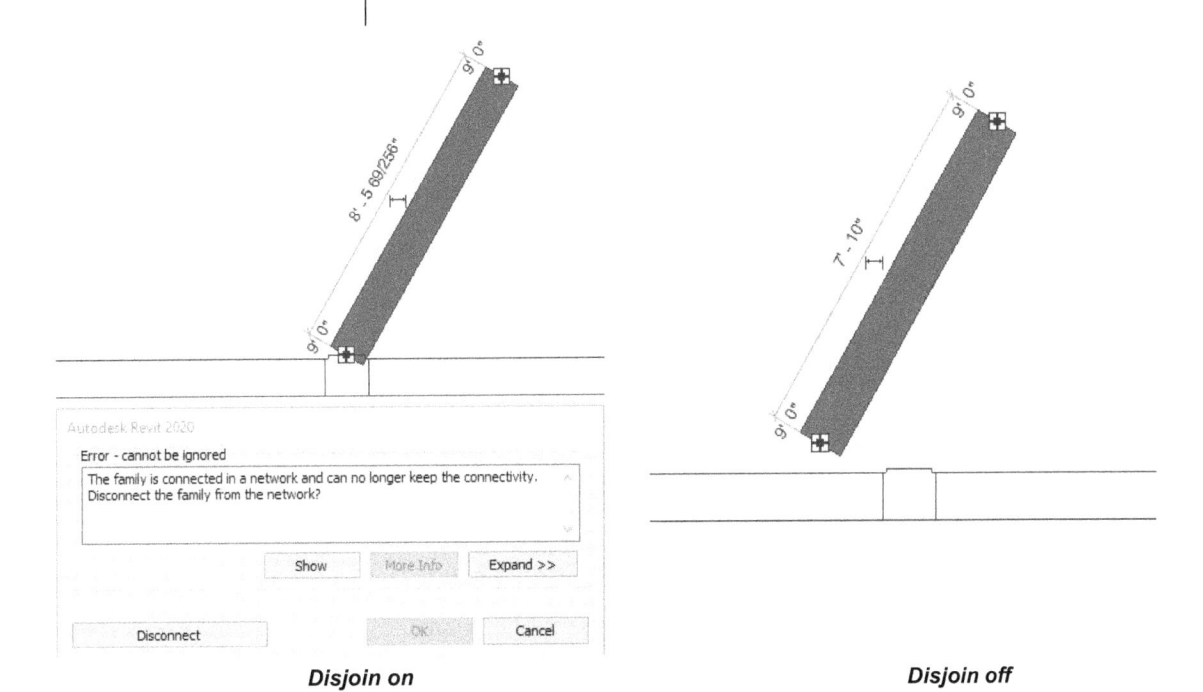

Disjoin on   *Disjoin off*

Figure 2–52

- Rotating connected MEP elements can easily cause connection and system problems.

Mirroring Elements

The **Mirror** command enables you to mirror elements about an axis defined by a selected element, as shown in Figure 2–53, or by selected points.

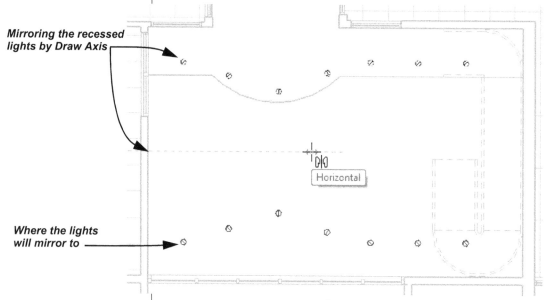

Mirroring the recessed lights by Draw Axis

Where the lights will mirror to

Figure 2–53

How To: Mirror Elements

1. Select the element(s) to mirror.
2. In the Modify panel, select the method you want to use:

   - Click ⬚ (Mirror - Pick Axis) or type the shortcut **MM**. This prompts you to select an element as the **Axis of Reflection** (mirror line).

   - Click ⬚ (Mirror - Draw Axis) or type the shortcut **DM**. This prompts you to select two points to define the axis about which the elements mirror.

3. The new mirrored element(s) remain highlighted, enabling you to start another command, or return to **Modify** to finish.

   - By default, the original elements that were mirrored remain. To delete the original elements, clear the **Copy** option in the Options Bar.

Hint: Scale

The Autodesk Revit software is designed with full-size elements. Therefore, not much can be scaled. However, you can use 🔲 (Scale) in reference planes, images, and imported files from other programs.

Creating Linear and Radial Arrays

The **Array** command creates multiple copies of selected elements in a linear or radial pattern, as shown in Figure 2–54. For example, you can array a row of columns to create a row of evenly spaced columns on a grid, or array a row of parking spaces. The arrayed elements can be grouped or placed as separate elements.

- A linear array creates a straight line pattern of elements, while a radial array creates a circular pattern around a center point.

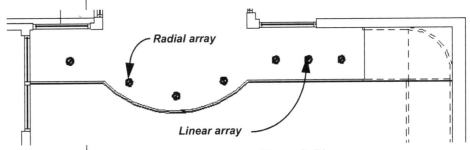

Figure 2–54

How To: Create a Linear Array

1. Select the element(s) to array.

2. In the Modify panel, click 🔳 (Array) or type the shortcut **AR**.

3. In the Options Bar, click ⬒ (Linear).
4. Specify the other options as needed.
5. Select a start point and an end point to set the spacing and direction of the array. The array is displayed.

6. If the **Group and Associate** option is selected, you are prompted again for the number of items, as shown in Figure 2–55. Type a new number or click on the screen to finish the command.

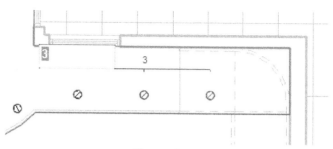

Figure 2–55

- To make a linear array in two directions, you need to array one direction first, select the arrayed elements, and then array them again in the other direction.

Array Options

In the Options Bar, set up the **Array** options for **Linear Array** (top of Figure 2–56) or **Radial Array** (bottom of Figure 2–56).

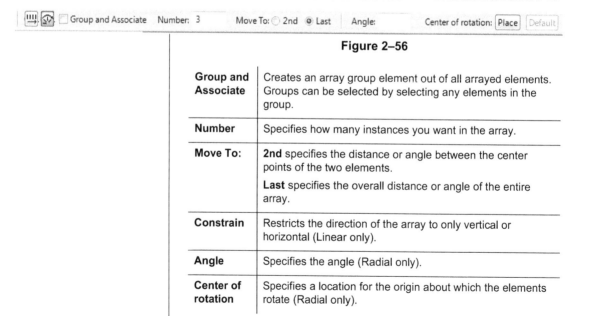

Figure 2–56

Group and Associate	Creates an array group element out of all arrayed elements. Groups can be selected by selecting any elements in the group.
Number	Specifies how many instances you want in the array.
Move To:	**2nd** specifies the distance or angle between the center points of the two elements. **Last** specifies the overall distance or angle of the entire array.
Constrain	Restricts the direction of the array to only vertical or horizontal (Linear only).
Angle	Specifies the angle (Radial only).
Center of rotation	Specifies a location for the origin about which the elements rotate (Radial only).

How To: Create a Radial Array

1. Select the element(s) to array.

2. In the Modify panel, click ⬚⬚ (Array).

3. In the Options Bar, click ⟳ (Radial).

4. Drag ⟳ (Center of Rotation) or in the Options Bar click **Place** to the move the center of rotation to the appropriate location, as shown in Figure 2–57.

Remember to set the
Center of Rotation
control first, before
specifying the angle.

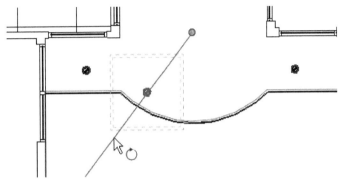

Figure 2–57

5. In the Options Bar, type an angle and press <Enter>, or specify the rotation angle by selecting points on the screen.
6. Specify the other options as needed.

Modifying Array Groups

When you select an element in an array that has been grouped, you can change the number of instances in the array, as shown in Figure 2–58. For radial arrays you can also modify the distance to the center.

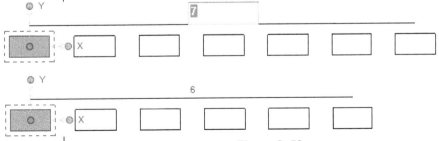

Figure 2–58

• Dashed lines surround the element(s) in a group, and the XY control lets you move the origin point of the group

If you move one of the elements in the array group, the other elements move in response based on the distance and/or angle, as shown in Figure 2–59.

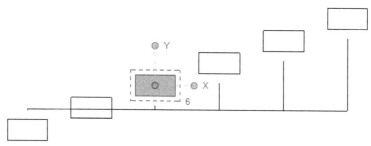

Figure 2–59

- To remove the array constraint on the group, select all of the elements in the array group and, in the *Modify* contextual tab>Group panel, click (Ungroup).

- If you select an individual element in an array and click (Ungroup), the element you selected is removed from the array, while the rest of the elements remain in the array group.

- You can use (Filter) to ensure that you are selecting only **Model Groups**.

Practice 2c

Work with Basic Modify Tools

Practice Objective

- Use basic modify tools, including Move, Copy, Rotate, Mirror, and Array.

In this practice, you will copy air terminals to several rooms and move some so they fit the room logically. You will array plumbing fixtures in a restroom and then mirror them to the other restroom. Finally, you will rotate lighting fixtures to fit an angled ceiling grid, as shown in Figure 2–60.

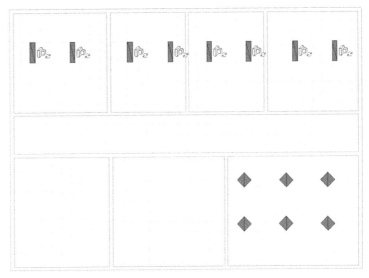

Figure 2–60

Task 1 - Copy elements.

1. In the practice files *Basics* folder, open **Simple-Building-Modify.rvt**.

2. Open the Mechanical>HVAC>Floor Plans>**1 - Mech** view.

3. Select the four air terminals.

4. In the *Modify | Air Terminals* tab>Modify panel, click (Copy).

5. In the Options Bar, select **Multiple**.

6. Select the following points, as shown in Figure 2–61:
   - *First point:* **Lab 101**
   - *Second point:* **Lab 104**
   - *Third point:* **Lab 107**

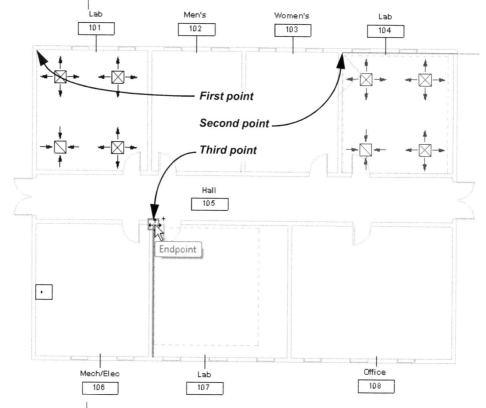

Figure 2–61

7. The air terminals are copied into each room.

8. Click ⬉ (Modify).

9. In the *Modify* tab>Modify panel, click ⬍ (Move).

10. As there is no current selection, you need to select the elements to move. In **Lab 107**, select the two air terminals on the right and then press <Enter>.

11. Select a base point on one of the air terminals and then use temporary dimensions to move the air terminals **4'-0"** to the right, as shown in Figure 2–62.

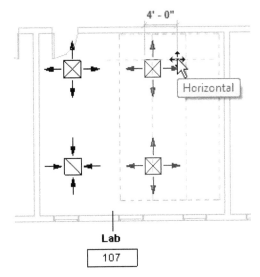

Figure 2–62

12. Save the project.

Task 2 - Array and mirror elements.

1. Open the Plumbing>Floor Plans>**1 - Plumbing** view.

2. Select the water closet (toilet) and lavatory (sink).

3. In the *Modify | Plumbing Fixtures* tab>Modify panel, click ⊞ (Array).

4. In the Options Bar, review the defaults.

5. Pick the lavatory as the first point and pick a second point **3'-0"** below. You are prompted for the number of elements, as shown in Figure 2–63.

6. Change the number to **4**, and then press <Enter>. The additional fixtures are placed, as shown in Figure 2–64.

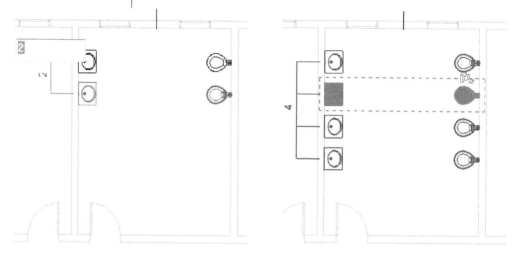

Figure 2–63   **Figure 2–64**

7. Click (Modify) and select all of the fixtures. They are grouped together.

8. In the *Modify | Model Groups* tab>Group panel, click (Ungroup). Each element can now be moved separately.

9. Click (Modify) and select all the water closets.

10. In the *Modify | Plumbing Fixtures* tab>Modify panel, click (Mirror - Pick Axis). Hover the cursor on the wall between rooms 102 and 103. The center of the wall should highlight. Use <Tab> to cycle through the wall's faces. Select the center of the wall, as shown in Figure 2–65.

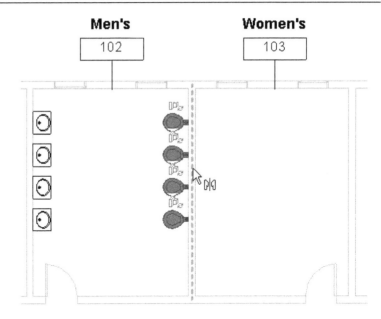

Figure 2–65

Note that mirroring the lavatories reverses the hot and cold water connectors.

11. Select one of the lavatories, right-click and select **Create Similar**.

12. Place the lavatory across from the water closet in the Women's room.

13. Click ⬚ (Modify) and select and drag the lavatory into place so it aligns with the water closet, as shown in Figure 2–66.

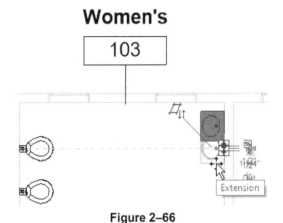

Figure 2–66

14. With the lavatory still selected, start the **Array** command.

15. In the Options Bar, clear the **Group and Associate** option and set *Number* to **4**.

16. Click a base point on the lavatory's upper left corner, then click a second point **3'-0"** below it. Four lavatories are now placed, which do not need to be ungrouped.

17. Select two of the water closets in Room 102. In the Type selector, change the type to **Urinal - Wall Hung: 3/4" Flush Valve**.

18. Save the project.

Task 3 - Copy and rotate elements.

---

1. Open the Electrical>Lighting>Ceiling Plans>**1 - Ceiling Elec** view.

2. Copy the lighting fixtures to the other rooms on the same side of the hall, similar to the example shown in Figure 2–67.

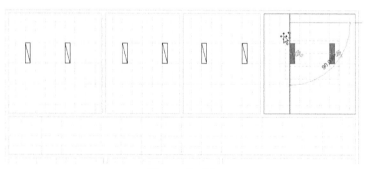

Figure 2–67

3. Add a **Plain Recessed Lighting Fixture: 2x2 - 277** type lighting fixture to the room with the 45 degree ceiling. (Remember to use **Place on Face**.)

4. Click ⌖ (Modify) and select the new square lighting fixture.

5. In the *Modify | Lighting Fixtures tab*>Modify panel, click ↻ (Rotate).

6. Drag the center control over to the edge, as shown in Figure 2–68. Click when the cursor displays a horizontal line and then on the nearby 45 degree angled line, as shown in Figure 2–69. The fixture now fits in the grid.

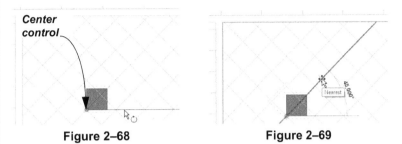

Figure 2–68   Figure 2–69

7. Copy the fixture to additional places in the room.

8. Save and close the project.

2.5 Working with Additional Modify Tools

As you work on a project, there are some additional tools on the *Modify* tab>Modify panel, as shown in Figure 2–70, that can help you with placing, modifying, and constraining elements. **Align** can be used with a variety of elements, while **Split Element**, **Trim/Extend**, and **Offset** can only be used with linear elements.

Figure 2–70

Aligning Elements

The **Align** command enables you to line up one element with another. Most Autodesk Revit elements can be aligned. For example, you can line up an air terminal with ceiling grids, as shown in Figure 2–71.

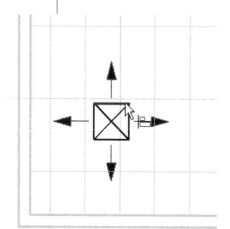 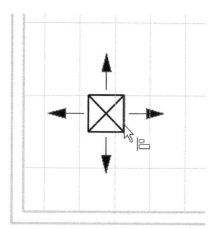

Figure 2–71

How To: Align Elements

1. In the *Modify* tab>Modify panel, click ⬚ (Align).
2. Select a line or point on the element that is going to remain stationary. For walls, press <Tab> to select the correct wall face.
3. Select a line or point on the element to be aligned. The second element moves into alignment with the first one.

- The **Align** command works in all model views, including parallel and perspective 3D views.

- You can lock alignments so that the elements move together if either one is moved. Once you have created the alignment, a padlock is displayed. Click on the padlock to lock it, as shown in Figure 2–72.

Locking elements enlarges the size of the project file, so use this option carefully.

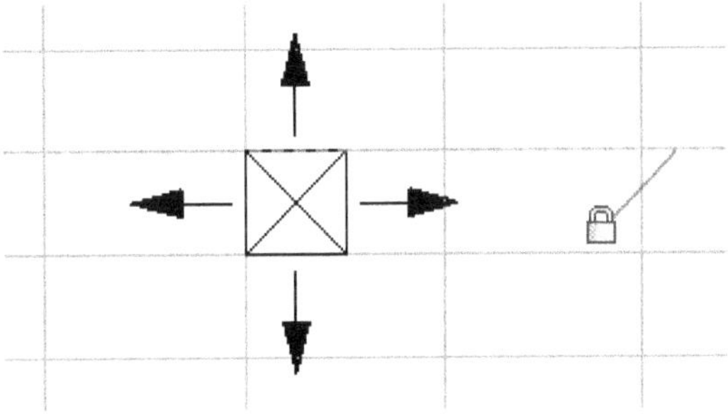

Figure 2–72

- From the Options Bar, select **Multiple Alignment** to select multiple elements to align with the first element. You can also hold <Ctrl> to select multiple elements to align.

- For walls, you can specify if you want the command to prefer **Wall centerlines**, **Wall faces**, **Center of core**, or **Faces of core**, as shown in Figure 2–73. The core refers to the structural members of a wall as opposed to facing materials, such as sheet rock.

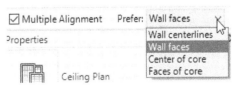

Figure 2–73

Splitting Linear Elements

The **Split** Element command enables you to break a linear element at a specific point. You can use alignment lines, snaps, and temporary dimensions to help place the split point. After you have split the linear element, you can use other editing commands to modify the two parts, or change the type of one part, as shown with walls in Figure 2–74.

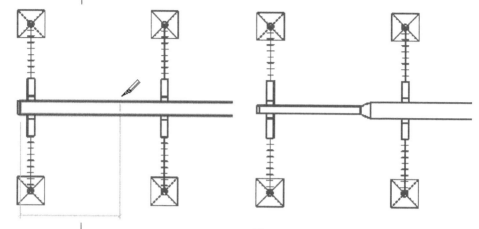

Figure 2–74

How To: Split Linear Elements

1. In the *Modify* tab>Modify panel, click ⊏╪⊐ (Split Element) or type the shortcut **SL**.
2. In the Options Bar, select or clear the **Delete Inner Segment** option.
3. Move the cursor to the point you want to split and select the point.
4. Repeat for any additional split locations.
5. Modify the elements that were split, as needed.

- The **Delete Inner Segment** option is used when you select two split points along a linear element. When the option is selected, the segment between the two split points is automatically removed.

Trimming and Extending

There are three trim/extend methods that you can use with linear elements: **Trim/Extend to Corner**, **Trim/Extend Single Element**, and **Trim/Extend Multiple Elements**.

- When selecting elements to trim, click the part of the element that you want to keep. The opposite part of the line is then trimmed.

How To: Trim/Extend to Corner

1. In the *Modify* tab>Modify panel, click ⇗ (Trim/Extend to Corner) or type the shortcut **TR**.
2. Select the first linear element on the side you want to keep.
3. Select the second linear element on the side you want to keep, as shown in Figure 2–75.

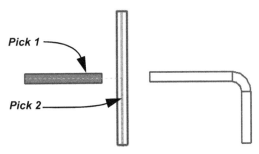

Figure 2–75

How To: Trim/Extend a Single Element

1. In the *Modify* tab>Modify panel, click ⇒ (Trim/Extend Single Element).
2. Select the cutting or boundary edge.
3. Select the linear element to be trimmed or extended, as shown in Figure 2–76.

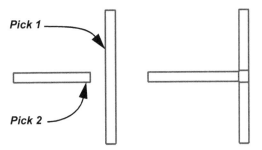

Figure 2–76

How To: Trim/Extend Multiple Elements

1. In the *Modify* tab>Modify panel, click ⇒ (Trim/Extend Multiple Elements).
2. Select the cutting or boundary edge.

3. Select the linear elements that you want to trim or extend by selecting one at a time, or by using a crossing window, as shown in Figure 2–77. For trimming, select the side you want to keep.

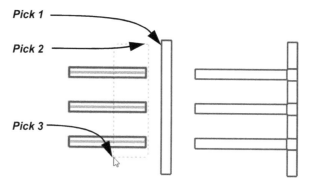

Figure 2–77

- You can click in an empty space in the view to clear the selection and select another cutting edge or boundary.

Offsetting Elements

MEP elements can be offset, but you should typically use other tools to create parallel elements, such as ducts, pipes, and conduits.

The **Offset** command is an easy way of creating parallel copies of linear elements at a specified distance, as shown in Figure 2–78. Walls, beams, braces, and lines are among the elements that can be offset.

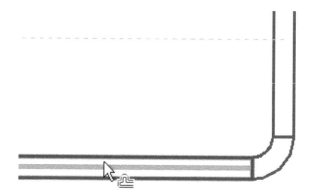

Figure 2–78

The offset distance can be set by typing the distance (**Numerical** method shown in Figure 2–79) or by selecting points on the screen (**Graphical** method).

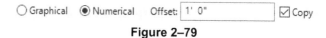

Figure 2–79

How To: Offset Using the Numerical Method

*The **Copy** option (which is on by default) makes a copy of the element being offset. If this option is not selected, the **Offset** command moves the element the set offset distance.*

1. In the *Modify* tab>Modify panel, click 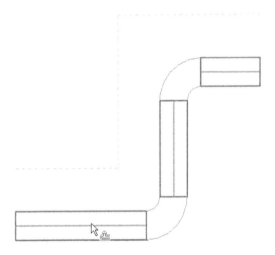 (Offset) or type the shortcut **OF**.
2. In the Options Bar, select the **Numerical** option.
3. In the Options Bar, type the required distance in the *Offset* field.
4. Move the cursor over the element you want to offset. A dashed line previews the offset location. Move the cursor to flip the sides, as required.
5. Click to create the offset.
6. Repeat Steps 4 and 5 to offset other elements by the same distance, or to change the distance for another offset.

- With the **Numerical** option, you can select multiple connected linear elements for offsetting. Hover the cursor over an element and press <Tab> until the other related elements are highlighted, as shown in Figure 2–80. Select the element to offset all of the elements at the same time.

The offset is from centerline to centerline of elements, such as duct or pipe.

Most linear elements connected at a corner automatically trim or extend to meet at the offset distance.

Figure 2–80

How To: Offset Using the Graphical Method

1. Start the **Offset** command.
2. In the Options Bar, select the **Graphical** option.
3. Select the linear element to offset.
4. Select two points that define the distance of the offset and which side to apply it. You can type an override in the temporary dimension for the second point.

Hint: Using Thin Lines

The software automatically applies line weights to views, as shown for a section on the left in Figure 2–81. If a line weight seems heavy or obscures your work on the elements, toggle off the line weights. In the Quick Access Toolbar or in the *View* tab>Graphics panel, click 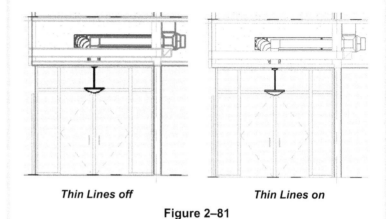 (Thin Lines) or type **TL**. The lines display with the same weight, as shown on the right in Figure 2–81.

Thin Lines off	*Thin Lines on*

Figure 2–81

- The **Thin Line** setting is remembered until you change it, even if you shut down and restart the software.

Practice 2d

Work with Additional Modify Tools

Practice Objective

- Use Align, Split, Offset, and Trim/Extend.

In this practice, you will discover and delete excess piping and clean it up with modify tools. You will align air terminals to ceiling grids. Finally you will offset cable trays and use trim/extend commands to link them. You will also split and resize part of the tray, as shown in Figure 2–82.

- Additional linear elements, including pipes and cable trays, have been added to this practice.

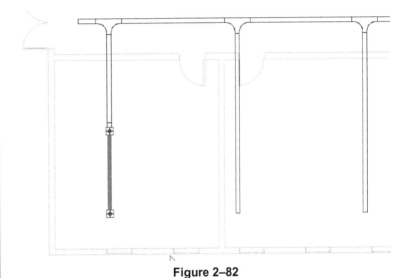

Figure 2–82

Task 1 - Clean up excess piping.

1. In the practice files *Basics* folder, open **Simple-Building-Align.rvt**.

2. **3D Plumbing** is the default view. Zoom in on the **Tee - Generic** connection between the hot water heater and the pipe in the hall.

3. In the View Control Bar, change the *Detail Level* to ▨ (Fine) and the Visual Style to ◰ (Shaded) to help display the pipes more clearly.

4. If required, in the Quick Access Toolbar, click  (Thin Lines) to see the piping better.

5. Delete the highlighted pipe, tee, and transition connectors between the pipes, as shown in Figure 2–83.

Figure 2–83

6. In the *Modify* tab>Modify panel, click ⊐ (Trim/Extend to Corner.

7. Select the two pipes, as shown in Figure 2–84. Ensure that you select the smaller pipe first so that the elbow connector uses the size of the larger pipe, as shown in Figure 2–85.

Figure 2–84   Figure 2–85

8. Type **ZF** to zoom the model to fit the view.

9. Save the project

Task 2 - Align air terminals to ceiling grids.

---

1. Open the Mechanical>HVAC>Ceiling Plans>**1-Ceiling Mech** view.

2. Zoom in on the lab room in the upper left corner.

3. In the *Modify* tab>Modify panel, click ⊐ (Align).

4. Select a vertical grid line and then the side of the air terminal, as shown in Figure 2–86.

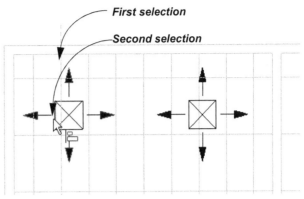

Figure 2–86

5. While still in the **Align** command, in the Options Bar, select **Multiple Alignment**.

6. Without stopping, select the following items in the order listed, as shown in Figure 2–87:
   - Horizontal grid line
   - Horizontal edge of the first air terminal
   - Horizontal edge of the 2nd air terminal

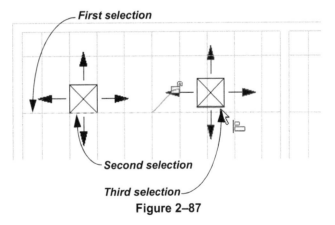

Figure 2–87

7. Press <Esc> once. This keeps you in the command but releases the alignment line.

8. Align the other air terminals to the ceiling grid, as shown in Figure 2–88.

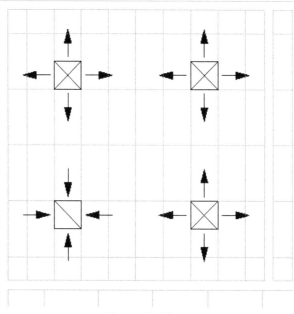

Figure 2–88

9. Use the **Align** tool with or without the multiple alignment (see which works the best for you) to move the air terminals in the other lab rooms.

10. Zoom to fit the view and then save the project.

Task 3 - Offset, trim, and split cable trays.

---

1. Open the Electrical>Power>Floor Plans>**1 - Power** view.

2. In the *Modify* tab>Modify panel, click (Offset).

3. In the Options Bar, select **Numerical**, set the *Offset* to **15'-0"**, and ensure that **Copy** is selected.

4. Hover the cursor over the vertical cable tray and ensure that the alignment line is to the right, as shown in Figure 2–89. Click to create the copy.

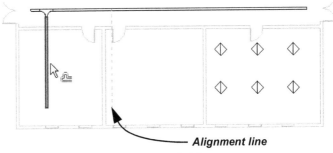

Alignment line

Figure 2–89

5. Select the new cable tray (ensuring that the offset is to the right) and continue until there are five total trays, as shown in Figure 2–90.

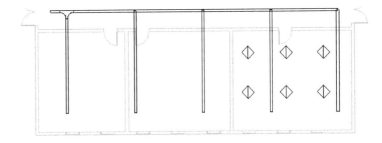

Figure 2–90

6. Click **Modify**.

7. In the *Modify* tab>Modify panel, click ⊟ (Trim/Extend Multiple Elements).

8. Select the horizontal cable tray and then draw a crossing window from right to left, as shown in Figure 2–91.

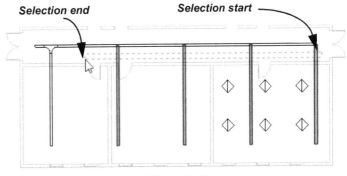

Selection end   **Selection start**

Figure 2–91

9. The cable trays are extended and fittings applied, as shown in Figure 2–92. The last cable tray does not clean up, use the 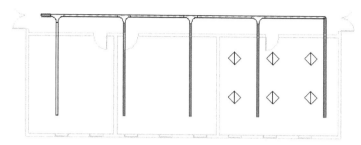 (Trim/Extend to Corner) command to finish it.

Figure 2–92

10. In the *Modify* tab>Modify panel, click ⊏⊐ (Split Element).

11. Select the point on the vertical cable tray shown in Figure 2–93. The cable tray is split and fittings are applied.

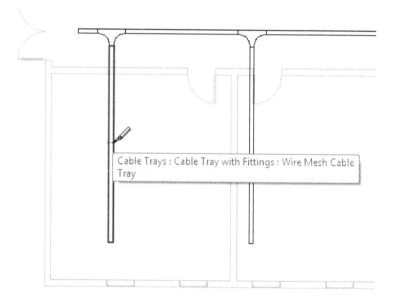

Cable Trays : Cable Tray with Fittings : Wire Mesh Cable Tray

Figure 2–93

12. Click **Modify** and select the lower part of the tray. In the Options Bar, change the *Width* to **4"**. The size changes and the fitting is applied.

- **Note:** You will learn how to justify cable trays in *Section 12.5 Adding Cable Trays and Conduit.*

13. Save the project.

Chapter Review Questions

1. What is the purpose of an alignment line?

   a. Displays when the new element you are placing or drawing is aligned with the grid system.

   b. Indicates that the new element you are placing or drawing is aligned with an existing element.

   c. Displays when the new element you are placing or drawing is aligned with a selected tracking point.

   d. Indicates that the new element is aligned with true north rather than project north.

2. Which of the following commands imports a component that is not available in your project?

   a. **Load Family**

   b. **Load Equipment**

   c. **Load Component**

   d. **Load Fixture**

3. How do you select all Lighting Fixture of various sizes, but no other elements in a view?

   a. In the Project Browser, select the *Lighting Fixtures* category.

   b. Select one Lighting Fixture, right-click and select **Select All Instances>Visible in View**.

   c. Select all of the elements in the view and use ▽ (Filter) to clear the other categories.

   d. Select one Lighting Fixture and click ▧ (Select Multiple) in the ribbon.

4. What are the two methods for starting commands such as **Move**, **Copy**, **Rotate**, **Mirror**, and **Array**?

   a. Start the command from the *Modify* tab and select the elements, or select the elements and then start the command.

   b. Start the command from the *Modify* tab and select the elements, or select the elements and then select the command from the Status Bar.

   c. Start the command from the *Modify* tab and select the elements, or select the elements, right-click, and select the command from the list.

5. Where do you change the type for a selected plumbing fixture, as shown in Figure 2–94?

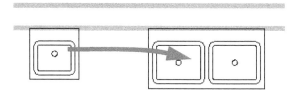

Figure 2–94

a. In the *Modify | Plumbing Fixtures* tab>Properties panel, click ⊞ (Type Properties) and select a new type in the dialog box.

b. In the Options Bar, click **Change Element Type**.

c. Select the dynamic control next to the selected plumbing fixture and select a new type in the drop-down list.

d. In Properties, select a new type in the Type Selector drop-down list.

6. Both Rotate and Array with Radial have a center of rotation that defaults to the center of the element or group of elements you have selected. How do you move the center of rotation to another point, as shown in Figure 2–95? (Select all that apply.)

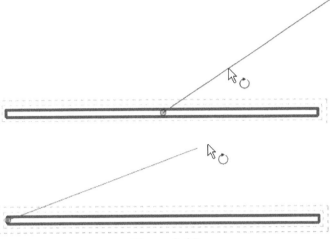

Figure 2–95

a. Select the center of rotation and drag it to a new location.

b. In the Options Bar, click **Place** and select the new point.

c. In the *Modify* tab>Placement panel, click ⌀ (Center) and select the new point.

d. Right-click and select **Snap Overrides>Centers** and select the new point.

7. Which command would you use to break part of a duct so that you can change the duct type?

a. ⊡ (Align)

b. ⇔ (Split)

c. ⇥ (Trim)

d. ⏠ (Offset)

Command Summary

Button	Command	Location
Modify Tools		
	Array	• **Ribbon:** *Modify* tab>Modify panel • **Shortcut:** AR
	Copy	• **Ribbon:** *Modify* tab>Modify panel • **Shortcut:** CO
	Copy to Clipboard	• **Ribbon:** *Modify* tab>Clipboard panel • **Shortcut:** <Ctrl>+<C>
	Delete	• **Ribbon:** *Modify* tab>Modify panel • **Shortcut:** DE
	Mirror - Draw Axis	• **Ribbon:** *Modify* tab>Modify panel • **Shortcut:** DM
	Mirror - Pick Axis	• **Ribbon:** *Modify* tab>Modify panel • **Shortcut:** MM
	Move	• **Ribbon:** *Modify* tab>Modify panel • **Shortcut:** MV
	Paste	• **Ribbon:** *Modify* tab>Clipboard panel • **Shortcut:** <Ctrl>+<V>
	Pin	• **Ribbon:** *Modify* tab>Modify panel • **Shortcut:** PN
	Rotate	• **Ribbon:** *Modify* tab>Modify panel • **Shortcut:** RO
	Scale	• **Ribbon:** *Modify* tab>Modify panel • **Shortcut:** RE
	Unpin	• **Ribbon:** *Modify* tab>Modify panel • **Shortcut:** UP
Modify Tools		
	Align	• **Ribbon:** *Modify* tab>Modify panel • **Shortcut:** AL
	Offset	• **Ribbon:** *Modify* tab>Modify panel • **Shortcut:** OF
	Split Element	• **Ribbon:** *Modify* tab>Modify panel • **Shortcut:** SL
	Trim/Extend Multiple Elements	• **Ribbon:** *Modify* tab>Modify panel

	Trim/Extend Single Element	• **Ribbon:** *Modify* tab>Modify panel
	Trim/Extend to Corner	• **Ribbon:** *Modify* tab>Modify panel • **Shortcut:** TR

Select Tools

	Drag elements on selection	• **Ribbon:** All tabs>Select panel • **Status Bar**
	Filter	• **Ribbon:** *Modify	Multi-Select* tab> Filter panel • **Status Bar**
	Select Elements By Face	• **Ribbon:** All tabs>Select panel • **Status Bar**
	Select Links	• **Ribbon:** All tabs>Select panel • **Status Bar**
	Select Pinned Elements	• **Ribbon:** All tabs>Select panel • **Status Bar**
	Select Underlay Elements	• **Ribbon:** All tabs>Select panel • **Status Bar**

Chapter

3

Introduction to Worksets

Autodesk® Revit® worksharing allows multiple team members connected on the same network the ability to co-author a single project model (one .RVT file). The appropriate team member creates a central model and worksets. Team members open and work in a local copy of the model that is linked back to the central model through saving and synchronizing.

This chapter has no practices and is meant as an introduction to worksharing because it is important to understand the terminology and proper workflow of worksharing. For more information about establishing and using worksets, refer to the ASCENT guide *Autodesk Revit: Collaboration Tools*.

Learning Objectives in This Chapter

- Review worksharing terminology and workflow.
- Learn about opening a local file to make changes to your part of a project.
- Review how to synchronize your local file with the central file, which contains changes from all the local files.

3.1 Introduction to Worksets

When a project becomes too big for one person, it needs to be subdivided so that a team of people working on the same network can work on it. Since Autodesk Revit projects include the entire building model in one file, the file needs to be separated into logical components, as shown in Figure 3–1, without losing the connection to the whole. This process is called *worksharing* and the main components are worksets.

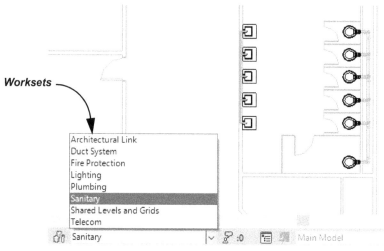

Figure 3–1

When worksets are established in a project, there is one **central file** and as many **local files** as needed for each person on the team to have a file, as shown in Figure 3–2.

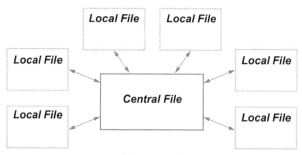

Figure 3–2

- The **central file** is created by the BIM Manager, Project Manager, or Project Lead and is stored on a server, enabling multiple users to access it.

- A **local file** is a copy of the central file that is stored on your computer.

- All local files are saved back to the central file, and updates to the central file are sent out to the local files. This way, all changes remain in one file, while the project, model, views, and sheets are automatically updated.

Workset Terminology

Workset: A collection of related elements in a project. Each user-created workset matches a part of the project that an individual team member would work on (such as specific sections of the building or the exterior shell, site, or interior partitions). There are also worksets created automatically for Families, Project Standards (such as materials and line styles), and Views. Worksets can be checked out so that others cannot modify them without permission.

Workshared file: A Revit project model that worksets have been enabled in that everyone can access and work on simultaneously.

Active workset: The active workset is the workset that all new elements are added to. It is important to verify which workset you are in before adding new elements.

Central file/model: The master project model that stores all of the worksets. This is the file to which everyone saves their changes. You should never edit this model directly.

Local file/model: A copy of the central file that is saved to your local computer. This is the file that you modify. You then save the file locally and synchronize it with the central file.

Element borrowing: Refers to the process of modifying items in the project that are not part of the workset you have checked out. This either happens automatically (if no one else has checked out a workset) or specifically, when you request to have control of the elements (if someone else has a workset checked out).

General Process of Using Worksets

1. Create a local file from the central file that is set up by the appropriate team member.
2. Open the local file and select the workset on which you need to work to make it active. This is the workset on which any new elements are placed.
3. Add, delete, and modify elements, as needed.
   - You may need to request access to elements in worksets that are currently checked out by other team members.

4. Save the local model as frequently as you would save any other project.

5. Synchronize the local model with the central model several times a day or as needed by company policy or project status.

- This reloads any changes from the central model to your local model and vice versa.

- If the option to **Save Local File before and after synchronizing with central** is checked, your local file will be saved. It is always recommended to save the local file every time you synchronize to the central file.

How To: Create a Local File

1. In the *File* tab or Quick Access Toolbar, click  (Open). In the Open dialog box, navigate to the central file server location and select the central file. Do not work in this file. Select **Create New Local**, as shown in Figure 3–3, and click **Open**.

File name:	Modern-Hotel-Life.rvt	⌄
Files of type:	All Supported Files (*.rvt, *.rfa, *.adsk, *.rte)	⌄

Worksharing

☐ Audit ☐ Detach from Central ☑ Create New Local [Open] [▼] [Cancel]

Figure 3–3

2. A copy of the project is created. It is named the same as the central file, but with your *User Name* added to the end.

- If you are working with a recently used central file, it may display in the Home Screen with the icon shown in Figure 3–4. Clicking this file automatically creates a local copy of the model. The first time you use this option, a warning displays, as shown in Figure 3–5.

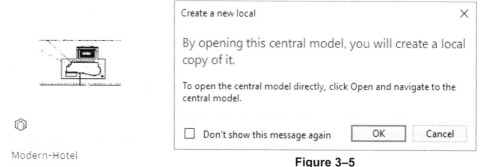

Modern-Hotel

Figure 3–4

Create a new local   ✕

By opening this central model, you will create a local copy of it.

To open the central model directly, click Open and navigate to the central model.

☐ Don't show this message again   [OK]   [Cancel]

Figure 3–5

3. You can save the file using the default name, or use

   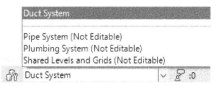 (Save As) and name the file according to your office's standard. It should include *Local* in the name to indicate that it is saved on your local computer, or that you are the only one working with that version of the file.

• Delete any old local files to ensure that you are working on the latest version.

How To: Work in a Workset-Related File

1. Open your local file.
2. In the Status Bar, expand the Active Workset drop-down list and select a workset, as shown in Figure 3–6. By setting the active workset, other people can work in the project but cannot edit elements that you add to the workset.

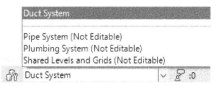

Figure 3–6

3. Work on the project as needed.

Saving Workset-Related Files

When you are using a workset-related file, you need to save the file locally and centrally.

• Save the local file frequently (every 15-30 minutes). In the Quick Access Toolbar, click 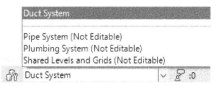 (Save) to save the local file just as you would any other project.

• Synchronize the local file with the central file periodically (every hour or two) or after you have made major changes to the project

Hint: Set up Notifications to Save and Synchronize

You can set up reminders to save and synchronize files to the central file in the Options dialog box, on the *General* pane, as shown in Figure 3–7.

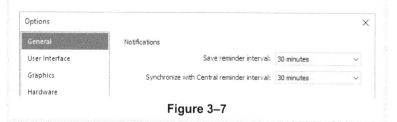

Figure 3–7

Synchronizing to the Central File

There are two methods for synchronizing to the central file. They are located in the Quick Access Toolbar or the *Collaborate* tab> Synchronize panel.

Click (Synchronize Now) to update the central file and then the local file with any changes to the central file since the last synchronization. This does not prompt you for anything. It automatically relinquishes elements borrowed from a workset used by another person, but retains worksets used by the current person.

Click (Synchronize and Modify Settings) to open the Synchronize with Central dialog box, as shown in Figure 3–8, where you can set the location of the central file, add comments, save the file locally before and after synchronization, and set the options for relinquishing worksets and elements.

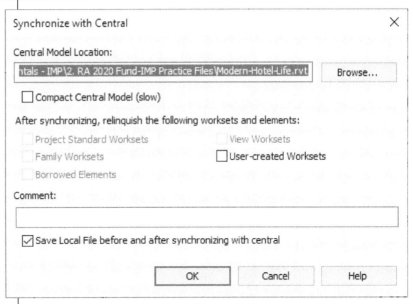

Figure 3–8

- Ensure that **Save Local file before and after synchronizing with central** is checked before clicking **OK**. Changes from the central file might have been copied into your file.

- When you close a local file without saving to the central file, you are prompted with options, as shown in Figure 3–9.

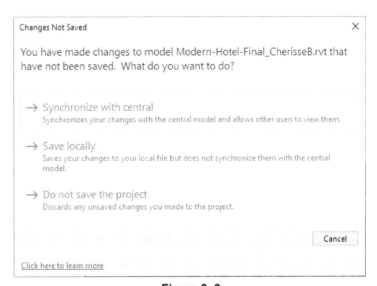

Figure 3–9

Command Summary

Button	Command	Location
💾	Save	• **Quick Access Toolbar** • **File tab:** Save • **Shortcut:** <Ctrl>+<S>
	Synchronize and Modify Settings	• **Quick Access Toolbar** • **Ribbon:** *Collaborate* tab> Synchronize panel>expand Synchronize with Central
	Synchronize Now	• **Quick Access Toolbar** • **Ribbon:** *Collaborate* tab> Synchronize panel>expand Synchronize with Central

Starting Systems Projects

MEP projects are typically started after an architectural project is underway and need to use information provided by the architect as the base for the project. You should never start your work inside of the architectural model.

You first need to create your project by starting with either the default Revit system or mechanical template or your company's custom template. Then, you will link the Revit® architectural model into your model and build the systems around them, copying and monitoring the required information from the architectural model into the systems model.

Learning Objectives in This Chapter

- Linking and importing CAD files.
- Link Revit models into the project so that you can design the systems project.
- Add levels to define floor-to-floor heights and other vertical references.
- Copy and monitor elements from linked Revit models so that you know when changes have been made.
- Run Coordination Reviews to identify changes between the current project and any linked models.
- Batch Copy elements such as air terminals, lighting fixtures, and plumbing fixtures from a linked model.

4.1 Linking and Importing CAD Files

While the Autodesk® Revit® software has become a major player in the AEC community, many firms have legacy drawings from other CAD programs and could be working with consultants that use other programs. You can import, link, and export data from a variety of programs. These can include 2D details, like a VAV Box as shown in Figure 4–1, and 3D models.

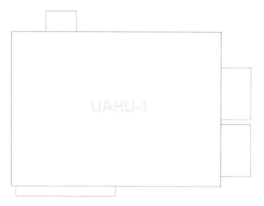

Figure 4–1

- CAD file formats that can be imported or linked include AutoCAD® (DWG and DXF), MicroStation (DGN), 3D ACIS modeling kernel (SAT), Trimble, and SketchUp (SKP).

Linking vs. Importing

- **Link:** A connection is maintained with the original file and the link updates if the original file is updated.

- **Import:** No connection is maintained with the original file. It becomes a separate element in the Autodesk Revit model.

How To: Link or Import a CAD File

1. Open the view into which you want to link or import the file.

   - For a 2D file, this should be a 2D view. For a 3D file, open a 3D view.

2. In the *Insert* tab>Link panel, click  (Link CAD), or in the *Insert* tab>Import panel, click (Import CAD).

3. In the Link CAD Formats or Import CAD Formats dialog box (shown in Figure 4–2), select the file that you want to import.

   - Select a file format in the Files of Type drop-down list to limit the files that are displayed.

Figure 4–2

4. Set the other options as shown in Figure 4–3.

Figure 4–3

5. Click **Open**.

The dialog boxes for Link CAD Formats and Import CAD Formats are the same.

Hint: Link or Import PDFs

You can link or import a PDF into Autodesk Revit as a raster image. If the PDF contains vector data, you can snap to the elements in the PDF.

- From the *Insert* tab>Import panel, click (Import PDF).
- From the *Insert* tab>Link panel, click (Link PDF).

Link and Import Options

Current view only	Determine whether the CAD file is placed in every view, or only in the current view. This is especially useful if you are working with a 2D floor plan that you only need to have in one view.
Colors	Specify the color settings. Typical Autodesk Revit projects are mainly black and white. However, other software frequently uses color. You can **Invert** the original colors, **Preserve** them, or change everything to **Black and White**.
Layers	Indicates which CAD layers are going to be brought into the model. Select how you want layers to be imported: **All**, **Visible**, or **Specify...**.
Import units	Select the units of the original file, as required. **Auto-Detect** works in most cases.
Correct Lines...	If lines in a CAD file are off axis by less than 0.1 degree selecting this option straightens them. It is selected by default.
Positioning	Specify how you want the imported file to be positioned in the current project: **Auto - Center to Center**, **Auto - Internal Origin to Internal Origin**, **Auto - By Shared Coordinates**, **Auto - Project Base Point to Project Base Point**, **Manual - Internal Origin**, **Manual - Base Point**, or **Manual - Center**. The default position is **Auto - Internal Origin to Internal Origin**.
Place at	Select a level in which to place the imported file. If you selected **Current view only**, this option is grayed out.
Orient to View	Used to orient the CAD file on import/link.

- When a file is positioned **Auto - Internal Origin to Internal Origin**, it is pinned in place and cannot be moved. To move the file, click on the pin to unpin it, as shown in Figure 4–4.

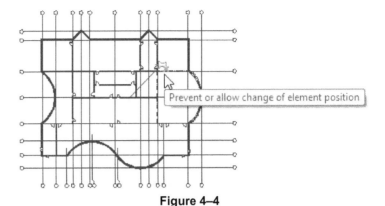

Figure 4–4

Setting an Imported or Linked File to Halftone

To see the difference between the host model elements and the linked or imported file, you can set the linked/imported file to Halftone, as shown in Figure 4–5.

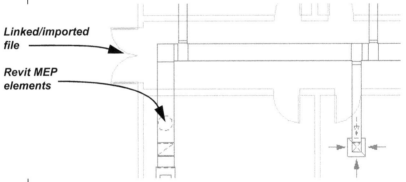

Figure 4–5

How To: Set an Element to Halftone

1. Select the imported file.
2. Right-click and select **Override Graphics in View>By Element...**.

3. In the View Specific Element Graphics dialog box, select **Halftone**, as shown in Figure 4–6.

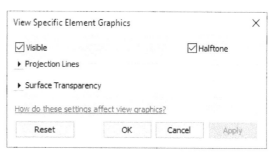

Figure 4–6

4. Click **OK**.

• You can use this method to set any element or category to halftone.

Hint: Draw Layer

Linked CAD files are typically in the background of a view. To change this, select the CAD file and in the Options Bar or in Properties, in the *Other* area, change the *Draw Layer* to **Foreground**.

4.2 Linking in Revit Models

You can link Autodesk Revit architectural or structural models directly into your systems project, which in turn becomes the host project because it will now be hosting linked models. A linked model automatically updates if the original file is changed. When the model is linked into the host project, the architectural and structural elements display in halftone, as shown in Figure 4–7.

A linked model automatically updates when the original file is changed.

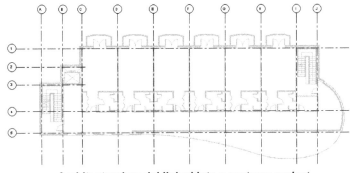

Architectural model linked into a systems project

Figure 4–7

• You can only link a model into a host project once.

• Architectural, structural, and MEP models created in the Autodesk Revit software can be linked to each other as long as they are from the same release cycle.

• When you use linked models, clashes between disciplines can be detected and information can be passed between disciplines.

How To: Add a Linked Model to a Host Project

1. In the *Insert* tab>Link panel, click (Link Revit).
2. In the Import/Link RVT dialog box, select the file that you want to link. Before opening the file, set the *Positioning*, as shown in Figure 4–8.

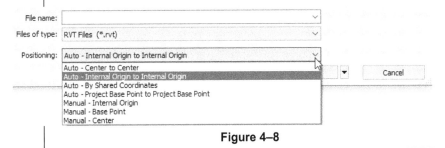

Figure 4–8

---

3. Click **Open**.

- Depending on how you decide to position the file, it is automatically placed in the project or you can manually place it with the cursor.

- As the links are loading, do not click on the screen or click any buttons. The more links present in a project, the longer it takes to load.

Hint: Preventing a Linked Model from Being Moved

Once a linked model is in the correct location, you can lock it in place to ensure it does not get moved by mistake or prevent the linked model from being selected.

- To pin the linked model in place, select it and in the *Modify* tab>Modify panel, click ⊣⊐ (Pin).

- To prevent pinned elements from being selected, in the Status Bar, click 🖳 (Select Pinned Elements).

- To toggle off the ability to select links, in the Status Bar, click 🖙 (Select Links).

If a linked model is moved, you can reposition it to the Project Base Point or Internal Origin. Right-click on the model and select the appropriate option, as shown in Figure 4–9.

Figure 4–9

Multiple Copies of Linked Models

Copied instances of a linked model are typically used when creating a master project with the same building placed in multiple locations, such as a university campus with six identical student residence halls.

- Linked models can be moved, copied, rotated, arrayed, and mirrored. There is only one linked model, and any copies are additional instances of the link.

- Copies are numbered automatically. You can change their names in Properties when the instance is selected.

- When you have placed a link in a project, you can drag and drop additional copies of the link into the project from the Project Browser>**Revit Links** node, as shown in Figure 4–10.

Figure 4–10

Managing Links

The Manage Links dialog box (shown in Figure 4–11) enables you to reload, unload, add, and remove links, and it also provides access to set other options. To open the Manage Links dialog box, in the *Insert* tab>Link panel, click 🔲 (Manage Links). Alternatively, you can go to the *Manage* tab>Manage Projects panel and click 🔲 (Manage Links).

- You can also select the link and click 🔲 (Manage Links) in the *Modify | RVT Links* tab>Link panel.

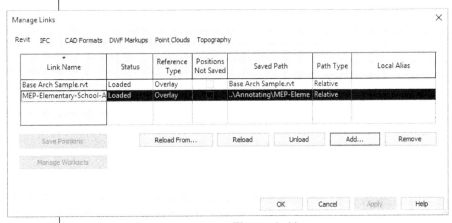

Figure 4–11

The options available include the following:

*Some of these options are also available in the Project Browser. Expand the Revit Links node, then right-click on the Revit Link and select **Reload**, **Unload** or **Reload From...**.*

- **Reload From:** Opens the Add Link dialog box, which enables you to select the file you want to reload. Use this if the linked file location or name has changed.

- **Reload:** Reloads the file without additional prompts.

- **Unload:** Unloads the file so that it the link is kept, but the file is not displayed or calculated in the project. Use **Reload** to restore it.

- **Add:** Opens the Import/Link RVT dialog box which enables you to link additional models into the host project.
- **Remove:** Deletes the link from the file.

Links can be nested into one another. How a link responds when the host project is linked into another project depends on the option in the *Reference Type* column:

- **Overlay**: The nested linked model is not referenced in the new host project.
- **Attach:** The nested linked model displays in the new host project.

The option in the *Path Type* column controls how the location of the link is remembered:

- **Relative**
  - Searches the root folder of the current project.
  - If the file is moved, the software still searches for it.
- **Absolute**
  - Searches the entire file path where the file was originally saved.
  - If the original file is moved, the software is not able to find it.
- Other options control how the linked file interfaces with Worksets and Shared Positioning.

Hint: Visibility Graphics and Linked Files

When you open the Visibility/Graphics dialog box (type **VV** or **VG**), you can modify the graphic overrides for Revit links as shown in Figure 4–12. This can help you clean up the view, or assign a view to build on.

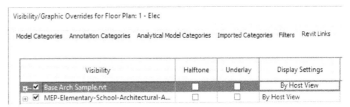

Figure 4–12

The *Display Settings* include:

- **By host view:** The display of the Revit link is based on the view properties of the current view in the host model.

- **By linked view:** The appearance of the Revit link is based on the view properties of the selected linked view and ignores the view properties of the current view.

- **Custom:** You can override all of the graphical elements.

Practice 4a

Start a Systems Project

Practice Objectives

- Start a new project from a template.
- Link an architectural model into a systems project.

In this practice, you will create a new systems project file and link a Revit architectural model into it. You will then pin the linked model in place and modify the elevation view marker locations, as shown in Figure 4–13. You will also view the linked model in 3D.

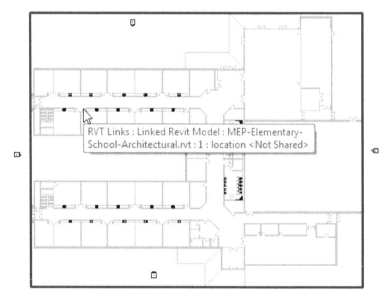

Figure 4–13

Task 1 - Create a new project.

1. In the *File* tab, click ⬜ (New).

2. In the New Project dialog box, click **Browse...**.

3. In the Choose Template dialog box, select **Imperial-Systems-Template**, click **Open**, and then click **OK**.

4. Save the project in the practice files *Starting* folder as **School-MEP.rvt**.

Task 2 - Link in a architectural model.

1. In the *Insert* tab>Link panel, click (Link Revit).

2. In the Import/Link RVT dialog box, navigate to the practice files *Starting* folder and select **School-Arch.rvt**.

3. Verify that the *Positioning* is set to **Auto - Internal Origin to Internal Origin** and then click **Open**.

4. Type **ZF** (Zoom to Fit). The new building displays in the active view and is linked into the new Revit MEP project.

Click the Select drop-down list under the Modify tool and make sure that Select Links is checked.

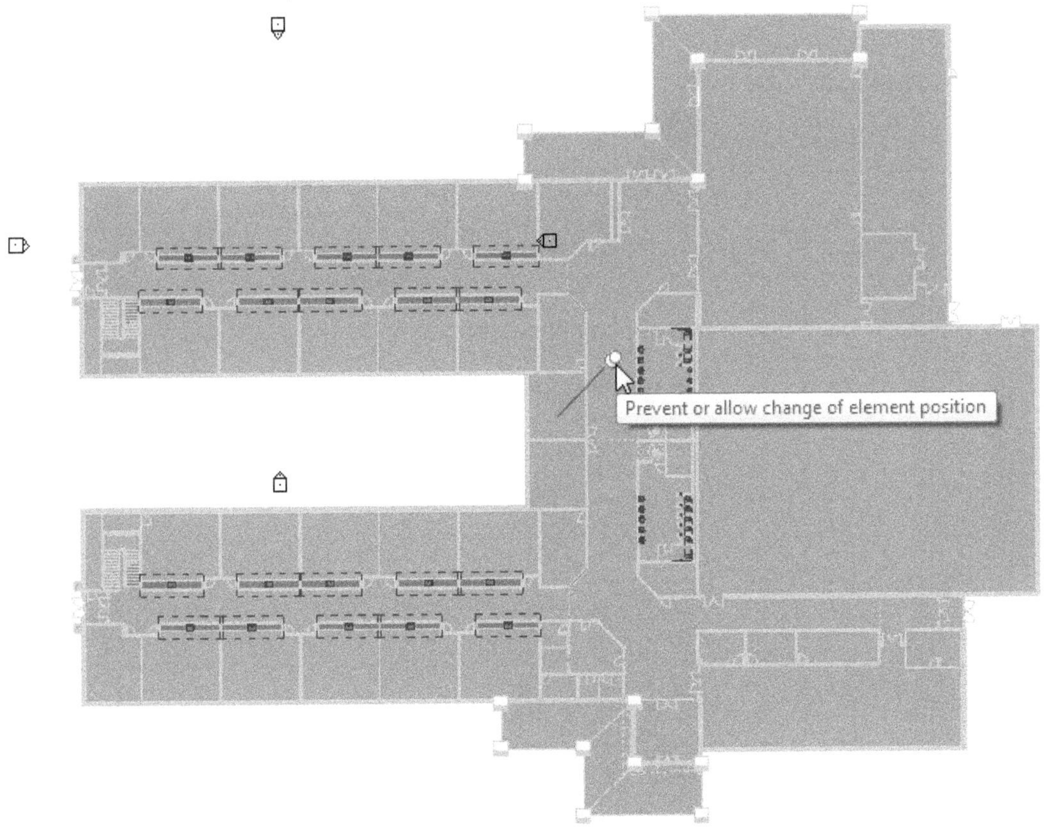

5. Select the linked model. In the *Modify | RVT Links* tab>Modify panel, click ⚲ (Pin). The pin icon displays on the linked file as shown in Figure 4–14. This keeps the linked model from being moved by accident.

Prevent or allow change of element position

Figure 4–14

6. Click in an empty space in the view to clear the selection of the linked model.

7. Move the elevation markers outside of the building, (Hint: Drag a window from left to right around each marker to select both parts.)

8. In the Quick Access Toolbar, click 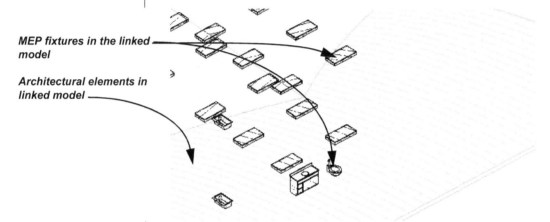 (Default 3D View.)

9. Zoom in to look at the model. All of the MEP-related elements in the architectural model display in black, while the architectural elements are grayed out, as shown in Figure 4–15.

MEP fixtures in the linked model

Architectural elements in linked model

Figure 4–15

10. Zoom to fit the view.

11. Save and close the project.

4.3 Setting Up Levels

Levels define stories and other vertical heights, as shown in Figure 4–16. The default systems template includes two levels, but you can define as many levels in a project as required. They can go below 0'-0" or in the negative (for basements) as well.

Floor levels are frequently set by the architect and need to be copied and monitored into the systems model. You can also draw levels directly in a project, as required.

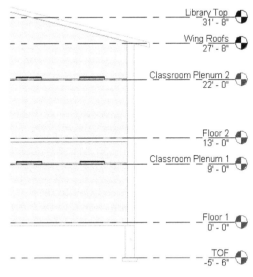

Library Top
31' - 8"

Wing Roofs
27' - 8"

Classroom Plenum 2
22' - 0"

Floor 2
13' - 0"

Classroom Plenum 1
9' - 0"

Floor 1
0' - 0"

TOF
-5' - 6"

Figure 4–16

- You must be in an elevation or section view to define levels.

- Once you constrain an element to a level it moves with the level when the level is changed.

How To: Create Levels

1. Open an elevation or section view.

2. In the *Architecture* tab>Datum panel, click ⌖ (Level), or type **LL**.

3. In the Type Selector, set the Level type if needed.

4. In the Options Bar, select or clear **Make Plan View** as needed. You can also click **Plan View Types...** to select the types of views to create when you place the level.

5. In the *Modify | Place Level* tab>Draw panel, click:

   - ╱ (Line) to draw a level.

   - ⬦ (Pick Lines) to select an element using an offset.

   Be careful when you use **Pick Lines** that you do not place levels on top of each other or other elements by mistake.

- Level names are automatically incremented as you place them. This automatic numbering is most effective when you use names such as Floor 1, Floor 2, etc. (as opposed to First Floor, Second Floor, etc.). This also makes it easier to find the view in the Project Browser.

- A fast way to create multiple levels is to use the ✎ (Pick Lines) option using an *Offset*. In the Options Bar, specify an *Offset,* select an existing level, and then pick above or below to place the new level, as shown in Figure 4–17.

You specify above or below the offset by hovering the cursor on the needed side.

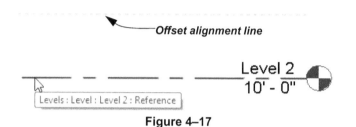

Figure 4–17

- When using the ✎ (Line) option, alignments and temporary dimensions help you place the line correctly, as shown in Figure 4–18.

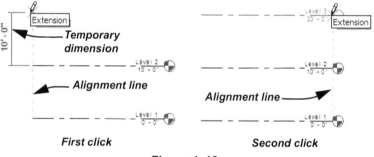

First click   Second click

Figure 4–18

- Sketch the level lines from left to right or right to left to keep consistent.

- You can also use ⟳ (Copy) to duplicate level lines. The level names are incremented but a plan view is not created.

- Levels display in the default 3D view. They can be modified and copied but you cannot create them in this view.

- Levels can be hidden in any view.

Modifying Levels

You can change levels using standard controls and temporary dimensions, as shown in Figure 4–19. You can also make changes in the Properties palette.

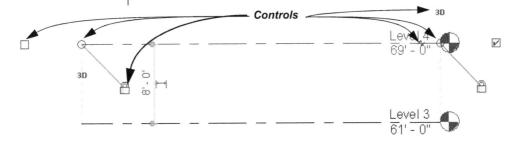

Figure 4–19

- ☑ ☐ (Hide / Show Bubble) displays on either end of the level line and toggles the level head symbol and level information on or off.

- 2D   3D (Switch to 3d / 2d extents) controls whether any movement or adjustment to the level line is reflected in other views (3D) or only affects the current view (2D).

- ↻ (Modify the level by dragging its model end) at each end of the line enables you to drag the level head to a new location.

- 🔒 🔓 (Create or remove a length or alignment constraint) controls whether the level is locked in alignment with the other levels. If it is locked and the level line is stretched, all of the other level lines stretch as well. If it is unlocked, the level line stretches independent of the other levels.

- Click ⌁ (Add Elbow) to add a jog to the level line as shown in Figure 4–20. Drag the shape handles to new locations as needed. This is a view-specific change.

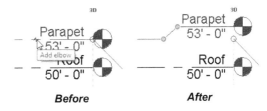

Before   *After*

Figure 4–20

• To change the level name or elevation, double-click on the information next to the level head, or select the level and modify the *Name* or *Elevation* fields in Properties, as shown in Figure 4–21.

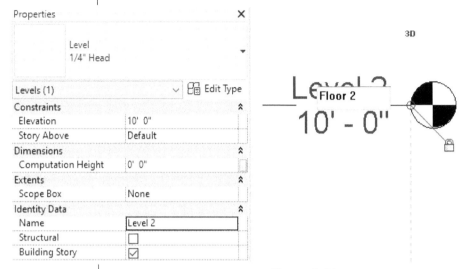

Figure 4–21

• When you rename a level, an alert box opens prompting you to rename the corresponding views, as shown in Figure 4–22.

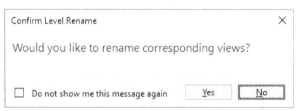

Figure 4–22

- If you delete a level, the views related to that level are also delete. A warning displays as shown in Figure 4–23.

Figure 4–23

Hint: Propagating Datum Extents

Datum elements such as levels and column grids might not always display as expected in a view. Select the levels or grids in a view in which they are displayed. In the *Modify contextual tab>Datum panel*, click (Propagate Extents). In the Propagate datum extents dialog box (shown in Figure 4–24), select the views to project the levels or grid lines to.

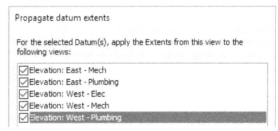

Figure 4–24

- (Propagate Extents) is particularly useful to make levels and grids display the same in all views.

Creating Plan Views

By default, when you place a level, plan views for that level are automatically created. If **Make Plan View** was toggled off when adding the level, or if the level was copied, you can create plan views to match the levels.

- Level heads with views are blue and level heads without associated views are black, as shown in Figure 4–25.

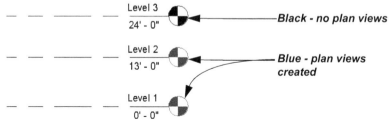

Figure 4–25

How To: Create Plan Views

1. In the *View* tab>Create panel, expand 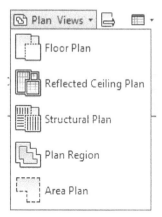 (Plan Views) and select the type of plan view you want to create, as shown in Figure 4–26.

Figure 4–26

The dialog box will be different depending on which Plan View you are creating.

2. In the New Plan dialog box, uncheck **Do not duplicate existing views**.
   - When **Do not duplicate existing views** is selected, views without the selected plan type display in the list.
3. To specify a view template, click **Edit Type**.
4. In the Type Properties dialog box, select the button beside *View Template applied to new views*.

Hold <Ctrl> or <Shift> to select more than one level.

5. In the Apply View Template dialog box, select the appropriate view template name. Click **OK** twice.
6. In the New Plan dialog box, select the levels for which you want to create plan views, as shown in Figure 4–27.

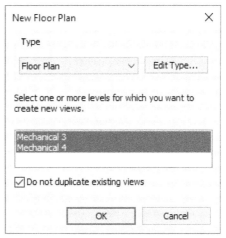

Figure 4–27

• System projects are typically divided into disciplines and sub-disciplines, as shown in Figure 4–28.

• You can specify the discipline after the plan is created in Properties, as shown in Figure 4–29.

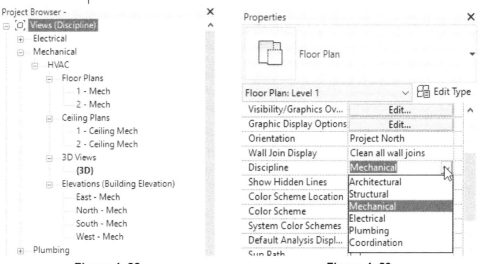

Figure 4–28   **Figure 4–29**

4.4 Copying and Monitoring Elements

Once a linked architectural model is in place, the next step is to copy and/or monitor elements that you need from the linked file into the systems project. These elements most often include grids and levels. Other elements commonly include lighting fixtures (as shown in Figure 4–30), plumbing fixtures, mechanical equipment, and sprinklers. A monitoring system keeps track of the copied elements and prompts for updates if something is changed. The ⌊∿⌋ (Monitor) icon indicates the element(s) is being monitored.

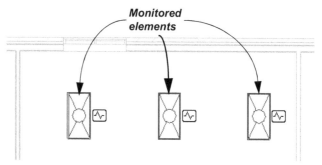

Figure 4–30

When starting the Copy/Monitor command, you can choose **Use Current Project** or **Select Link**. Use Select Link to monitor a linked file's elements if they could potentially be moved and affect your system.

- **Copy:** Copies the selected element from the linked model to the current model or host model, then monitors the element for any changes that may happen in the linked model.

- **Monitor:** Compares two elements of the same type against each other, either from a linked model to the current project (as shown in Figure 4–31) or in the current project.

Figure 4–31

How To: Copy and Monitor Elements from a Linked File

1. In the *Collaborate* tab>Coordinate panel, expand (Copy/Monitor) and click (Select Link).
2. Select the link.
3. In the *Copy/Monitor* tab>Tools panel, click (Copy) or (Monitor).
4. If copying from the linked file, select each element that you want to copy. Alternatively, use the **Multiple** option:
   - In the Options Bar, select **Multiple**, as shown in Figure 4–32.

Figure 4–32

   - Hold <Ctrl> and select the elements that you want to copy into your model individually, or use a pick and drag window around multiple elements.
   - In the Options Bar, click **Finish**.

   If monitoring elements in the current project with elements in the linked model, first select the element in the current project, and then select the element in the linked model.

5. Click (Finish) to end the session of Copy/Monitor.

Warnings about duplicated or renamed types might display.

How To: Copy and Monitor Elements in the Current Project.

1. In the *Collaborate* tab>Coordinate panel, expand

    (Copy/Monitor) and click   (Use Current Project).

2. In the *Copy/Monitor* tab>Tools panel, click   (Copy) or

    (Monitor).

3. Select the two elements you want to monitor.

4. Repeat the process for any additional elements.

5. Click   (Finish) to end the command.

- The elements do not have to be at the same elevation or location for the software to monitor them.

Practice 4b | Copy and Monitor Elements

Practice Objectives

- Modify existing levels.
- Copy and monitor levels.
- Add levels.

In this practice, you will use **Copy/Monitor** to copy and monitor levels from the architectural model to the MEP project, as shown in Figure 4–33. You will also add levels and then monitor them against other levels.

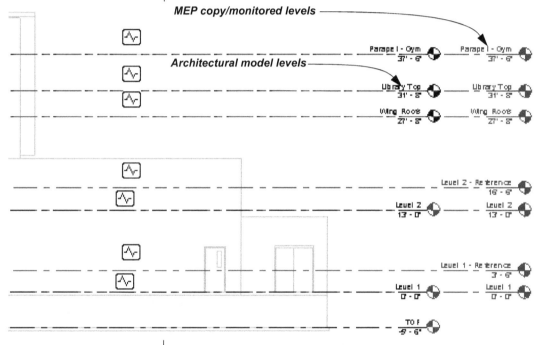

Figure 4–33

Task 1 - Match existing levels to levels in the linked model.

1. In the practice files *Starting* folder, open **Levels-School-MEP.rvt**.

2. Open the Mechanical>HVAC>Elevations (Building Elevations)>**East - Mech** view.

3. There are two levels in the host project. Select the linked architectural model to help you distinguish between them, as shown in Figure 4–34.

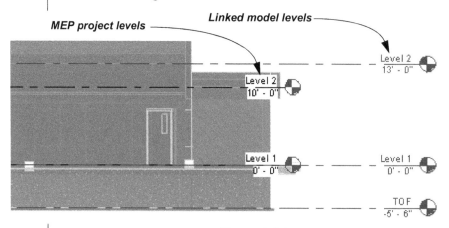

Figure 4–34

4. Click ⬉ (Modify).

5. In the *Modify* tab>Modify panel, click ⬚ (Align).

If required, press <Tab> to select the level in the host project, and not the linked model.

6. In the linked model, select **Level 2** and in the host project, select **Level 2**. The levels are now at **13'-0"**.

7. Click ⬉ (Modify) and select one of the level lines in the host project. Select the control and drag it to the side, as shown in Figure 4–35.

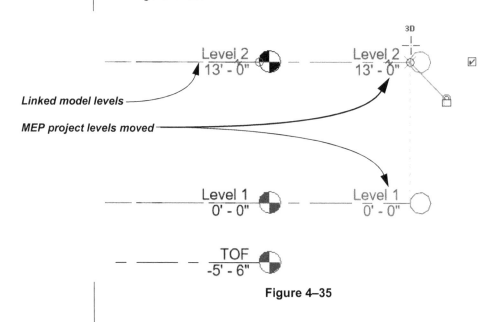

Figure 4–35

8. Save the project.

Task 2 - Copy and monitor levels.

1. In the *Collaborate* tab>Coordinate panel, expand 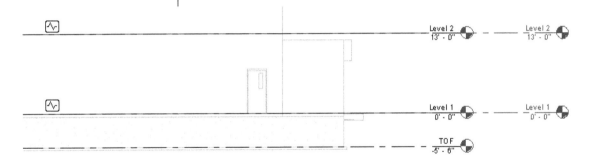 (Copy/Monitor) and click (Select Link).

2. Select the architectural linked model.

3. In the *Copy/Monitor* tab>Tools panel, click (Monitor).

4. In the host project, select **Level 1**. In the linked model, select **Level 1**. Repeat for **Level 2.**

5. In the Copy/Monitor panel, click (Finish). The levels are now monitored. You will see the monitored symbol when you select on the levels, as shown in Figure 4–36.

Figure 4–36

6. Select **Level 2** in the host project. Change the *Height* to **14'-0"** (use temporary dimensions or change the number below the level name). A Warning dialog box opens as shown in Figure 4–37.

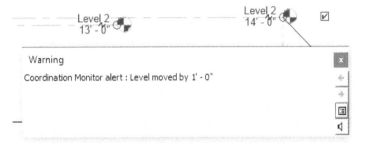

Figure 4–37

7. Close the Warning dialog box and undo the level height change.

8. In the *Collaborate* tab>Coordinate panel, expand (Copy/Monitor) and click (Select Link).

9. Select the architectural linked model.

10. In the *Copy/Monitor* tab>Tools panel, click (Copy).

11. Select the top three levels. They are reference levels used to create the heights of spaces. Close any alert dialog boxes that may pop up.

12. In the Copy/Monitor panel, click (Finish).

13. Drag the level bubbles over so that they match with the levels you moved earlier.

14. Save the project.

Task 3 - Add and monitor levels.

---

1. In the *Architecture* tab>Datum panel, click (Level).

2. In the *Modify | Place Level* tab>Draw panel, click (Pick Lines).

3. In the Options Bar, clear **Make Plan View** and set the *Offset* to **3'-6"**.

4. Hover the cursor over **Level 1** and verify that the alignment line for the offset is above the level as shown in Figure 4–38.

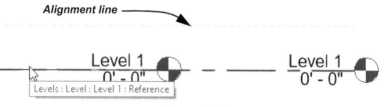

Figure 4–38

5. Click on **Level 1** to place the new level.

6. Repeat with **Level 2** and then click (Modify) to end the command.

7. Click on the name of new level above **Level 1** and change it to **Level 1 - Reference**, as shown in Figure 4–39. Repeat with the new level above **Level 2** and name it **Level 2 - Reference**.

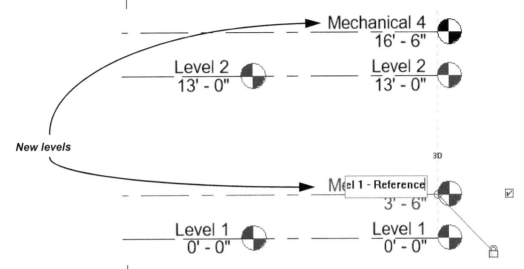

Figure 4–39

8. In the *Collaborate* tab>Coordinate panel, expand (Copy/Monitor) and click (Select Link).

9. Select the architectural linked model.

10. In the *Copy/Monitor* tab>Tools panel, click (Monitor).

11. In the host project, select **Level 1 - Reference**. In the linked model, select **Level 1**. Repeat for **Level 2 - Reference** and **Level 2.**

12. In the Copy/Monitor panel, click (Finish).

13. Zoom out, save, and close the project.

By monitoring the reference levels to the levels in the linked project, any changes to the linked project (such as a name change) are automatically updated in the reference levels as well.

4.5 Coordinating Linked Models

Monitoring elements identifies changes in the data and changes in placement. For example, if you move a grid line, a Coordination Monitor alert displays, as shown in Figure 4–40. You can run a Coordination Review to correct or accept these changes.

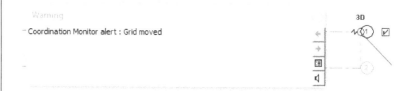

Figure 4–40

- If you open a project with a linked file that contains elements that have been modified and monitored, the Warning shown in Figure 4–41 displays.

Figure 4–41

- Warnings do not prevent you from making a change, but rather they alert you that the element is monitored and requires further coordination.

- If you no longer want an element to be monitored, select it and in the associated *Modify* tab>Monitor panel, click (Stop Monitoring).

How To: Run a Coordination Review

1. In the *Collaborate* tab>Coordinate panel, expand 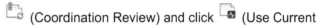 (Coordination Review) and click ⬛ (Use Current Project) or ⬛ (Select Link). The Coordination Review dialog box lists any conflicts detected, as shown in Figure 4–42.

   • If there are no conflicts, the *Message* area is empty.

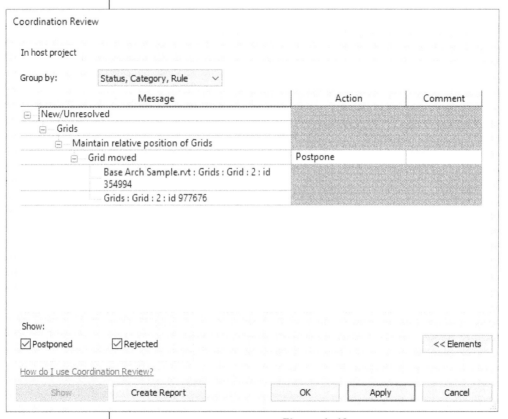

Figure 4–42

2. Use the Group by: drop-down list to group the information by **Status**, **Category**, and **Rule** in a variety of different ways. This is important if you have many elements to review.

3. Select an Action for each conflict related to the elements involved, as shown in Figure 4–43.

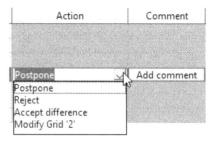

Figure 4–43

- **Postpone:** Do nothing, but leave it to be handled later.
- **Reject:** Do not accept the change. The change needs to be made in the other model.
- **Accept Difference:** Make no change to the monitored element in the current project, but accept the change (such as a distance between the elements) in the monitor status.
- **Rename/Modify/Move:** Apply the change to the monitored element.
- Other options display when special cases occur. See the Autodesk Revit help files for more information.

4. Add a comment, click **Add comment** in the column to the right. This enables you to make a note about the change, such as the date of the modification
5. Select the element names or click **Show** to display any items in conflict. Clicking **Show** changes the view to center the elements in your screen. Selecting the name does not change the view.
6. Click **Create Report** to create an HTML report that you can share with other users, as shown in Figure 4–44.

Revit Coordination Report

In host project

New/Unresolved	Plumbing Fixtures	Maintain relative position of Fixtures	Relative position of two Fixtures changed	Plumbing Fixtures : Sink_Kitchen-Single[1] : Mark 1 : id 734856 MEP-Elementary-School-Architectural.rvt : Plumbing Fixtures : Sink_Kitchen-Single[1] : Mark 80 : id 329165

Figure 4–44

Practice 4c

Coordinate Linked Models

Practice Objectives

- Make a modification to an architectural model.
- Run a Coordination Review.

In this practice, you will make a modification to the architectural model, and then open the systems project which prompts you of the change. You will then run a Coordination Review and update the systems project to match the change in the architectural model, as shown in Figure 4–45.

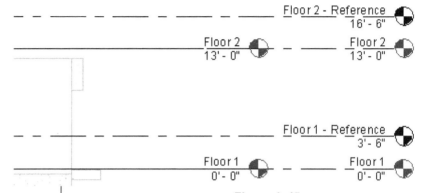

Figure 4–45

1. Close the previous practice's project if you have not already done so. You cannot open a linked file with it open.

2. In the practice files *Starting* folder, open the project **School-Arch.rvt**. This is the file that is linked into the MEP project.

3. In the Project Browser, open the Elevations (Building Elevation)>Architectural>**East** view.

4. Zoom in on the level names to the right of the elevation.

5. Select **Level 1** and change the *name* to **Floor 1**, as shown in Figure 4–46.

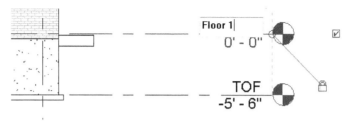

Figure 4–46

6. Repeat with **Level 2** and rename it to **Floor 2**.

7. Save and close the project.

8. In the practice files *Starting* folder, open the project **Coordinate-School-MEP.rvt**. A Warning dialog box opens, prompting you that the linked model needs a Coordination Review.

9. Click **OK**.

10. Open the Mechanical>HVAC>Elevation (Building Elevation)> **East - Mech** view and zoom in on the level names. The linked model displays the updated names but the host file has not yet been updated as shown in Figure 4–47.

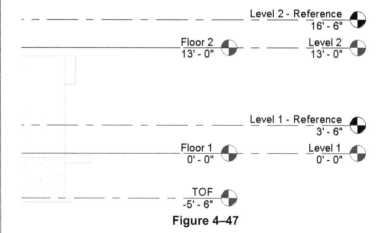

Figure 4–47

11. Select the linked model.

12. In the *Modify | RVT Links* tab>Monitor panel, click (Coordination Review).

13. In the Coordination Review dialog box, expand each of the New/Unresolved>Levels>Maintain Name>*Name changed* categories to display the proposed changes.

14. Select one of the **Name changed** options to display the related levels highlighted in the view as shown in Figure 4–48. In the example, the software recognizes the monitoring connection between **Level 2** in the host project with **Floor 2** in the linked model.

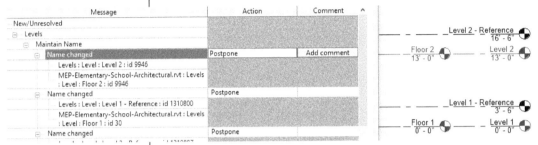

Figure 4–48

15. Next to each N*ame changed* message, expand the list in the *Action* column and select **Rename Element** as shown for Level 2 in Figure 4–49.

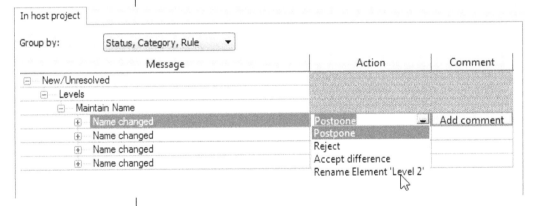

Figure 4–49

16. Click **OK**.

17. The levels in the host project are renamed as shown in Figure 4–50.

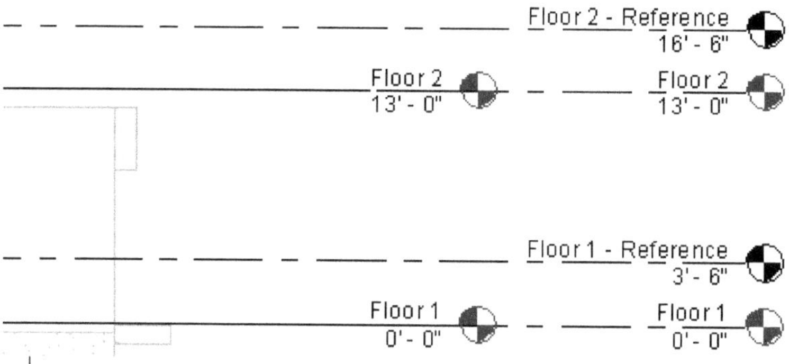

Figure 4–50

18. Save and close the model.

4.6 Batch Copying Fixtures

MEP fixtures can be copied and monitored from linked models. To make the process of copy/monitor more effective, you can set the behavior of various categories as they are copied, as shown in the Coordination Settings dialog box in Figure 4–51. In this dialog box, you can also prepare elements to be batch copy/monitored.

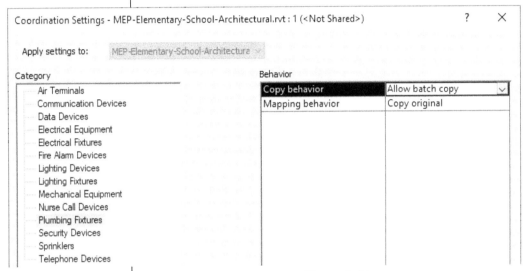

Figure 4–51

- Only Autodesk Revit MEP fixtures in the linked model can be copied and monitored. This process cannot be used for non-MEP elements in the host project.

- If a linked model has nested links you can only copy and monitor fixtures from primary linked model.

- Create the default settings before you start to copy and monitor. This saves you time and reduces errors.

How To: Define Default Coordination Settings

1. In the *Collaborate* tab>Coordinate panel, expand

    (Copy/Monitor) and click (Select Link). Alternatively, you can go to the *Collaborate* tab>Coordinate panel and click

    (Coordination Settings).
2. Select the linked model you want to work with.

3. In the *Copy/Monitor* tab>Tools panel, click 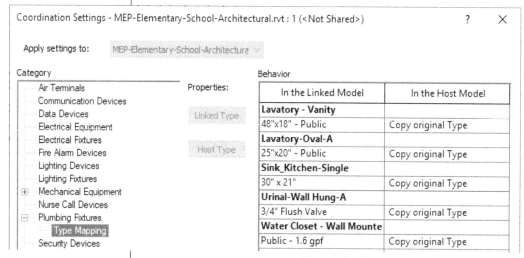 (Coordination Settings).

4. In the Coordination Settings dialog box, in the *Category* area, select the type of fixtures you want to modify.

5. In the *Behavior* area, specify the following:

Copy behavior	**Allow batch copy:** You can use the batch copy command on this category.
	Copy individually: You need to select each element in this category you want to copy.
	Ignore category: Prevents you from copying elements from this category.
Mapping behavior	**Copy original:** Copy exact replicas of the fixtures in this category.
	Specify type mapping: Specify the fixtures you want to use in place of the linked models component.

6. If you select **Specify type mapping**, in the *Category* area, select **Type Mapping**. Then you can set up the coordination between the linked model and the host project, as shown in Figure 4–52.

Coordination Settings - MEP-Elementary-School-Architectural.rvt : 1 (<Not Shared>)   ?   ×

Apply settings to: MEP-Elementary-School-Architecture

Category

- Air Terminals
- Communication Devices
- Data Devices
- Electrical Equipment
- Electrical Fixtures
- Fire Alarm Devices
- Lighting Devices
- Lighting Fixtures
- ⊞ Mechanical Equipment
- Nurse Call Devices
- ⊟ Plumbing Fixtures
  - Type Mapping
- Security Devices

Properties: Linked Type   Host Type

Behavior

In the Linked Model	In the Host Model
Lavatory - Vanity	
48"x18" - Public	Copy original Type
Lavatory-Oval-A	
25"x20" - Public	Copy original Type
Sink_Kitchen-Single	
30" x 21"	Copy original Type
Urinal-Wall Hung-A	
3/4" Flush Valve	Copy original Type
Water Closet - Wall Mounte	
Public - 1.6 gpf	Copy original Type

Figure 4–52

7. Click **Save & Close**.

Batch Copying Fixtures

When working with a project in which the architect has placed most of the fixtures and devices, you can use a batch copying process that saves you the time it would take to select each element.

- It is recommended that you set up the Coordination Settings for the linked model before you start the process. However, you can also do this before copying in the fixtures.

- Copy levels first before you copy fixtures into the project.

How To: Batch Copy Fixtures

1. Start the **Copy/Monitor** process and set the **Coordination Settings** for a selected linked model.

2. In the *Copy/Monitor* tab>Tools panel, click 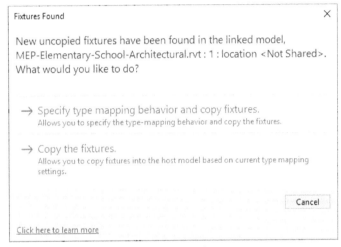 (Batch Copy).

3. In the Fixtures Found dialog box shown in Figure 4–53, select **Specify type mapping behavior and copy fixtures** or **Copy the fixtures**.

Fixtures Found ✕

New uncopied fixtures have been found in the linked model, MEP-Elementary-School-Architectural.rvt : 1 : location <Not Shared>. What would you like to do?

→ Specify type mapping behavior and copy fixtures.
Allows you to specify the type-mapping behavior and copy the fixtures.

→ Copy the fixtures.
Allows you to copy fixtures into the host model based on current type mapping settings.

Cancel

Click here to learn more

Figure 4–53

4. The elements are copied into the host project and set to be monitored, as shown in Figure 4–54.

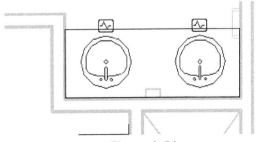

Figure 4–54

If an element of that name already exists in the project, a Warning dialog box opens prompting you the copied element has been given a new name.

- If batch copied elements are added to the linked file, they are copied into the project when it is reloaded or reopened.

Practice 4d | Batch Copy Fixtures - Mechanical

Practice Objectives

- Set up the coordination settings.
- Batch copy fixtures from the architectural model.

In this practice, you will set up coordination settings to select the types of elements you want to copy and monitor. You will then use **Batch Copy** to copy in MEP fixtures, as shown in Figure 4–55.

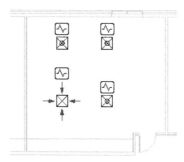

Figure 4–55

1. In the practice files *Starting* folder, open the project **Batch-School-MEP.rvt**.

2. Open the Mechanical>HVAC>Floor Plans>**1 - Mech** view.

3. Air terminals in the linked model display darker in this view, but are not in the host project.

4. In the *Collaborate* tab>Coordinate panel, expand

   ![icon] (Copy/Monitor) and click ![icon] (Select Link), then select the linked model.

5. In the *Copy/Monitor* tab>Tools panel, click ![icon] (Coordination Settings).

6. Select the **Air Terminals** category and set the *Copy behavior* to **Allow batch copy** and the *Mapping behavior* to **Specify type mapping**, as shown in Figure 4–56.

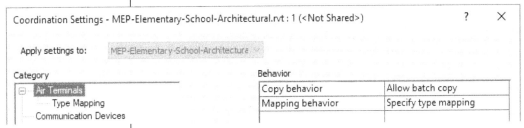

Figure 4–56

7. In the *Category* area, select **Air Terminals>Type Mapping**.

It is important to select the MEP fixtures because they have connectors. Architectural fixtures typically do not have connectors.

8. In the *Behavior* area, in the *In the Host Model* column, set the following, as shown in Figure 4–57:

- *Return Diffuser - Hosted: 24 x 24:* **Return Diffuser: 24 x 24 Face 12 x 12 Connection**
- *Supply Diffuser: 24 x 12:* **Don't copy this Type**
- *Supply Diffuser: 24 x 24:* **Supply Diffuser - Round Neck - Ceiling Mounted: 24x24x10 In Neck**

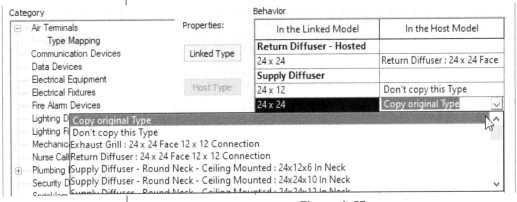

Figure 4–57

9. Click **Save & Close**.

10. In the *Copy/Monitor* tab>Tools panel, click (Batch Copy).

11. In the Fixtures Found dialog box, select **Copy the fixtures**.

12. In the Copy/Monitor panel, click (Finish).

13. Zoom in on some of the classrooms and draw a window selection around the air terminals to show the monitoring icon, as shown in Figure 4–58.

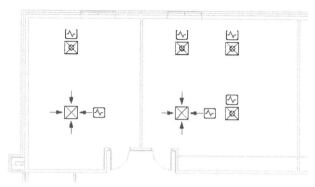

Figure 4–58

14. Zoom out to see the full view.

15. Save and close the project.

Practice 4e

Batch Copy Fixtures - Electrical

Practice Objectives

- Set up the coordination settings.
- Batch copy fixtures from the architectural model.

In this practice, you will set up coordination settings to select the types of elements you want to copy and monitor. You will then use **Batch Copy** to copy in MEP fixtures, as shown in Figure 4–59.

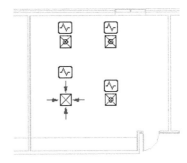

Figure 4–59

1. In the practice files *Starting* folder, open the project **Batch-School-MEP.rvt**.

2. Open the Electrical>Lighting>Floor Plans>**1 - Lighting** view.

3. The lighting fixtures in the linked model display darker in this view but are not yet copied into the host project. Zoom into the upper left rooms to see the style of the lighting fixture, as shown in Figure 4–60.

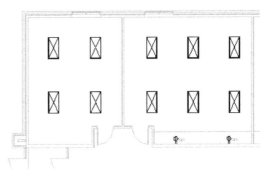

Figure 4–60

4. In the *Collaborate* tab>Coordinate panel, expand
   ![icon] (Copy/Monitor) and click ![icon] (Select Link), then select the linked model.

5. In the *Copy/Monitor* tab>Tools panel, click ![icon] (Coordination Settings).

6. Select the **Lighting Fixtures** category and set the *Copy behavior* to **Allow batch copy** and the *Mapping behavior* to **Specify type mapping**, as shown in Figure 4–61.

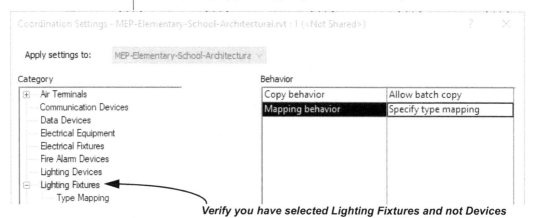

Verify you have selected Lighting Fixtures and not Devices

Figure 4–61

7. In the *Category* area, select **Lighting Fixtures>Type Mapping**.

It is important to select the MEP fixtures because they have connectors. Architectural fixtures typically do not have connectors.

8. In the *Behavior* area, in the *In the Host Model* column, set the following, as shown in Figure 4–62:
   * *Troffer Light - 2x4: 2 Lamp - 120V:* **Troffer Light - 2x4 Parabolic: 2'x 4' (2 Lamp) - 120V**
   * *Troffer Light - 2x4: 2 Lamp -227V:* **Don't copy this Type**
   * *Troffer Light - 2x4: 4 Lamp -120V:* **Don't copy this Type**
   * *Troffer Light - 2x4: 4 Lamp -227V:* **Don't copy this Type**

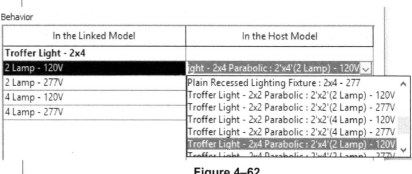

Figure 4–62

9. Click **Save & Close**.

10. In the *Copy/Monitor* tab>Tools panel, click 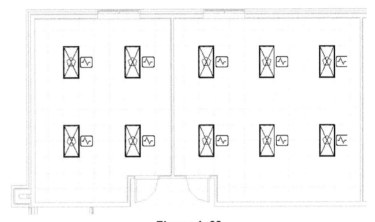 (Batch Copy).

11. In the Fixtures Found dialog box, select **Copy the fixtures**.

12. In the Copy/Monitor panel, click (Finish).

13. Zoom in on some of the classrooms and draw a window selection around both of the lighting fixtures. They have been copied into the project and the monitoring icon displays as shown in Figure 4–63.

Figure 4–63

14. Zoom out to see the full view.

15. Save and close the project.

Practice 4f

Batch Copy Fixtures - Plumbing

Practice Objectives

- Set up the coordination settings.
- Batch copy fixtures from the architectural model.

In this practice, you will set up coordination settings to select the types of elements you want to copy and monitor. You will then use **Batch Copy** to copy in MEP fixtures, as shown in Figure 4–64.

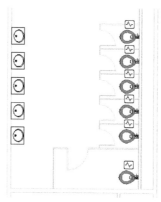

Figure 4–64

1. In the practice files *Starting* folder, open the project **Batch-School-MEP.rvt**.

2. Open the Plumbing>Floor Plans>**1 - Plumbing** view.

3. Plumbing fixtures in the linked model display darker in this view but are not yet copied into the host project.

4. In the *Collaborate* tab>Coordinate panel, expand (Copy/Monitor) and click (Select Link), then select the linked model.

5. In the *Copy/Monitor* tab>Tools panel, click (Coordination Settings).

6. Select the **Plumbing Fixtures** category and set the *Copy behavior* to **Allow batch copy** and the *Mapping behavior* to **Specify type mapping**, as shown in Figure 4–65.

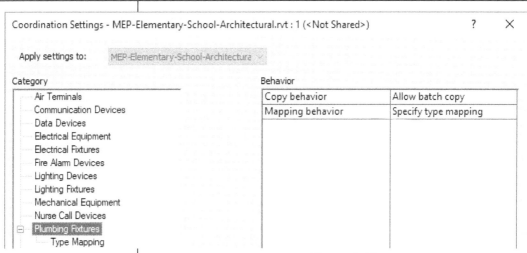

Figure 4–65

7. In the *Category* area, select **Plumbing Fixtures>Type Mapping**.

8. In the *Behavior* area, in the *In the Host Model* column, set the following, as shown in Figure 4–66:
   - *Lavatory - Vanity:* **Don't copy this Type**
   - *Lavatory-Oval-A:* **Don't copy this Type**
   - *Sink_Kitchen-Single:* **Don't copy this Type**
   - *Urinal-Wall Hung-A:* **Urinal - Wall Hung: ¾" Flush Valve**
   - *Water Closet - Wall Mounted:* **Water Closet - Flush Valve - Wall Mounted: Public - 1.6gpf**

It is important to select the MEP fixtures because they have connectors. Architectural fixtures typically do not have connectors.

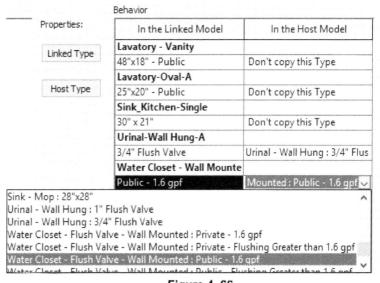

Figure 4–66

9. Click **Save & Close**.

10. In the *Copy/Monitor* tab>Tools panel, click (Batch Copy).

11. In the Fixtures Found dialog box, select **Copy the fixtures**.

12. In the Copy/Monitor panel, click ✓ (Finish).

13. Zoom in on one of the restrooms and draw a window selection around both the lavatories and water closets. Only the water closets are copied into the project, as shown in Figure 4–67.

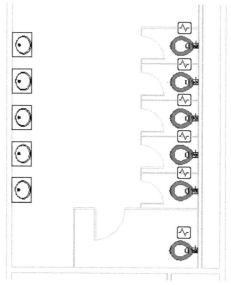

Figure 4–67

14. Zoom out to see the full view.

15. Save and close the project.

Chapter Review Questions

1. What type of view do you need to be in to add a level to your project?

   a. Any non-plan view.

   b. As this is done using a dialog box, the view does not matter.

   c. Any view except for 3D.

   d. Any section or elevation view.

2. Which of the following elements can be copied and monitored? (Select all that apply.)

   a. Plumbing Fixtures

   b. Levels

   c. Ducts

   d. Electrical Fixtures

3. Which of the following elements can be batch copied and monitored? (Select all that apply.)

   a. Plumbing Fixtures

   b. Levels

   c. Ducts

   d. Electrical Fixtures

4. On which of the following element types can a coordination review with the host project be performed?

   a. CAD link

   b. CAD import

   c. Revit link

   d. Revit import

5. When linking an architectural model, what should be done to keep the linked model from moving?

   a. Lock the model.

   b. Pin the model.

   c. Center the model.

   d. Coordinate the model.

6. How many times can one project file be linked into another project?

   a. Once

   b. It is limited by the size of the link.

   c. As many as you want.

Command Summary

Button	Command	Location
General Tools		
	Level	• **Ribbon:** *Architecture* tab>Datum panel • Shortcut: LL
	Override By Category	• **Ribbon:** *Modify* tab>View panel, expand Override Graphics in View • **Shortcut Menu:** Override Graphics in View>By Category...
	Override By Element	• **Ribbon:** *Modify* tab>View panel, expand Override Graphics in View • **Shortcut Menu:** Override Graphics in View>By Element...
	Pin	• **Ribbon:** *Modify* tab>Modify Panel
Linked Revit and CAD Files		
	Coordination Review	• **Ribbon:** *Collaborate* tab>Coordinate panel
	Copy (from linked file)	• **Ribbon:** *Copy/Monitor* tab>Tools panel
	Copy/Monitor> Select Link	• **Ribbon:** *Collaborate* tab>Coordinate panel, expand Copy/Monitor
	Copy/Monitor> Use Current Project	• **Ribbon:** *Collaborate* tab>Coordinate panel, expand Copy/Monitor
	Import CAD	• **Ribbon:** *Insert* tab>Import panel
	Link CAD	• **Ribbon:** *Insert* tab>Link panel
	Link Revit	• **Ribbon:** *Insert* tab>Link panel
	Manage Links	• **Ribbon:** *Manage* tab>Manage Projects panel or *Insert* tab>Link panel
	Monitor	• **Ribbon:** *Copy/Monitor* tab>Tools panel
	Options (Copy/Monitor)	• **Ribbon:** *Copy/Monitor* tab>Tools panel

Chapter

5

Working with Views

Views are the cornerstone of working with Autodesk® Revit® models as they enable you to see the model in both 2D and 3D. As you are working, you can duplicate and change views to display different information based on the same view of the model. Callouts, elevations, and sections are especially important views for construction documents.

Learning Objectives in This Chapter

- Change the way elements display in different views to show required information and set views for construction documents.
- Duplicate views so that you can modify the display as you are creating the model, as well as set the display for construction documents.
- Create callout views of parts of plans, sections, or elevations for detailing.
- Add building and interior elevations that can be used to demonstrate how a building will be built.
- Create building and wall sections to help you create the model and to include in construction documents.
- Create 3D section views using Selection Boxes and Orient to View.

5.1 Modifying the View Display

Views are a powerful tool that enables you to create multiple versions of a model without having to recreate building elements. For example, you can have views that are specifically used for working on the model, while other views are annotated and used for construction documents. Different disciplines can have different views that show only the features they require, as shown in Figure 5–1. Properties of one view can be independent of the properties in other views.

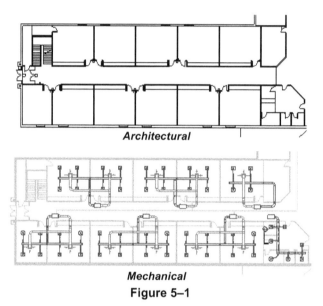

Architectural

Mechanical

Figure 5–1

The view display can be modified in the following locations:

- View Control Bar
- Properties
- Shortcut menu
- Visibility/Graphic Overrides dialog box

View Properties

The most basic properties of a view are accessed using the View Control Bar, shown in Figure 5–2. These include the *Scale*, *Detail Level*, and *Visual Style* options. Additional options include temporary overrides and other advanced settings.

1/8" = 1'-0"

Figure 5–2

- The **Detail Level** controls whether you see schematic elements (Coarse or Medium Detail) or full scale elements (Fine Detail), as shown in Figure 5–3.

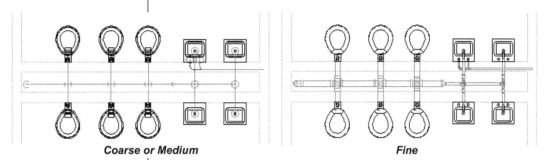

Coarse or Medium   *Fine*

Figure 5–3

Other modifications to views are available in Properties, as shown in Figure 5–4. These properties include *Underlays* and *View Range* as well as many others. The *Discipline* and *Sub-Discipline* of a view can also be set here. This is especially important for MEP projects.

The options in Properties vary according to the type of view. A plan view has different properties than a 3D view.

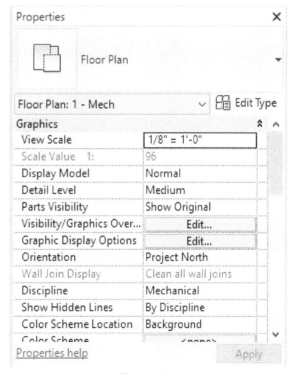

Figure 5–4

Setting an Underlay

Setting an *Underlay* is helpful if you need to display elements on a different level, such as the basement plan shown with an underlay of the first floor plan in Figure 5–5. You can then use the elements to trace over or even copy to the current level of the view.

Underlays are only available in Floor Plan and Ceiling Plan views.

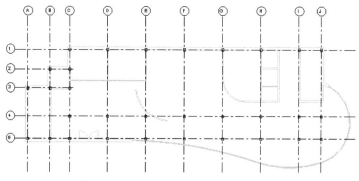

Figure 5–5

In Properties in the *Underlay* area, specify the *Range: Base Level* and the *Range: Top Level*. You can also specify the Underlay Orientation to **Look down** or **Look up**, as shown in Figure 5–6.

Underlay		☆
Range: Base Level	Floor 2	
Range: Top Level	Floor 3	
Underlay Orientation	Look down	

Figure 5–6

- To prevent moving elements in the underlay by mistake, in the Select panel, expand the panel title, and clear **Select underlay elements**. You can also toggle this on/off using

   (Select Underlay Elements) in the Status Bar.

Setting the View Range

The View Range controls the cut planes that control the visibility of plan views, as shown in the Sample View Range key in Figure 5–7. Elements outside the cut planes do not display unless you include an underlay.

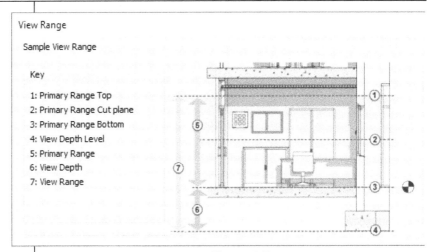

Figure 5–7

How To: Set the View Range

1. In Properties, in the *Extents* area, beside *View Range*, select **Edit...** or type **VR**.
2. In the View Range dialog box, as shown in Figure 5–8, modify the Levels and Offsets for the *Primary Range* and *View Depth*.

   • Click **<<Show** to display the Sample View Range key.

3. Click **OK**.

Figure 5–8

- If the settings used cannot be represented graphically, a warning displays, stating the inconsistency.

- A Reflected Ceiling Plan (RCP) is created, as if the ceiling is reflected by a mirror on the floor, so that the ceiling is the same orientation as the floor plan. The cutline is placed just below the ceiling to ensure that any windows and doors below do not display.

Setting the Discipline of a View

Disciplines are frequently used with MEP projects.

Many times when you duplicate or create a view it will not be in the expected grouping in the Project Browser. The view properties of *Discipline* and *Sub-Discipline*, as shown in Figure 5–9, control the visibility of some elements and applies grouping in the Project Browser. For example, you can separate the Plumbing Plans from the Fire Plumbing plans, as shown in Figure 5–10.

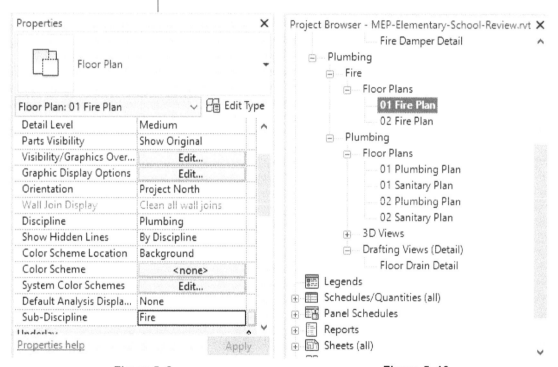

Figure 5–9   Figure 5–10

- You can add additional sub-disciplines by typing in a new name but the list of disciplines is set by the software.

Hiding and Overriding Graphics

Two common ways to customize a view are to:

- Hide individual elements or categories
- Modify how graphics display for elements or categories (e.g., altering lineweight, color, or pattern)

Note that an element is an individual item (i.e., one piece of equipment in a view), while a category includes all instances of a selected element (i.e., all of the equipment in a view).

For example, you can customize the view shown in Figure 5–11 by changing the grid category in a floor plan to halftone.

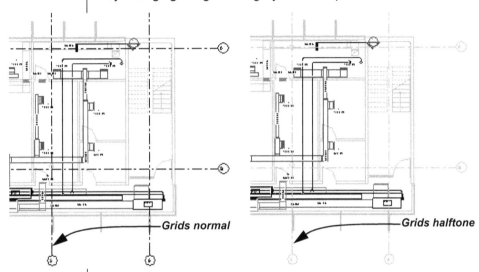

Grids normal   Grids halftone

Figure 5–11

How To: Hide Elements or Categories in a View

1. Select the elements or categories you want to hide.
2. Right-click and select **Hide in View>Elements** or **Hide in View>Category**, as shown in Figure 5–12.
3. The elements or categories are hidden in current view only.

A quick way to hide entire categories is to select an element(s) and type **VH**.

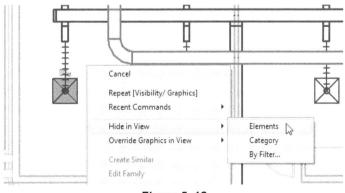

Figure 5–12

How To: Override Graphics of Elements or Categories in a View

1. Select the element(s) you want to modify.
2. Right-click and select **Override Graphics in View>By Element** or **By Category**. The View-Specific Element (or Category) Graphics dialog box opens, as shown in Figure 5–13.

The exact options in the dialog box vary depending on the type of elements selected.

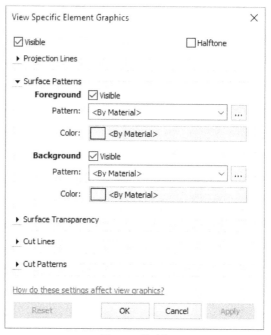

Figure 5–13

3. Select the changes you want to make and click **OK**.

View-Specific Options

- Clearing the **Visible** option is the same as hiding the elements or categories.

- Selecting the **Halftone** option grays out the elements or categories.

- The options for *Projection Lines* and *Cut Lines* include **Weight**, **Color**, and **Pattern**. The options for *Surface Patterns* and *Cut Patterns* include **Visibility**, **Pattern**, and **Color** for the Foreground and Background.

- **Surface Transparency** can be set by moving the slider bar, as shown in Figure 5–14.

▾ Surface Transparency

Transparency: ——————◻—————— 33

Figure 5–14

- The View-Specific Category Graphics dialog box includes **Open the Visibility Graphics dialog...**, which opens the full dialog box of options.

The Visibility/Graphic Overrides Dialog Box

The options in the Visibility/Graphic Overrides dialog box (shown in Figure 5–15) control how every category and sub-category of elements is displayed per view. You can toggle categories on and off, override the *Projection/Surface* and *Cut* information, set categories to **Halftone**, and change the *Detail Level*.

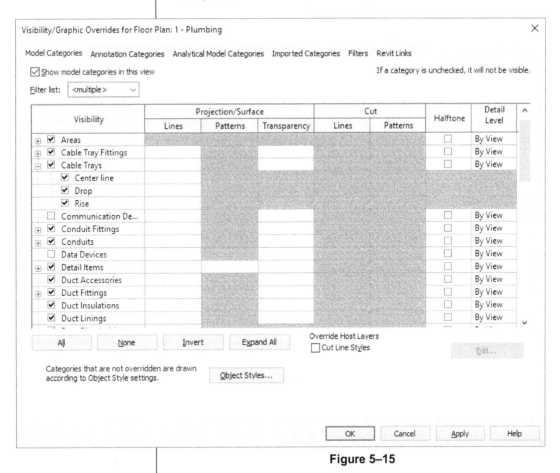

Figure 5–15

To open the Visibility/Graphic Overrides dialog box, type **VV** or **VG**. It is also available in Properties: in the *Graphics* area, beside *Visibility/Graphic Overrides*, click **Edit...**.

- The Visibility/Graphic Overrides are divided into *Model, Annotation, Analytical Model, Imported,* and *Filters* categories.

- Other categories might be available if specific data has been included in the project, including *Design Options, Linked Files*, and *Worksets*.

- To limit the number of categories showing in the dialog box select a discipline from the *Filter list,* as shown in Figure 5–16.

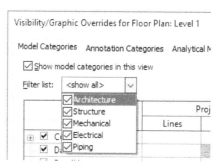

Figure 5–16

- To help you select categories, use the **All**, **None**, and **Invert** buttons. The **Expand All** button displays all of the sub-categories.

Hint: Restoring Hidden Elements or Categories

If you have hidden categories, you can display them using the Visibility/Graphic Overrides dialog box. To display hidden elements, however, you must temporarily reveal the elements first.

1. In the View Control Bar, click 💡 (Reveal Hidden Elements). The border and all hidden elements are displayed in magenta, while visible elements in the view are grayed out, as shown in Figure 5–17.

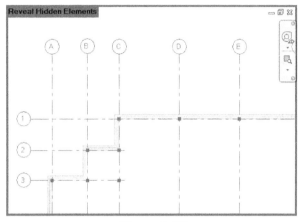

Figure 5–17

2. Select the hidden elements you want to restore, right-click, and select **Unhide in View>Elements** or **Unhide in View>Category**. Alternatively, in the *Modify* | contextual tab>Reveal Hidden Elements panel, click 🖼 (Unhide Element) or 🖼 (Unhide Category).

3. When you are finished, in the View Control Bar, click 🖼 (Close Reveal Hidden Elements) or, in the *Modify* | contextual tab>Reveal Hidden Elements panel, click ❎ (Toggle Reveal Hidden Elements Mode).

Using View Templates

A powerful way to use views effectively is to set up a view and then save it as a View Template. You can apply view templates to views - individually or through the Properties palette. Setting the View Template using the Properties palette ensures that you do not accidentally modify the view while interacting with it.

How To: Create a View Template from a View

1. Set up a view, as needed.
2. In the Project Browser, right-click on the view and select **Create View Template from View**.
3. In the New View Template dialog box, type in a name and then click **OK**.
4. The new view template is listed in the View Templates dialog box. Make any modifications needed in the **View properties** section.
5. Click **OK**.

How To: Specify a View Template for a View

1. In the Project Browser, select the view or views to which you want to apply a view template.
2. In Properties, scroll down to the *Identity Data* section and click the button beside *View Template*.
3. In the Apply View Template dialog box, select the view template from the list, as shown in Figure 5–18.

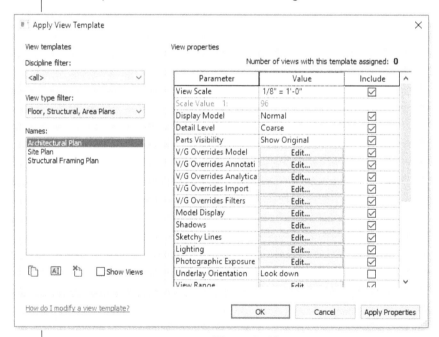

Figure 5–18

4. Click **OK**.

- In the View Control Bar, use ⬚ (Temporary View Properties) to temporarily apply a view template to a view.

MEP System Filters

Systems in Autodesk Revit MEP are color-coded. For example, supply ducts display in one color and return ducts display in a different color. The system colors display in all views (including 3D views), as shown in Figure 5–19.

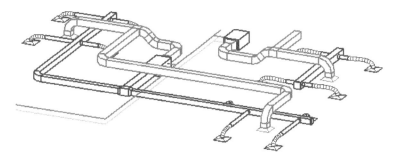

Figure 5–19

You can use filters to display only the systems you want to see in a view. For example, in a section view, you might want to display the sanitary piping only and omit the hot and cold water piping, as shown in Figure 5–20.

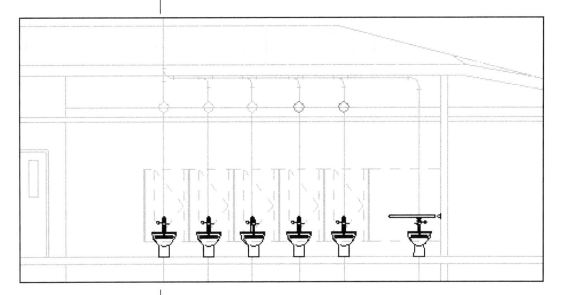

Figure 5–20

- When you create an elevation or section, it uses the basic filters from the original plan view, but some cleanup might be required using Visibility Graphics Overrides.

How To: Apply a View Filter to Override a View

1. Open the Visibility/Graphic Overrides dialog box.
2. In the dialog box, select the *Filters* tab. Some filters might already be available.
3. To add a new filter to this view, click **Add**.
4. In the Add Filters dialog box, as shown in Figure 5–21, select the type of systems you want to modify and click **OK**.

The list might vary depending on the filters that have been set up in the project.

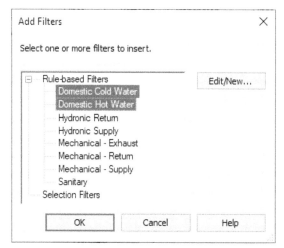

Figure 5–21

5. In the *Filters* tab, select **Visibility** and any other overrides you might want to use. In the example in Figure 5–22, the Domestic Cold and Hot Water have been toggled off while only the Sanitary systems display.

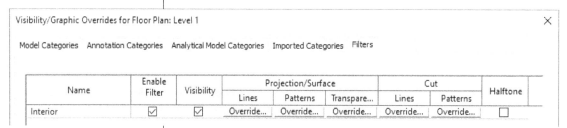

Figure 5–22

6. Click **OK** to close the dialog box.

- To toggle off other elements, such as levels or grids, use the other tabs in the Visibility/Graphics dialog box or use **Hide in View** or **Override Graphics in View**.

- View Filters override system graphics; so, any colors you set in this dialog box supersede those specified in the System Type.

5.2 Duplicating Views

Once you have created a model, you do not have to recreate the elements at different scales or copy them so that they can be used on more than one sheet. Instead, you can duplicate the required views and modify them to suit your needs.

Duplication Types

Duplicate creates a copy of the view that only includes the building elements, as shown in Figure 5–23. Annotation and detailing are not copied into the new view. Building model elements automatically change in all views, but view-specific changes made to the new view are not reflected in the original view.

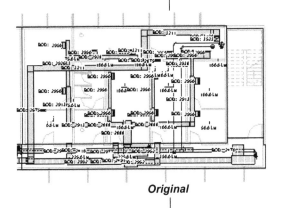

Original

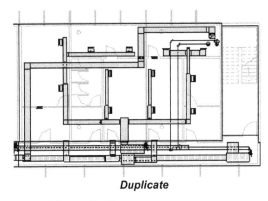

Duplicate

Figure 5–23

Duplicate with Detailing creates a copy of the view and includes all annotation and detail elements (such as tags), as shown in Figure 5–24. Any annotation or view-specific elements created in the new view are not reflected in the original view.

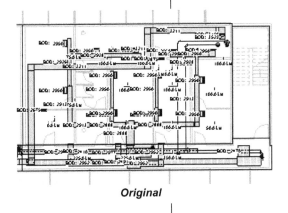

Original

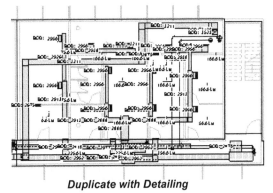

Duplicate with Detailing

Figure 5–24

Duplicate as a Dependent creates a copy of the view and links it to the original (parent) view, as shown in the Project Browser in Figure 5–25. View-specific changes made to the overall view, such as changing the *Scale*, are also reflected in the dependent (child) views and vice-versa.

Project Browser   ✕

⊟ ⌞O⌝ Views (all)   ∧

   ⊟ Floor Plans

     ⊟ Floor 1

       Floor 1 - Dependent 1

     Floor 2

     Floor 3

Figure 5–25

- Use dependent views when the building model is so large that you need to split the building onto separate sheets, while ensuring that the views are all same scale.

- If you want to separate a dependent view from the original view, right-click on the dependent view and select **Convert to independent view**.

How To: Create Duplicate Views

1. Open the view you want to duplicate.
2. In the *View* tab>Create panel, expand **Duplicate View** and select the type of duplicate view you want to create, as shown in Figure 5–26.

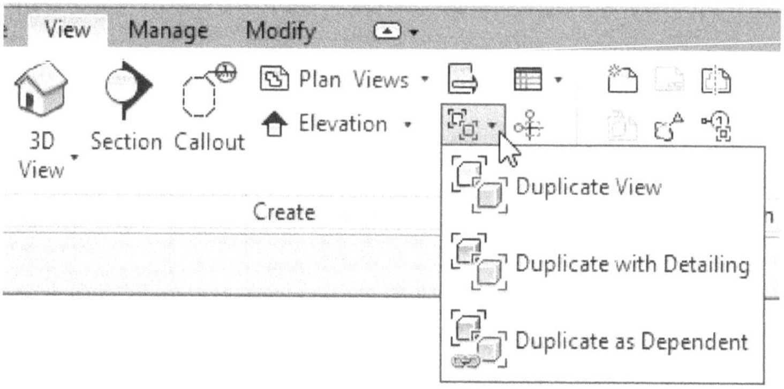

Most types of views can be duplicated.

Figure 5–26

- Alternatively, you can right-click on a view in the Project Browser and select the type of duplicate that you want to use, as shown in Figure 5–27.

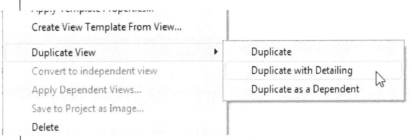

Figure 5–27

- To rename a view, double-click on the view name slowly and the text highlights, as shown in Figure 5–28. You can also right-click on a view name and select **Rename...** or press <F2>.

Figure 5–28

Practice 5a

Duplicate Views and Set the View Display - Mechanical

Practice Objectives

- Duplicate views.
- Apply view filters.
- Modify the view display using the Visibility/Graphic Overrides dialog box.

In this practice, you will duplicate views and modify them using filters and Visibility/Graphic Overrides.

1. In the practice files *Views* folder, open **Views-School-MEP.rvt**.

2. In the Project Browser, right-click on the **3D Plumbing** view and select **Duplicate View>Duplicate**.

3. Right-click on the new view name and select **Rename**, or double-click on the new view name, and type **3D HVAC**.

4. In Properties, change the *Discipline* to **Mechanical** and the *Sub-Discipline* to **HVAC**, as shown in Figure 5–29. The view moves to this category in the Project Browser.

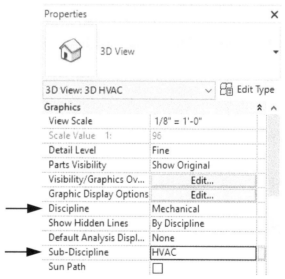

Figure 5–29

5. Open the Visibility/Graphic Overrides dialog box and in the *Filters* tab, uncheck anything that is checked and only select **Mechanical - Supply** and **Mechanical - Return**. Click **OK**.

6. Select one of the plumbing fixtures and type **VH** (for Hide category in view). Now only the HVAC systems display as shown in Figure 5–30.

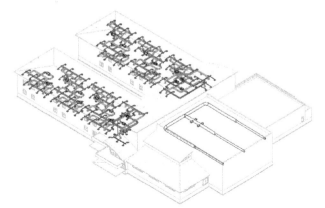

Figure 5–30

7. Save and close the project.

Practice 5b

Duplicate Views and Set the View Display - Electrical

Practice Objectives

- Duplicate views.
- Apply view filters.
- Modify the view display using the Visibility/Graphic Overrides dialog box.

In this practice, you will duplicate views and modify them using filters and Visibility/Graphic Overrides.

1. In the practice files *Views* folder, open **Views-School-MEP.rvt**.

2. In the Project Browser, right-click on the **3D Plumbing** view and select **Duplicate View>Duplicate**.

3. Double-click on the new view name and type **3D Electrical**.

4. In Properties, change the *Discipline* to **Electrical** and the *Sub-Discipline* to **Lighting**, as shown in Figure 5–31. The view moves to this category in the Project Browser.

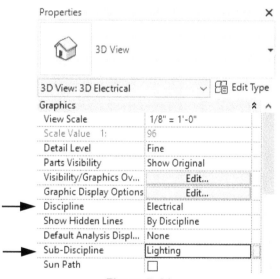

Figure 5–31

5. Select one of the plumbing fixtures and type **VH** (for Hide category in view).

6. Open the Visibility/Graphic Overrides dialog box and in the *Filters* tab, uncheck any selected filters. Click **Apply**.

7. In the *Model Categories* tab, set the *Filter list* to display only **Electrical**. Select the following Visibility categories, as shown in Figure 5–32: **Cable Tray Fittings**, **Cable Trays**, **Conduit Fittings**, **Conduits**, **Data Devices**, **Electrical Equipment**, **Electrical Fixtures**, **Lighting Devices**, and **Lighting Fixtures**.

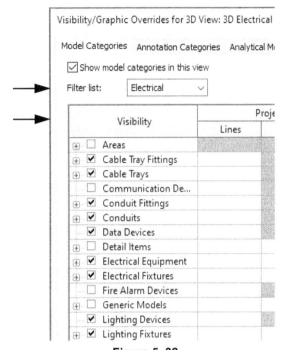

Figure 5–32

8. Click **OK**. Note that the lighting fixtures and electrical equipment now display, but that no cable trays or conduits have been added.

9. Save and close the project.

Practice 5c

Duplicate Views and Set the View Display - Plumbing

Practice Objectives

- Duplicate views.
- Apply view filters.
- Modify the view display using the Visibility/Graphic Overrides dialog box.

In this practice, you will duplicate views and modify them using filters and Visibility/Graphic Overrides.

1. In the practice files *Views* folder, open **Views-School-MEP.rvt**.

2. In the Project Browser, right-click on the **3D Plumbing** view and select **Duplicate View>Duplicate**.

3. Right-click on the new view name and select **Rename**, or double-click on the new view name, and type **3D Sanitary**.

4. Open the Plumbing>Plumbing>**3D Plumbing** view. Note that this view only displays the sanitary piping.

5. Open the Visibility/Graphic Overrides dialog box and in the *Filters* tab, select **Domestic Cold Water** and **Domestic Hot Water**, as shown in Figure 5–33.

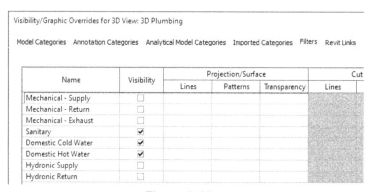

Figure 5–33

6. Click **OK** and the rest of the plumbing system elements display.

7. Save and close the project.

5.3 Adding Callout Views

Callouts are details of plan, elevation, or section views. When you place a callout in a view, as shown in Figure 5–34, it automatically creates a new view clipped to the boundary of the callout, as shown in Figure 5–35. You can create rectangular or sketched callout boundaries.

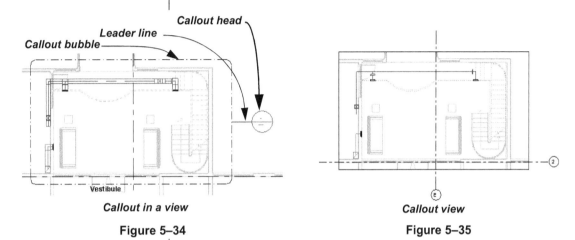

Callout in a view

Figure 5–34

Callout view

Figure 5–35

- Callout views are saved in the same node in the Project Browser as the original view. For example, the callout view of a floor plan is placed within the Floor Plans node.

- To open the callout view, double-click on its name in the Project Browser or on the callout head (verify that the callout bubble is not selected before you double-click on the callout head).

How To: Create a Rectangular Callout

1. In the *View tab>Create panel,* click ⌾ **(Callout)**.
2. Select points for two opposite corners to define the callout bubble around the area you want to detail.
3. Select the callout bubble and use the shape handles to modify the location of the bubble and any other edges that might need changing.
4. In the Project Browser, you can rename the callout view.

How To: Create a Sketched Callout

1. In the *View tab>Create panel,* expand ⌀ (Callout), and click 📝 (Sketch).
2. Sketch the shape of the callout bubble using the tools in the *Modify | Edit Profile* tab>Draw panel, as shown in Figure 5–36.

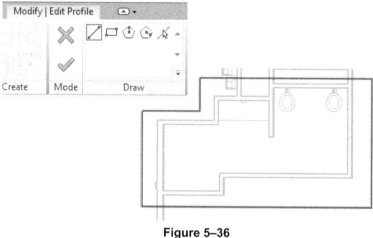

Figure 5–36

3. Click ✓ (Finish) to complete the boundary.
4. Select the callout bubble and use the shape handles to modify the location of the bubble and any other edges that might need to be changed.
5. In the Project Browser, rename the callout.

Modifying Callouts

Callouts are cropped versions of the original view. When you modify them you are changing the Crop Region of the view.

• If you change the size of the callout bubble in the original view, it automatically updates the callout view and vice-versa.

• Callouts can be reshaped. Select the callout bubble or crop region and, in the *Modify | Floor Plan* tab>Mode panel, click 📝 (Edit Crop) and use the Draw tools to modify the sketch.

• If you want to return a sketched or modified callout or crop region to a rectangular configuration, click 🔲 (Reset Crop).

Working with Crop Regions

Plans, sections, elevations, and 3D views can all be modified by changing how much of the model is displayed in a view. One way to do this is to set the Model crop region. If there are dimensions, tags, or text near the crop region, you can also use the Annotation crop region to include these, as shown in Figure 5–37.

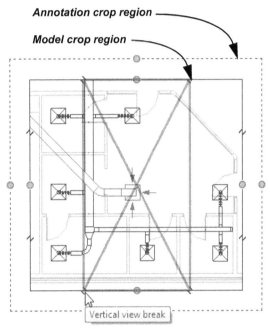

Figure 5–37

Zoom out if you do not see the crop region when you set it to be displayed.

- To display the crop region, in the View Control Bar, click ⊞ (Show Crop Region). Alternatively, in Properties, in the *Extents* area, select **Crop Region Visible**. **Annotation Crop** is also available in this area.

- It is best practice to hide a crop region before placing a view on a sheet. In the View Control Bar, click ⊞ (Hide Crop Region).

- Resize the crop region using the ◯ control on each side of the region.

Breaking the crop region is typically used with sections or details.

- Click ↗ (Break Line) control to split the view into two regions, horizontally or vertically. Each part of the view can then be modified in size to display what is needed and be moved independently.

- The annotation crop region crops any annotation outside of the crop region and any annotations that it touches. If the model crop region crops an element that is tagged, the tag or annotation will automatically be cropped. You can turn on Annotation Crop and resize the crop region closer to the model crop region using the grip controls or by using the Crop Region Size dialog box, as shown in Figure 5–38. In the *Modify | Floor Plan* tab>Crop panel, click (Size Crop) to open the dialog box.

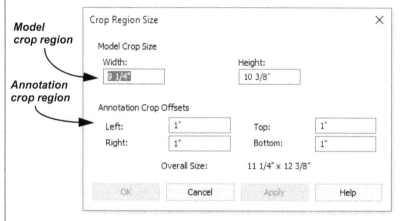

Figure 5–38

Plan Regions

When you have a plan view with multiple levels of floors or ceilings, you can create plan regions that enable you to set a different view range for part of a view (as shown in Figure 5–39) for a set of clerestory windows.

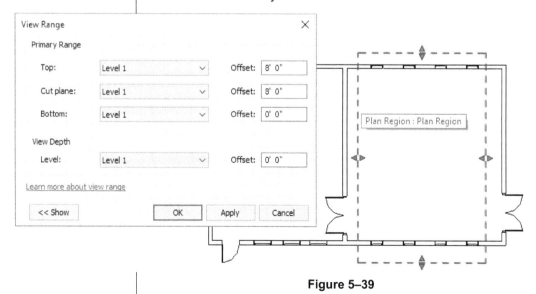

Figure 5–39

How To: Create Plan Regions

1. In a plan view, in the *View* tab>Create panel, expand

   ▣ (Plan Views) and select ▣ (Plan Region).
2. In the *Modify | Create Plan Region Boundary* tab>Draw panel, select a draw tool and create the boundary for the plan region.

   - The boundary must be closed and cannot overlap other plan region boundaries, but the boundaries can be side by side.

3. Click ✓ (Finish Edit Mode).
4. In the *Modify | Plan Region* tab>Region panel, click 🗲 (View Range).
5. In the View Range dialog box, specify the offsets for the plan region and click **OK**. The plan region is applied to the selected area.

- Plan regions can be copied to the clipboard and then pasted into other plan views.

- You can use shape handles to resize plan region boundaries without having to edit the boundary.

- If a plan region is above a door, the door swing displays, but the door opening does not display, as shown in Figure 5–40.

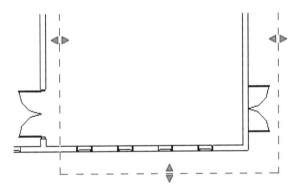

Figure 5–40

- Plan Regions can be toggled on and off in the Visibility/ Graphic Overrides dialog box on the *Annotation Categories* tab. If they are displayed, the plan regions are included when printing and exporting.

Hint: Depth Clipping and Far Clipping

Depth Clipping, shown in Figure 5–41, is a viewing option which sets how sloped walls are displayed if the *View Range* of a plan is set to a limited view.

Far Clipping (shown in Figure 5–42) is available for section and elevation views.

Figure 5–41   Figure 5–42

- An additional Graphic Display Option enables you to specify *Depth Cueing*, so that items that are in the distance will be made lighter.

Practice 5d

Add Callout Views - Mechanical

Practice Objectives

- Create callouts.
- Adjust crop region display.

In this practice, you will create a callout view of one wing of the building. In the new callout view, you will then create an additional callout view, as shown in Figure 5–43.

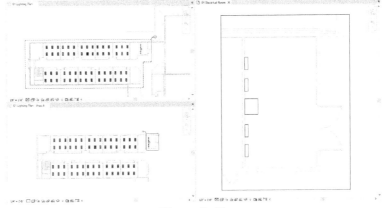

Figure 5–43

1. In the practice files *Views* folder, open **Callout-School-MEP.rvt**.

2. Open the Mechanical>HVAC>Floor Plans>**01 Mechanical Plan** view.

3. In the *View* tab>Create panel, expand ⌀̃ (Callout) and select ✎̃ (Sketch).

4. Sketch a boundary similar to that shown in Figure 5–44.

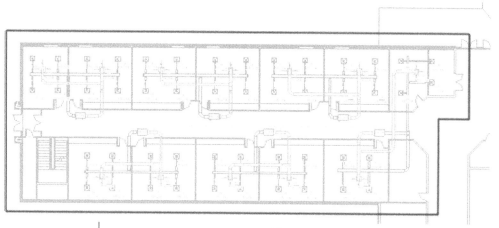

Figure 5–44

5. Click ✓ (Finish Edit Mode). Use the blue grip controls to move the bubble as shown in Figure 5–45.

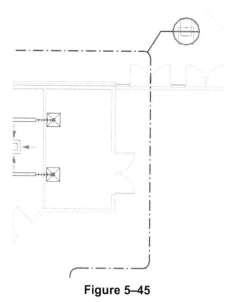

Figure 5–45

6. In the Project Browser, double-click on the new callout view to open it. Rename the callout **01 Mechanical Plan-Area A**.

• In the View Control Bar, notice that the *Scale* is automatically increased to be two times the previous view.

7. In the View Control Bar, click 📏 (Hide Crop Region).

8. In the *View* tab>Create panel, click 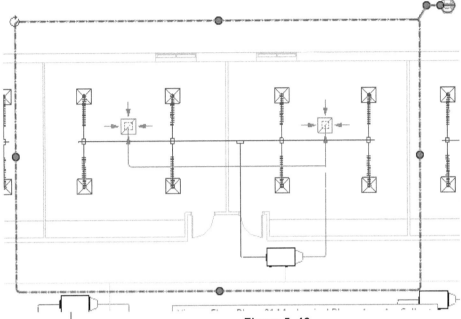 (Callout).

9. Draw a callout box around one set of two classrooms and move the bubble as shown in Figure 5–46.

Figure 5–46

10. In the Project Browser, rename the new callout **Typical Classroom Mechanical**. Open the view and you can see that the scale was doubled again from the previous callout view.

11. Reopen the **01 Mechanical Plan** view. Note that the larger callout displays, but the second callout created does not.

12. Save and close the project.

Practice 5e

Add Callout Views - Electrical

Practice Objectives

- Create callouts.
- Adjust crop region display.
- Apply a view template.

In this practice, you will create a callout view of one wing of the building. In the new callout view, you will then create an additional callout view.

1. In the practice files *Views* folder, open **Callout-School-MEP.rvt**.

2. Open the Electrical>Lighting>Floor Plans>**01 Lighting Plan** view.

3. In the *View* tab>Create panel, expand ⌖ (Callout) and select ⌖ (Sketch).

4. Sketch a boundary similar to that shown in Figure 5–47.

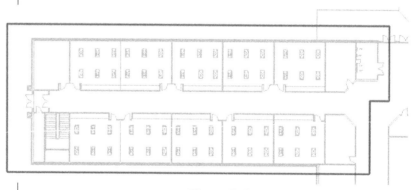

Figure 5–47

5. Click ✓ (Finish Edit Mode). Use the blue grip controls to move the bubble as shown in Figure 5–48.

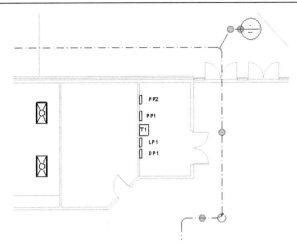

Figure 5–48

6. In the Project Browser, double-click on the new callout view to open it. Rename the callout **01 Lighting Plan-Area A**.

7. In the View Control Bar, notice that the *Scale* is automatically increased to two times the previous view.

8. In the View Control Bar, click 🗂 (Hide Crop Region).

9. In the *View* tab>Create panel, click ⬭ (Callout).

10. Draw a callout box around the electrical room and move the bubble as shown in Figure 5–49.

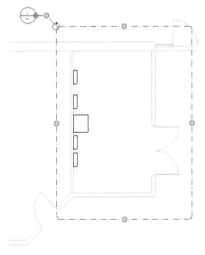

Figure 5–49

11. Open the view and note that the scale was doubled again from the previous callout view.

12. In the Project Browser, rename the new callout **01 Electrical Room**.

13. Right-click on the view name and select **Apply Template Properties**.

14. In the Apply View Template dialog box, select **Power Plan** and click **OK**. The view moves to the **Power** node.

15. Note that the view scale is changed by the view template. Change *Scale* to **1/4" = 1'-0"**, which works best for this size of plan.

16. Reopen the **01 Lighting Plan** view. The larger callout displays, but the second callout created does not.

17. Save and close the project.

Practice 5f

Add Callout Views - Plumbing

Practice Objective

- Create callouts.
- Adjust crop region display.

In this practice, you will create a callout view of one wing of the building. In the new callout view, you will then create an additional callout view.

1. In the practice files *Views* folder, open **Callout-School-MEP.rvt**.

2. Open the Plumbing>Plumbing>Floor Plans>**01 Plumbing Plan** view.

3. In the *View* tab>Create panel, expand ⌀ (Callout) and select ✐ (Sketch).

4. Sketch a boundary similar to that shown in Figure 5–50.

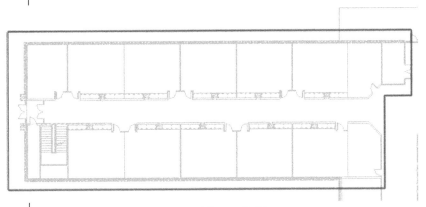

Figure 5–50

5. Click ✔ (Finish Edit Mode). Use the blue grip controls to move the bubble as shown in Figure 5–51.

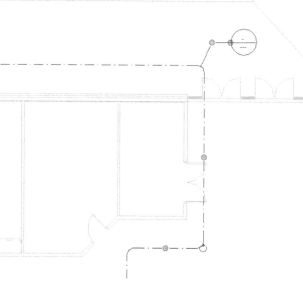

Figure 5–51

6. In the Project Browser, double-click on the new callout view to open it. Rename the callout **01 Plumbing Plan-Area A**.

7. In the View Control Bar, note that the *Scale* is automatically increased to two times the previous view.

8. In the View Control Bar, click ⬚ (Hide Crop Region).

9. In the *View* tab>Create panel, click ⬚ (Callout).

10. Draw a callout box around one of the classroom sinks and move the bubble, as shown in Figure 5–52.

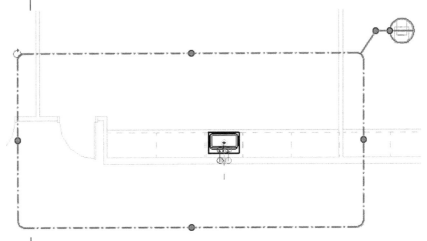

Figure 5–52

11. In the Project Browser, rename the new callout **Typical Classroom Plumbing**. Open the view and note that the scale was doubled again from the previous callout view.

12. Reopen the **01 Plumbing Plan** view. The larger callout displays, but the second callout created does not.

13. Save and close the project.

5.4 Creating Elevations and Sections

Elevations and sections are critical elements of construction documents and can assist you as you are working on a model. Any changes made in one of these views (such as the section in Figure 5–53), changes the entire model and any changes made to the project model are also displayed in the elevations and sections.

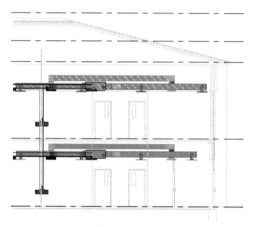

Figure 5–53

- In the Project Browser, elevations are separated by elevation type and sections are separated by section type, as shown in Figure 5–54.

Figure 5–54

- To open an elevation or section view, double-click on the marker arrow or on its name in the Project Browser.

- To give the elevation or section a new name, in the Project Browser, slowly double-click on the name or right-click on it and select **Rename...**.

Elevations

Elevations are *face-on* views of the interiors and exteriors of a building. Four Exterior Elevation views are defined in the default template: **North**, **South**, **East**, and **West**. You can create additional building elevation views at other angles or interior elevation views, as shown in Figure 5–55.

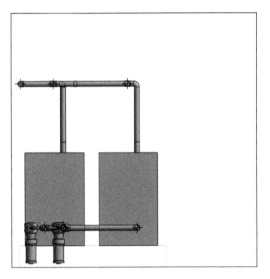

Figure 5–55

- Elevations markers must be placed in plan views.

- When you add an elevation or section to a sheet, the detail and sheet number are automatically added to the view title and elevation/section marker.

How To: Create an Elevation

The software remembers the last elevation type used, so you can click the top button if you want to use the same elevation command.

1. In the *View* tab>Create panel, expand ⬆ (Elevation) and click ⬆ (Elevation).
2. In the Type Selector, select the elevation type. Two types come with the templates: **Building Elevation** and **Interior Elevation**.
3. Move the cursor near one of the walls that defines the elevation. The marker follows the angle of the wall.
4. Click to place the marker.

- The length, width, and height of an elevation are defined by the walls and ceiling/floor at which the elevation marker is pointing.

- When creating interior elevations, ensure that the floor or ceiling above is in place before creating the elevation or you will need to modify the elevation crop region so that the elevation markers do not show on all floors.

Sections

Sections are slices through a model. You can create a section through an entire building, as shown in Figure 5–56, or through one wall for a detail. Sections can be created in plan, elevation, and other section views.

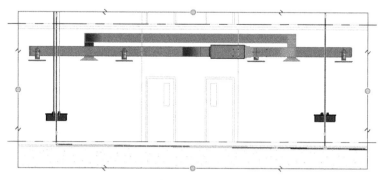

Figure 5–56

You can flip, resize, or split a section. Figure 5–57 shows all the components of a section marker.

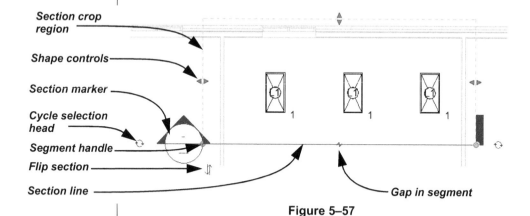

Section crop region
Shape controls
Section marker
Cycle selection head
Segment handle
Flip section
Section line
Gap in segment

Figure 5–57

How To: Create a Section

1. In the *View* tab>Create panel or in the Quick Access Toolbar, click (Section).

2. In the Type Selector, select **Section: Building Section** or **Section: Wall Section.** If you want a section in a Drafting view select **Detail View: Detail.**
3. In the view, select a point where you want to locate the crop region and section marker.
4. Select the second or end point that defines the section.
5. The shape controls display. You can flip the arrow and change the size of the cutting plane, as well as the location of the bubble and flag.

- When placing a section you can snap to other elements in the model as the start and end points of the section line. You can also use the Align command to reorient a section line to an element such as an angled wall.

- Section lines can also be used as an alignment object and can be snapped to when placing other geometry.

Modifying Elevations and Sections

There are two parts to modifying elevations and sections:

- To modify the markers (as shown in Figure 5–58), use the controls to change the length and depth of elevations and sections. There are other specific type options as well.

- To modify the view (as shown in Figure 5–59), use the controls to modify the size or create view breaks.

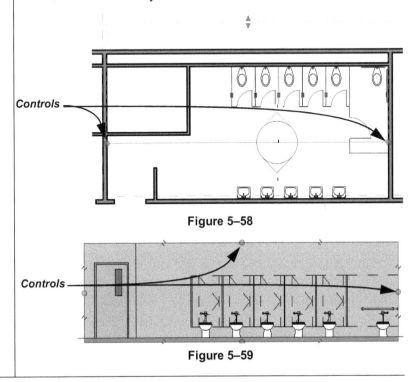

Figure 5–58

Figure 5–59

Modifying Elevation Markers

When you modify elevation markers, you can specify the length and depth of the clip plane, as shown in Figure 5–60.

- Select the arrowhead of the elevation marker (not the circle portion) to display the clip plane.

- Drag the round shape handles to lengthen or shorten the elevation.

- Adjust the ▲▼ (Drag) controls to modify the depth of the elevation.

To display additional interior elevations from one marker, select the circle portion (not the arrowhead) and place a check mark in the Show Arrow box in the directions that you want to display, as shown in Figure 5–60.

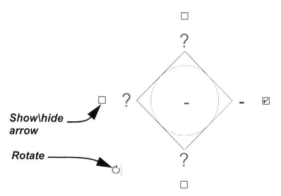

Figure 5–60

- Use the ↻ (Rotate) control to angle the marker (e.g., for a room with angled walls).

Modifying Section Markers

When you modify section markers, various shape handles and controls enable you to modify a section, as shown in Figure 5–61.

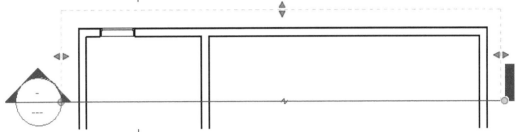

Figure 5–61

- Adjust the ▲▼ (Drag) controls to change the length and depth of the cut plane.

- Drag the segment handle controls at either end of the section line to change the location of the arrow or flag without changing the cut boundary.

- Click ↩ (Flip Section) to change the direction of the arrowhead, which also flips the entire section.

- Click ↻ (Cycle Section Head/Tail) to switch between an arrowhead, flag, or nothing on each end of the section.

- Click ↙ (Gaps in Segments) to create an opening in section lines, as shown in Figure 5–62. Select it again to restore the full section cut.

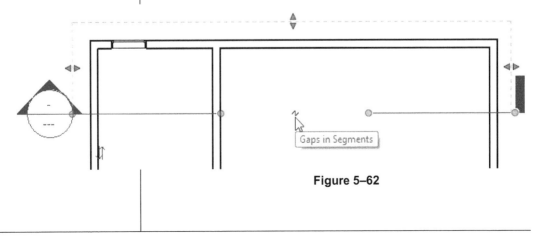

Figure 5–62

How To: Add a Jog to a Section Line

1. Select the section line you want to modify.

2. In the *Modify | Views* tab> Section panel, click ⬚ (Split Segment).

3. Select the point along the section line where you want to create the split, as shown in Figure 5–63.

4. Specify the location of the split line, as shown in Figure 5–64.

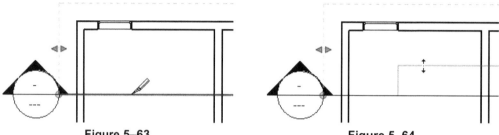

Figure 5–63   Figure 5–64

• If you need to adjust the location of any segment on the section line, modify it and drag the shape handles along each segment of the line, as shown in Figure 5–65.

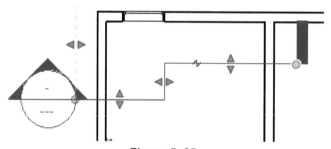

Figure 5–65

To bring a split section line back into place, use the shape handle to drag the jogged line until it is at the same level with the rest of the line.

3D Section Views

There are two ways you can create section views of your 3D model: creating a selection box, as shown in Figure 5–66, and orienting to a view. Both of these are very helpful as you are working and also can be used in construction documents and presentations.

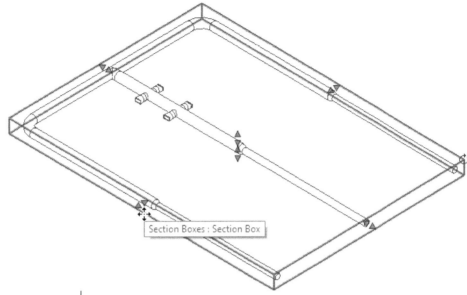

Figure 5–66

How To: Create a Selection Box

1. In a 3D view, select the elements you want to isolate. In the example shown in Figure 5–66, the front wall was selected.

2. In the *Modify* tab>View panel, click (Selection Box) or type **BX**.
3. The view is limited to a box around the selected item(s).
4. Use the controls of the Section Box to modify the size of the box to show exactly what you want.

- To toggle off a section box and restore the full model, in the view's Properties, in the *Extents* area, clear the check from **Section Box**.

How To: Orient a 3D View to a View

1. Open a 3D view.
2. Right-click on the ViewCube and select **Orient to View>Floor Plans**, **Elevations**, **Sections**, or **3D Views**, as shown in Figure 5–67, and select the view from the list.

Figure 5–67

3. The view displays as shown, in the partial floor plan view of an electrical room, in Figure 5–68. Use the 3D view rotation tools to navigate around the 3D model, as shown in Figure 5–69.

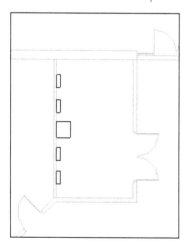

Figure 5–68

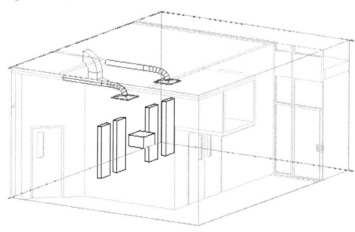

Figure 5–69

- **Orient to a Direction** allows you to rotate the view to a specific direction, as shown in Figure 5–70. This is similar to using the orientation planes of the ViewCube.

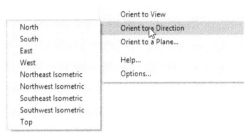

Figure 5–70

- **Orient to a Plane** opens the Select Orientation Plane dialog box and allows you to specify a Level, Grid, or named Reference Plane, or pick a plane or a line, as shown in Figure 5–71. The view is not cut at the plane but oriented in that direction.

Figure 5–71

Practice 5g

Create Elevations and Sections - Mechanical

Practice Objectives

- Create exterior and interior elevations.
- Add building sections and wall sections.
- Apply a view template.

In this practice, you will create building and wall sections, as well as exterior and interior elevations, to show mechanical fixtures. Then, you will apply a view template to apply preset settings.

1. In the practice files *Views* folder, open **Elevations-School-MEP.rvt**.

2. Open the Mechanical>HVAC>Floor Plans>**01 Mechanical Plan** view.

3. In the *View* tab>Create panel, click ⑨ (Section).

4. In the Type Selector, select **Section: Building Section**.

5. Draw a section through the north wing, as shown in Figure 5–72.

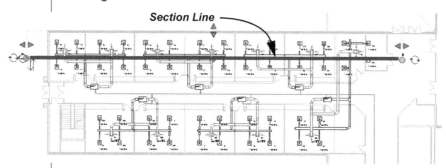

Figure 5–72

6. Press <Esc> and then double-click on the section marker to open the section view.

7. Expand the crop region so that the first floor and the full height of the roof is displayed, as shown in Figure 5–73.

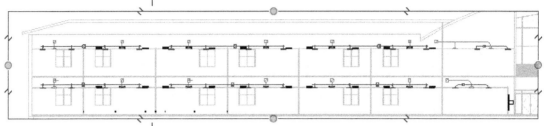

Figure 5–73

8. In the Project Browser, expand Mechanical>????>Sections (Building Section) and rename the new section **North Wing - HVAC**.

9. Right-click on the new section and select **Apply Template Properties**.

10. In the Apply View Template dialog box, select **Mechanical Section** and click **OK**.

11. In the 01 Mechanical Plan view, draw several other sections.

12. In the Project Browser, rename the sections and apply the **Mechanical Section** view template.

13. Save and close the project.

Practice 5h

Create Elevations and Sections - Electrical

Practice Objectives

- Create exterior and interior elevations.
- Add building sections and wall sections.
- Apply a view template.

In this practice, you will create building and wall sections, as well as exterior and interior elevations, to show electrical fixtures. Then, you will apply a view template to apply preset settings.

1. In the practice files *Views* folder, open **Elevations-School-MEP.rvt**.

2. Open the Electrical>Power>Floor Plans>**01 Electrical Room** view.

3. In the *View* tab>Create panel, click ⬆ (Elevation).

4. In the Type Selector, select **Elevation: Interior Elevation**.

5. Place an elevation marker facing the wall of electrical equipment.

6. Click ⬚ (Modify).

7. Select the circle part of the elevation marker and check the box facing the bottom of the view, as shown in Figure 5–74.

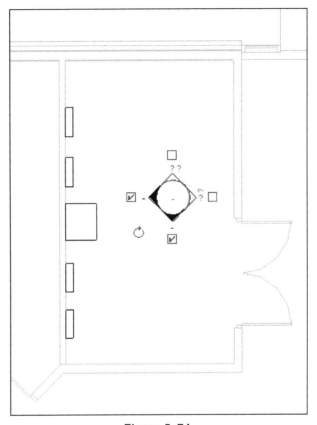

Figure 5–74

8. Press <Esc> to release the selection.

9. Select one of the arrows and zoom out to see the full length and depth of the section.

Note that the elevation does not automatically reflect the size of the room because it cannot read the location of the walls in the linked model.

10. Drag the ends back to the electrical room and modify the depth to encompass the room, as shown in Figure 5–75.

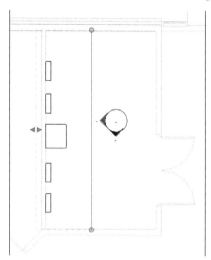

Figure 5–75

11. Repeat with the other direction.

12. In the Project Browser, expand Electrical>???>Elevations (Interior Elevation) and rename the new elevations **Electrical Room - South Elevation** and **Electrical Room - West Elevation**, as shown in Figure 5–76.

13. Open the section views and adjust the crop regions, as shown in Figure 5–76.

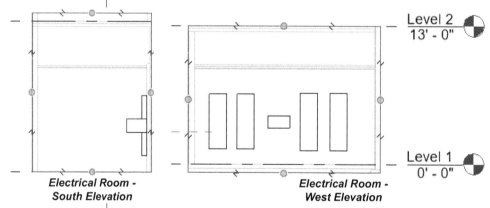

Electrical Room - South Elevation   *Electrical Room - West Elevation*

Figure 5–76

14. In the Project Browser, hold <Ctrl> and select both interior elevations, right-click, and select **Apply View Template...**.

15. In the Apply View Template dialog box, select **Electrical Elevation** and click **OK**.

16. Save and close the project.

Practice 5i

Create Elevations and Sections - Plumbing

Practice Objectives

- Create exterior and interior elevations.
- Add building sections and wall sections.

In this practice, you will create building and wall sections, as well as exterior and interior elevations, to show plumbing fixtures.

1. In the practice files *Views* folder, open **Elevations-School-MEP.rvt**.

2. Open the Plumbing>Plumbing>Floor Plans>**01 Plumbing Plan** view.

3. Zoom in on the restrooms near the gym.

4. In the *View* tab>Create panel, click (Elevation).

5. In the Type Selector, select **Elevation: Interior Elevation**.

6. Place an elevation facing the wall of sinks in one of the restrooms.

7. Click (Modify).

8. Select the circle part of the elevation marker and check the box on the opposite side, as shown in Figure 5–77.

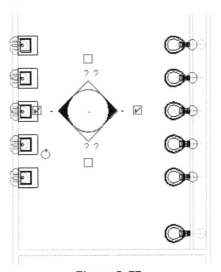

Figure 5–77

9. Press <Esc> to release the selection.

10. Select one of the arrows and zoom out to see the full length and depth of the section.

11. Drag the ends back to the restroom and modify the depth, as shown in Figure 5–78.

The elevation does not reflect the size of the room automatically because it cannot read the location of the walls in the linked model.

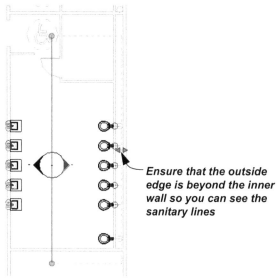

Ensure that the outside edge is beyond the inner wall so you can see the sanitary lines

Figure 5–78

12. Repeat with the other direction.

13. Double-click on the arrow pointing toward the water closets to open the corresponding view. The elevation cannot find the ceiling of the linked model so it selects the extents of the building model, as shown in Figure 5–79.

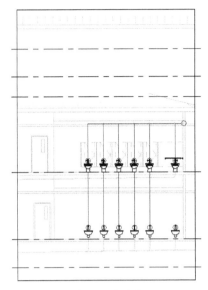

Figure 5–79

14. Select the crop region and resize the view so that only the lower floor restroom is displayed.

15. Return to plan view and open the arrow in the other direction. Repeat the process of resizing the crop region as shown in Figure 5–80.

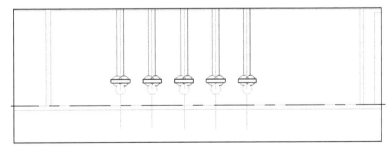

Figure 5–80

16. Return to plan view and select the entire elevation marker (the circle and both arrows).

17. Hold <Ctrl> and drag a copy of the marker up to the other restroom.

By setting up one elevation and then copying it to a location, you can save some steps.

18. Open each of the new elevation views and modify the crop regions as shown in Figure 5–81.

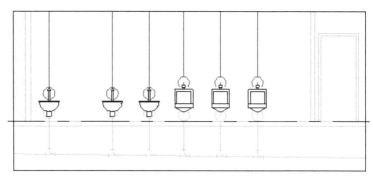

Figure 5–81

19. In the Project Browser expand Plumbing>???>Elevations (Interior Elevation), as shown in Figure 5–82.

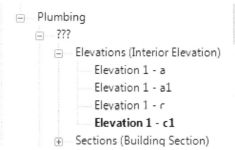

Figure 5–82

20. Right-click on the open elevation and give it a new title. For example, the elevation in Figure 5–81 would be **01 Men's East Elevation**.

21. Once you have finished renaming each of the elevations, hold <Ctrl> and select each of the new elevations.

22. In Properties, set the *Sub-Discipline* to **Plumbing**.

23. In the Project Browser, note that the elevations are now in the Plumbing sub-category, as shown in Figure 5–83.

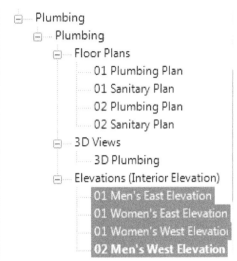

Figure 5–83

24. Save and close the project.

Chapter Review Questions

1. Which of the following commands creates a view that results in an independent view displaying the same model geometry and containing a copy of the annotation?

    a. Duplicate

    b. Duplicate with Detailing

    c. Duplicate as a Dependent

2. Which of the following is true about the Visibility Graphic Overrides dialog box?

    a. Changes made in the dialog box only affect the current view.

    b. It can only be used to toggle categories on and off.

    c. It can be used to toggle individual elements on and off.

    d. It can be used to change the color of individual elements.

3. What is the purpose of creating a callout?

    a. To create a boundary around part of the model that needs revising, similar to a revision cloud.

    b. To create a view of part of the model for export to the AutoCAD® software for further detailing.

    c. To create a view of part of the model that is linked to the main view from which it is taken.

    d. To create a 2D view of part of the model.

4. You placed dimensions in a view and some of them display and others do not (as shown on the left in Figure 5–84) but you were expecting the view to display as shown on the right in Figure 5–84. What do you need to modify to see the missing dimensions?

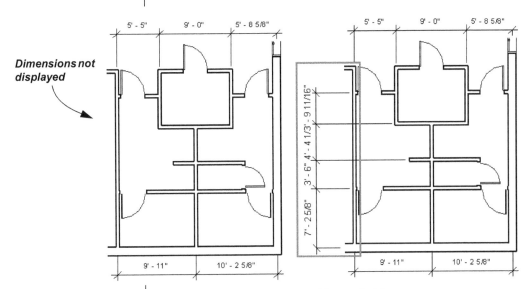

Figure 5–84

a. Dimension Settings

b. Dimension Type

c. Visibility Graphic Overrides

d. Annotation Crop Region

5. How do you create multiple interior elevations in one room?

a. Using the **Interior Elevation** command, place the elevation marker.

b. Using the **Elevation** command, from the properties type selector, change to **Interior Elevation** and place the first marker, select it and select the appropriate Show Arrow boxes.

c. Using the **Interior Elevation** command, place an elevation marker for each wall of the room you want to display.

d. Using the **Elevation** command, select a Multiple Elevation marker type, and place the elevation marker.

6. How do you create a jog in a building section, such as that shown in Figure 5–85?

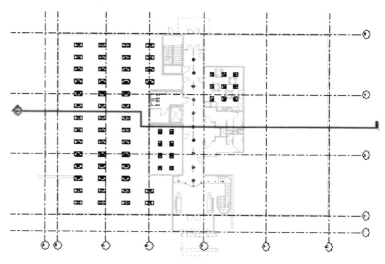

Figure 5–85

a. Use the **Split Element** tool in the *Modify* tab>Modify panel.

b. Select the building section and then click **Split Segment** in the contextual tab.

c. Select the building section and click the blue control in the middle of the section line.

d. Draw two separate sections, and use the **Section Jog** tool to combine them into a jogged section.

Command Summary

Button	Command	Location
Views		
	Elevation	• **Ribbon:** *View* tab>Create panel> expand Elevation
	Callout: Rectangle	• **Ribbon:** *View* tab>Create panel> expand Callout
	Callout: Sketch	• **Ribbon:** *View* tab>Create panel> expand Callout
	Duplicate	• **Ribbon:** *View* tab>Create panel> expand Duplicate View • **Right-click:** *(on a view in the Project Browser)* expand Duplicate View
	Duplicate as Dependent	• **Ribbon:** *View* tab>Create panel> expand Duplicate View • **Right-click:** *(on a view in the Project Browser)* expand Duplicate View
	Duplicate with Detailing	• **Ribbon:** *View* tab>Create panel> expand Duplicate View • **Right-click:** *(on a view in the Project Browser)* Duplicate View
	Plan Region	• **Ribbon:** *View* tab>Create panel> expand Plan Views
	Section	• **Ribbon:** *View* tab>Create panel • **Quick Access Toolbar**
	Split Segment	• **Ribbon:** *(when the elevation or section marker is selected)* Modify	Views tab> Section panel
Crop Views		
	Crop View	• **View Control Bar** • **View Properties:** Crop View *(check)*
	Do Not Crop View	• **View Control Bar** • **View Properties:** Crop View *(clear)*
	Edit Crop	• **Ribbon:** *(when the crop region of a callout, elevation, or section view is selected)* Modify	Views tab>Mode panel
	Hide Crop Region	• **View Control Bar** • **View Properties:** Crop Region Visible *(clear)*

	Reset Crop	• **Ribbon:** *(when the crop region of a callout, elevation or section view is selected) Modify	Views* tab>Mode panel
	Show Crop Region	• **View Control Bar** • **View Properties:** Crop Region Visible *(check)*
	Size Crop	• **Ribbon:** *(when the crop region of a callout, elevation or section view is selected) Modify	Views* tab>Mode panel

View Display

	Hide in View	• **Ribbon:** *Modify* tab>View Graphics panel>Hide>Elements *or* By Category • **Right-click:** *(when an element is selected)* Hide in View>Elements *or* Category
	Override Graphics in View	• **Ribbon:** *Modify* tab>View Graphics panel>Hide>Elements *or* By Category • **Right-click:** *(when an element is selected)* Override Graphics in View>By Element *or* By Category • **Shortcut:** *(category only)* VV or VG
	Plan Region	• **Ribbon:** *View* tab>Create panel expand Plan Views.
	Selection Box	• **Ribbon:** *Modify* tab>View panel • **Shortcut: BX.**
	Reveal Hidden Elements	• **View Control Bar**
	Temporary Hide/Isolate	• **View Control Bar**
	Temporary View Properties	• **View Control Bar**

Chapter

6

Setting Up Spaces

Spaces are used with most MEP disciplines to identify rooms and room numbers from the linked architectural model; however, they also include information about the 3D surroundings. Spaces are critical as the basis for analyzing heating and cooling loads and calculating light levels.

Learning Objectives in This Chapter

- Prepare a model so that you can add spaces.
- Create spaces individually or automatically.
- Add space separation lines to further divide spaces.
- Select spaces and modify them graphically and in Properties.
- Set up spaces for specific situations, including shafts, sliver spaces, cavities, and plenums.

6.1 Preparing a Model for Spaces

The Space element is a critical component in the process of establishing heating and cooling loads. Spaces are also used to calculate the light levels based on the number and types of lighting fixtures in a room. Spaces identify each room in a building providing area, perimeter, and volume information about each space, and information used in Electrical, Mechanical, and Energy Analysis, as shown in Properties in Figure 6–1.

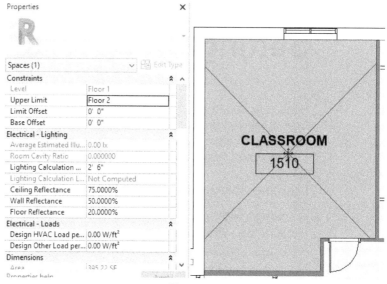

Figure 6–1

- Spaces are similar to rooms created in a Revit® architectural models. However, they contain more information for heating and cooling loads analysis and electrical lighting analysis.

- In MEP projects, you need to add spaces not only to occupiable rooms, but also to shafts, chases, plenums, and other enclosed areas that would not normally be assigned a room by the architect.

Before adding spaces to a project, you must:

- Set up the room bounding status of linked models so that the spaces identify elements such as walls and ceilings.
- Toggle on the area and volume computations so that the spaces will read the volume of the room correctly.
- Create views that display the spaces to make the process of adding and modifying spaces easier.

How To: Set a Linked Model to Room Bounding

1. Select the linked model.

2. In Properties, click ⊞ (Edit Type).

3. In the Type Properties dialog box, select the value for **Room Bounding**, as shown in Figure 6–2. Click **OK**.

Room bounding elements, whether in a linked model or the host project include: walls, roofs, floors, ceilings, columns, curtain systems, and room or space separation lines.

Type Properties		×
Family:	System Family: Linked Revit Model ∨	Load...
Type:	MEP-Elementary-School-Architectural-S∣ ∨	Duplicate...
		Rename...

Type Parameters

Parameter	Value	=
Constraints		☆
Room Bounding	☑	
Other		☆
Reference Type	Overlay	
Phase Mapping	Edit...	

Figure 6–2

How To: Set Area and Volume Computations

1. In the *Analyze* tab>Spaces & Zones panel, expand the panel title and click 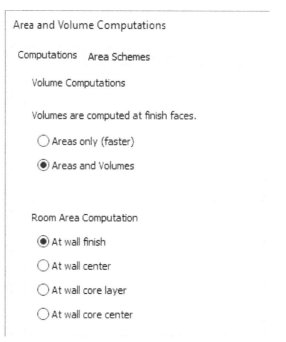 (Area and Volume Computations).
2. In the Area and Volume Computations dialog box, select **Area and Volumes** and **At wall finish**, as shown in Figure 6–3.

Area and Volume Computations

Computations   Area Schemes

Volume Computations

Volumes are computed at finish faces.

◯ Areas only (faster)

◉ Areas and Volumes

Room Area Computation

◉ At wall finish

◯ At wall center

◯ At wall core layer

◯ At wall core center

Figure 6–3

3. Click **OK**.

- As you add spaces, they fill the volume bounding area appropriately, as shown in Figure 6–4.

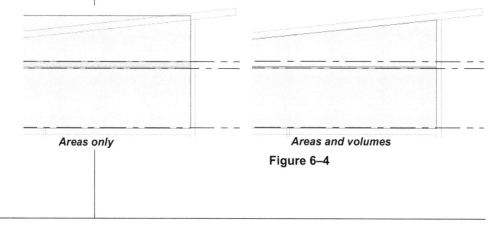

Areas only   *Areas and volumes*

Figure 6–4

How To: Create Views for Spaces

1. Duplicate a view and assign it to the *Coordination* discipline.
2. In the Visibility/Graphic Overrides dialog box, in the *Model Categories* tab, expand **Spaces** and select **Interior** and/or **Reference**, as shown in Figure 6–5 and Figure 6–6.

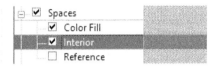

Figure 6–5

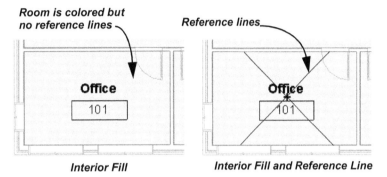

Interior Fill   *Interior Fill and Reference Line*

Figure 6–6

3. Toggle off any other categories that are not needed in the view.

6.2 Adding Spaces

Once you have set up views for the spaces, you can start applying them to the model, as shown in Figure 6–7. You can do this quickly by automatically filling each space, and then applying space names from a linked architectural model. You can also add spaces individually and divide them using Space Separators.

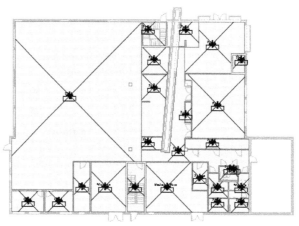

Figure 6–7

How To: Place Spaces Automatically

1. In the *Analyze* tab>Spaces & Zones panel, click ▦ (Space).
2. If you want to include a tag as you place the space, in the

   Modify | Place Space tab>Tag panel, click ⌐① (Tag on Placement).
3. In the Options Bar, you can set the *Orientation* of the tag and the *Leader*, if required.
4. In the Options Bar, set the *Upper Limit* and *Offset* (which controls the volume calculations), and set the height of the space, as shown in Figure 6–8.

Modify | Place Space | Upper Limit: Level 1 ▼ Offset: 9' 0" ⌐ Horizontal ▼ ☐ Leader Space: New ▼

Figure 6–8

- If you want elements (such as ceilings) to control the height of the space, set the *Upper Limit* to the level above and the *Offset* to **0**.

5. In the *Modify | Place Space* tab>Spaces panel, click

   ▦ (Place Spaces Automatically).

6. An alert box opens, prompting you about the number of spaces that were created. Click **Close**.
7. Spaces are added in each bounded area and a tag is placed if that option is selected in the ribbon.

- To help you understand the volume of the spaces as you create them, it helps to have a section view open, as shown in Figure 6–9.

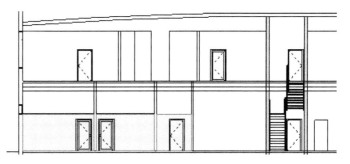

Figure 6–9

Naming Spaces

Spaces are named and numbered as they are placed, but they are probably not the names or numbers that are useful to you. Typically, you want the spaces to relate to the room names and numbers that were used in the architectural model. If a linked architectural model includes rooms, the associated *Room Name* and *Number* are displayed in the space's Properties (as shown in Figure 6–10), and can be set to match using the **Space Naming** command, which automatically updates space names based on the corresponding architectural model's room name.

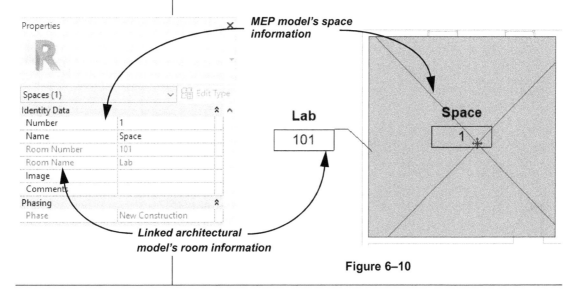

Figure 6–10

How To: Run the Space Naming Command

1. Add spaces to the model.

2. In the *Analyze* tab>Spaces & Zones panel, click 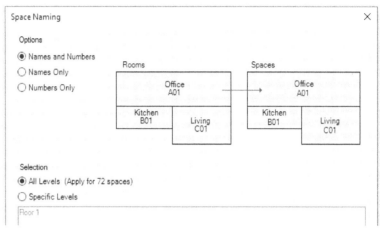 (Space Naming).

3. In the Space Naming dialog box (shown in Figure 6–11), select the Options and Selection for the spaces you want named and then click **OK**.

Figure 6–11

- Some spaces (such as plenums, cavities, and chases) are specific to MEP projects and are not named in the linked architectural model. Select the space(s) and change the name and number in Properties, or select the tag name or number to modify it, as shown in Figure 6–12.

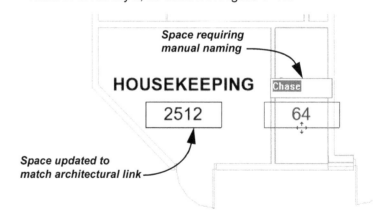

Figure 6–12

- If room names and numbers are changed in the linked architectural model, run the Space Naming tool again to update them.

Creating Individual Spaces

While most of the spaces you need can be created using the **Place Spaces Automatically** tool, you can also add individual spaces by selecting boundaries and by using Space Separators to sub-divide spaces. For example, in a lobby, there might be an area open to above that does not have a wall that defines the change in space height. Draw a space separation boundary as shown in Figure 6–13.

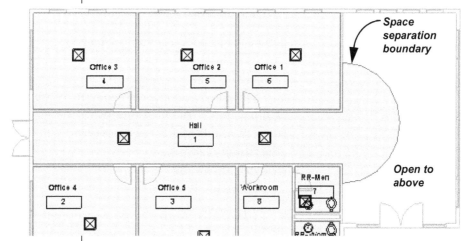

Figure 6–13

How To: Create Spaces by Selecting Boundaries

1. In the *Analyze* tab>Spaces & Zones panel, click ▦ (Space).
2. Specify tagging and other options.
3. Move the cursor into a boundary area and click to place the space. Continue adding spaces, as shown in Figure 6–14.

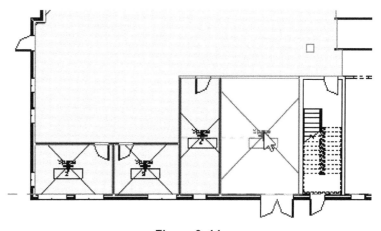

Figure 6–14

How To: Create Space Separation Boundaries

1. In the *Analyze* tab>Spaces & Zones panel, click 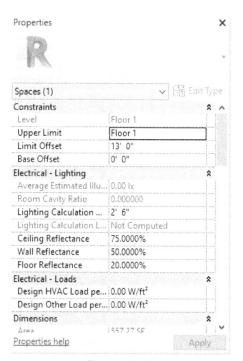 (Space Separator).
2. In the *Modify | Place Space Separation* tab>Draw panel, use the sketch tools to draw the edges of the boundary.

3. Use (Space) to add spaces in the areas bounded by the separation lines.

- You can edit space separation lines by splitting, trimming, etc.

Space Properties

You can modify the properties of a space by selecting it and using Properties, as shown in Figure 6–15, including:

- **Constraints:** Includes *Upper Limit* and *Limit Offset*, which displays the height of the space.
- **Electrical - Lighting**
- **Electrical - Loads**
- **Mechanical - Flow**
- **Energy Analysis**
- **Identity Data:** Includes the *Space Name* and *Space Number*.

This information is critical to set up before doing Heating and Cooling Loads and Lighting analysis.

Figure 6–15

Practice 6a | Add Spaces

Practice Objectives

- Set up the model to add spaces.
- Rename spaces to match rooms in a linked architectural model.
- Add spaces and space separator lines.

In this practice, you will set up a project by setting the linked model to Room Bounding, setting the area and volume computations, and creating a view where you can add spaces. You will also create a view template of that view to be used in similar views. You will then automatically add spaces and rename them to match the linked architectural model, as shown in Figure 6–16.

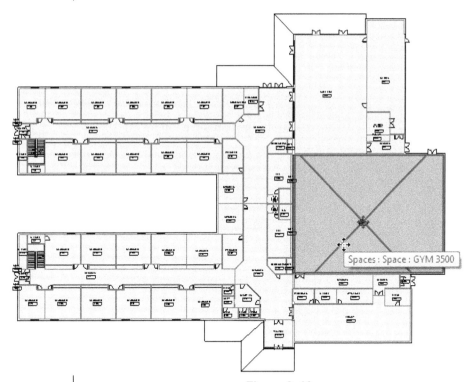

Figure 6–16

Task 1 - Set up a view in which you will define spaces.

1. In the practice files *Spaces* folder, open **Spaces-School-MEP.rvt**.

2. Select the linked model.

3. In Properties, click 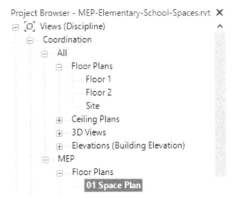 (Edit Type).

4. In the Type Properties dialog box, select **Room Bounding** and click **OK**.

5. In the *Analyze* tab, expand the Spaces & Zones panel and click (Area and Volume Computations).

6. In the Area and Volume Computations dialog box, select **Areas and Volumes** and keep **At wall finish** selected. Click **OK**.

7. In the Project Browser, expand Coordination>All>Floor Plans. Select the **Floor 1** view, right-click and select **Duplicate View>Duplicate**.

8. Rename the new view as **01 Space Plan**.

9. In Properties, change the *Sub-Discipline* to **MEP**.

   • Note that you want the *Discipline* to remain **Coordination** but *Sub-Discipline* to be **MEP** (rather than **All**), as spaces are used in multiple disciplines.

10. The new view moves to the **MEP** node, as shown in Figure 6–17.

Project Browser - MEP-Elementary-School-Spaces.rvt ✕
- Views (Discipline)
  - Coordination
    - All
      - Floor Plans
        - Floor 1
        - Floor 2
        - Site
      - Ceiling Plans
      - 3D Views
      - Elevations (Building Elevation)
    - MEP
      - Floor Plans
        - 01 Space Plan

Figure 6–17

11. No spaces display in this view. Type **VG** to open the Visibility/Graphics dialog box.

12. In the *Model Categories* tab, scroll down and first select **Spaces** to turn spaces on, then expand the Spaces node, select **Interior** (as shown in Figure 6–18), and click **OK**. Note that no spaces are placed yet.

Figure 6–18

13. In the Project Browser, right-click on the **01 Space Plan** view and select **Create View Template from View...**

14. In the New View Template dialog box, type **Space Plan** and click **OK**.

15. In the View Templates dialog box, clear the check from the *View Scale* option, as shown in Figure 6–19, and click **OK**.

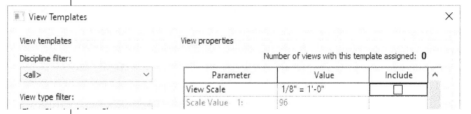

Figure 6–19

16. Duplicate the **Coordination>All>Floor Plans>Floor 2** view and rename it **02 Space Plan**.

17. Right-click on the new **02 Space Plan** view and select **Apply Template Properties**.

18. In the Apply View Template dialog box, select *Space Plan* and click **OK**. The view moves to the MEP *Sub-Discipline* and the view is ready to have spaces applied.

19. Save the project.

Task 2 - Add spaces.

---

1. Open the **01 Space Plan** view.

2. In the *Analyze* tab>Spaces & Zones panel, click ▦ (Space).

---

3. In the Options Bar, set the *Upper Limit* to **Floor 2** and the *Offset* to **0.**

4. In the *Modify | Place Space* tab>Tag panel, verify that (Tag on Placement) is selected.

5. In the Spaces panel, click (Place Spaces Automatically). The spaces are created as shown in Figure 6–20. Click **Close**.

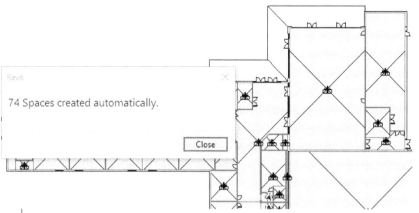

Figure 6–20

6. Zoom in to see the names of the spaces. Note that they are all named the same with numbers starting in the 3000's.

7. Open the **02 Space Plan** view and place spaces on the second floor with an *Upper Limit* of **Floor 2** and *an Offset* of **13'-0".**

8. Return to the **01 Space Plan** view.

9. In the *Analyze* tab>Spaces & Zones panel, click (Space Naming).

10. In the Space Naming dialog box, accept the default settings for **Names and Numbers** and **All Levels** and click **OK**. Most of the spaces are updated as shown in Figure 6–21.

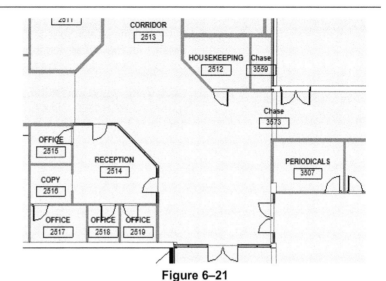

Figure 6–21

11. Open the **02 Space Plan** view. Most of the space names and numbers are also updated.

Task 3 - Add a space separation line and new space.

---

1. Open the **01 Space Plan** view.

2. Zoom in on the **KITCHEN STORAGE** space in the top right side of the building above the gym.

3. In the *Analyze* tab>Spaces & Zones panel, click ⬚ (Space Separator).

4. Draw a line across part of the storage area, as shown in Figure 6–22. Press <Esc> twice to end the command.

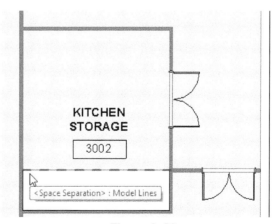

Figure 6–22

5. In the *Analyze* tab>Spaces & Zones panel, click 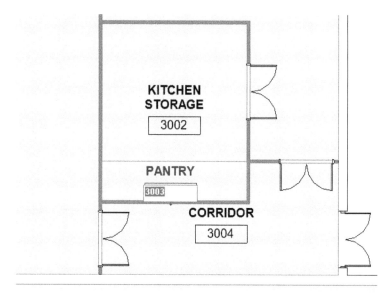 (Space). Verify that the *Upper Limit* is set to **Floor 2** and the *Offset* is set to **0'**, then click inside the empty area.

6. Click **Modify** and select the space tag. Click on the name and rename it **PANTRY**. Click on the number and enter **3003**, as shown in Figure 6–23.

Figure 6–23

7. Zoom out to fit the view.

8. Save and close the project.

6.3 Working with Spaces

As you are working with spaces in a project, it is important to place a space in every open area so that the energy analysis is computed correctly. Check the project in plan and in section to find elements, such as shafts and plenum spaces as shown in Figure 6–24. You also need to set up the properties of each space for correct calculation.

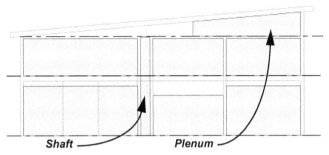

Shaft ———   Plenum ——

Figure 6–24

- You can change the height of a space in properties or visually in a section using controls, as shown in Figure 6–25, and temporary dimensions.

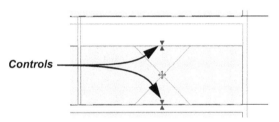

Controls ——

Figure 6–25

- When there are changes in the height of an area, the space must be placed at the tallest height as shown in Figure 6–26, where a Plenum level was added. You can then change the *Bottom Offset* in Properties to have the space extend down, as shown in Figure 6–27.

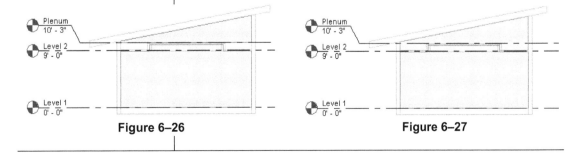

Figure 6–26	**Figure 6–27**

Special Space Situations

There are several situations in which you need to make modifications to spaces or the surrounding bounding areas to have them read correctly when analysis is done. These include shafts, sliver spaces, cavities, and plenum spaces.

Shafts and Interior/Exterior Bounding Elements

It is critical to place a space in every area in a building before you try to analyze the heating and cooling load because any wall that is not bounded by another space is considered an exterior wall. In the example shown in Figure 6–28, there are several spaces that have not been added, including a shaft, an elevator shaft, and a room. The open spaces are considered exterior rather than interior spaces.

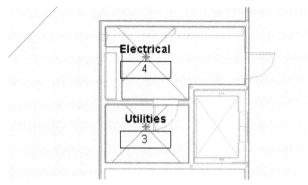

Figure 6–28

- Wall type functions can be specified in the Type Parameters as shown in Figure 6–29. **Interior** and **Core-shaft** *Function* types are considered interior whether they have a space on the other side of the wall or not.

When space boundary objects are contained in linked projects it might be required to coordinate these settings with the project Architect or Structural Engineer.

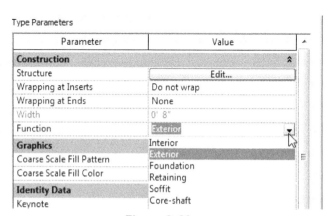

Figure 6–29

- Floor types can also have a *Function* of **Interior** or **Exterior**.

Sliver Spaces

Sliver spaces are shafts or other thin vertical areas that have parallel walls with spaces on all sides and meet a Sliver Space Tolerance setup in Energy Settings. The default is **1'-0"**. You cannot place a space in such areas, as shown in Figure 6–30.

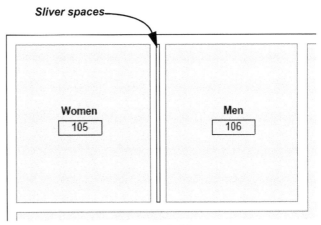

Figure 6–30

- To define the Sliver Space Tolerance, in the *Manage* tab> Settings panel, click (Project Information) and click **Edit...** next to the **Energy Settings** parameter.

Cavities

Cavities are small areas in which the walls are asymmetrical, such as a curved or triangular space that defines an odd shaped room, as shown in Figure 6–31. Typically, walls that define such spaces only extend to the ceiling or just above the ceiling. If you can add a space, do so. Check the area in section to verify that the entire space has been filled.

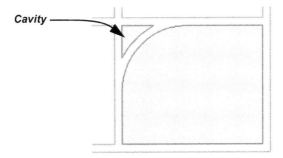

Figure 6–31

Plenum Spaces

Plenum spaces, as shown in Figure 6–32, are the areas between ceilings and the floor above, typically where ducts, piping, and electrical lines are run.

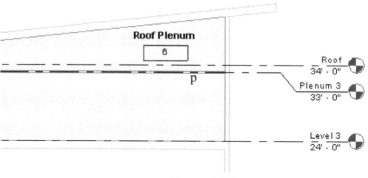

Figure 6–32

How To: Create Spaces in a Plenum

*Set the space **Upper Limit** to the level above, to have the space automatically stop at a boundary, such as a ceiling.*

1. In a plan view, create a section that cuts through the area in which the plenum runs, and in the section, verify that all of the spaces are touching the ceilings.
2. In the *Architecture* tab>Datum panel, click (Level).
3. In the Type Selector, select **Level: Plenum**.
4. In the Options Bar, select **Make Plan View**.
5. Draw a new level at the height of the ceiling and rename the level and any associated views with a name that fits the project, such as **Plenum 1** shown in Figure 6–33.

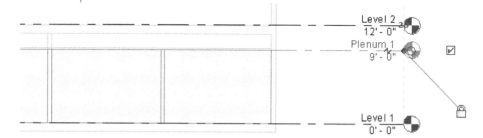

Figure 6–33

6. Open the new floor plan.
7. In Properties, edit the *View Range* and set the *cut plane offset* to **6"** (or other value that fits the height of the plenum.) Also, in the *Energy Analysis* area, select **Plenum**. This automatically clears and grays out *Occupiable* and sets *Condition Type* to **Unconditioned**.

8. In the plan view, place the spaces. They should fill the plenum area, as shown in the section view in Figure 6–34.

In this example, one wall touches the ceiling and another goes up to the floor above to indicate how the space in the plenum is divided.

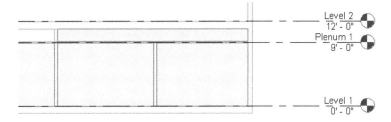

Figure 6–34

9. Repeat as required for all other plenum areas.

Hint: Troubleshooting Errors and Warnings

There are two types of error alerts. Those that you cannot ignore (shown in Figure 6–35) and those that can be ignored but need to be dealt with at a later time (shown in Figure 6–36).

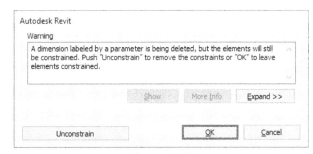

Figure 6–35

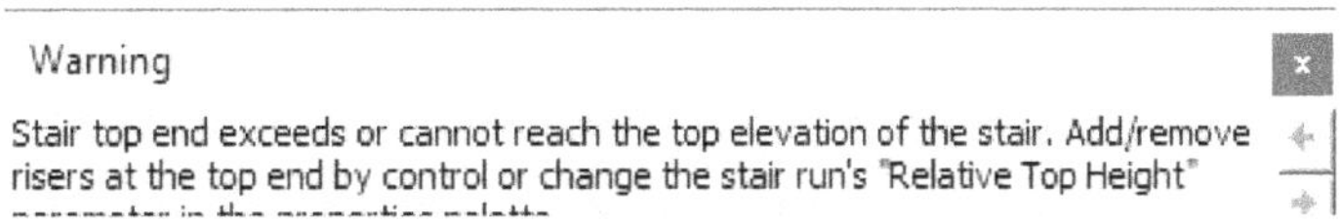

Warning

Stair top end exceeds or cannot reach the top elevation of the stair. Add/remove risers at the top end by control or change the stair run's "Relative Top Height"

Figure 6–36

- **Errors:** Force you to stop and fix the situation. In some cases, you can resolve the error if an option is provided, while in other cases, you have to cancel and try again.
- **Warnings**: Display when something is wrong, but you can keep on working. In many cases, you can close the dialog box and fix the issue or wait and fix it later.

When you select an element with issues, ⚠ (Show Related Warnings) displays in the contextual tab. To see all the warnings in a project, in the *Manage* tab>Inquiry panel, click

⚠ (Review Warnings).

Practice 6b | Work with Spaces

Practice Objectives

- Modify spaces.
- Add a plenum level.
- Correct space issues.

In this practice, you will modify the heights of spaces in the gym and cafeteria areas. You will also create a plenum level and add plenum spaces, as shown in Figure 6–37. You will investigate an overlap of spaces and add space separation lines to correct it.

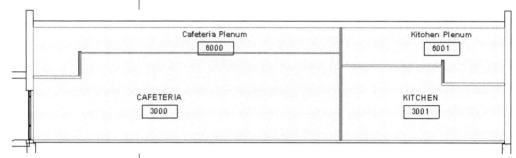

Figure 6–37

Task 1 - Modify the heights of spaces.

1. In the project files *Spaces* folder, open **Spaces-Modify-School-MEP.rvt**. This project file includes additional space elements for the practice.

2. Draw a section vertically across the far right end of the gym, as shown in Figure 6–38.

Draw the section so it does not display the far wall. This makes it easier to just display the gym and its space.

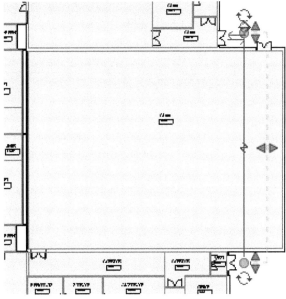

Figure 6–38

3. Click **Modify** and then double-click on the section marker to open the section.

4. In Properties, set the *Sub-Discipline* to **MEP** and the *View Name* to **Gym Section.**

5. In the Visibility/Graphics Overrides dialog box, in the *Model Categories* tab, verify that **Spaces** is checked and expand it to check **Interior**, as shown in Figure 6–39.

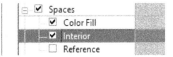

Figure 6–39

6. In the Project Browser, right-click on the Coordination> MEP>Section (Building Section)>**Gym Section** section view and select **Create View Template from View**.

7. In the New View Template dialog box, type **Space Section** and click **OK**.

8. In the View Templates dialog box, clear the check from the *View Scale* category and click **OK**. This template can be used again for any other section views that you create while working with spaces.

9. The space height in the gym is too low, as shown in Figure 6–40.

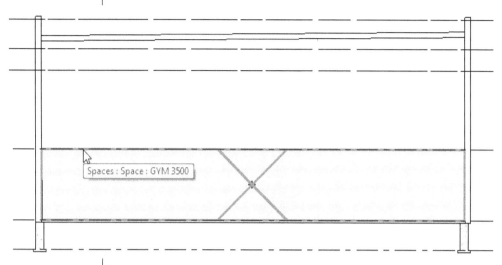

Figure 6–40

10. Select the space. Use the controls to extend the space above the roof of the gym or, in Properties, change the *Upper Limit* to **Reference 3**.

11. In the Project Browser, click on **01 Space Plan** to open the view or switch which view tab is being displayed.

12. Draw a section horizontally across the end of the Cafeteria and Kitchen, as shown in Figure 6–41.

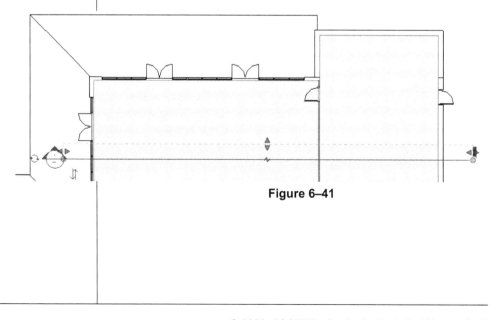

Figure 6–41

13. Click in empty space to clear the selection and then double-click on the section marker to open the section.

When a View Template is specified in Properties, you cannot make changes to many of the view properties.

14. In Properties, in the *Identity Data* area click the **<None>** button next to *View Template*. In the Apply View Template dialog box, select **Space Section** and click **OK**. The view inherits the settings of the View Template that you created earlier.

15. Change the name of the view to **Cafeteria Section**.

16. You can see that the Kitchen space (to the right in Figure 6–42) fills the height correctly but the Cafeteria (to the left in Figure 6–42) does not.

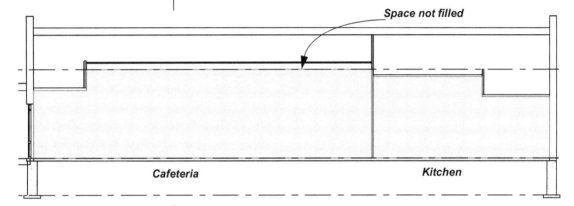

Figure 6–42

17. Select the Cafeteria space. In Properties, change *Upper Limit* to **Floor 2** and *Limit Offset* to **5'-0".**

18. The space is now filled in correctly as shown in Figure 6–43.

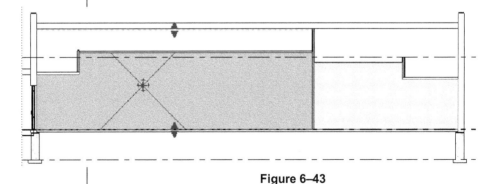

Figure 6–43

19. Save the project.

Task 2 - Add plenum spaces above the cafeteria and kitchen.

Ensure you select the Plenum Level type, as it can cause problems if it is drawn on a building story level.

1. In the *Architecture* tab>Datum panel, click ⁻⁺⁴ (Level).

2. In the Type Selector, select **Level: Plenum** and, in Properties, verify the **Building Story** option is not checked.

3. Draw a level line **14'-0"** above the First Floor and rename it as **Cafeteria Plenum** as shown in Figure 6–44. When prompted, rename the associated views.

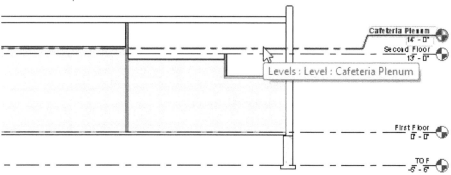

Figure 6–44

4. Double-click on the **Cafeteria Plenum** level head to open the floor plan view.

5. In Properties, apply the *View Template* **Space Plan** to this view.

6. In the *Analyze* tab>Spaces & Zones panel, click ⊞ (Space).

7. Add spaces to the Cafeteria and Kitchen areas, as shown in Figure 6–45.

The walls showing in your view may vary.

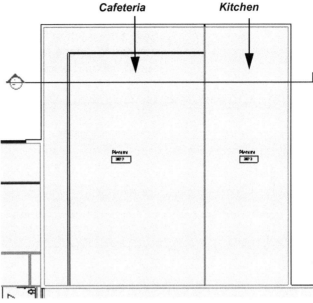

Figure 6–45

8. Click **Modify**.

9. Change the space name and number over the cafeteria to **Cafeteria Plenum** and **6000**. Change the space name and number over the kitchen to **Kitchen Plenum** and **6001**.

10. Switch to the Section 2 view tab. The height of the space is appropriate but the depth of some parts is not as shown in Figure 6–46.

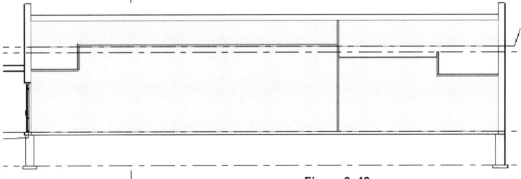

Figure 6–46

11. Select the Cafeteria Plenum space. In Properties, change the *Base Offset* to (negative) **-3'-0"**. The space expands down but not all of the way. Change the *Base Offset* to (negative) **-5'-0"**. The space expands down to fill the plenum area.

12. Select the Kitchen Plenum space. This time use the Drag controls to extend the space below the lowest ceiling. The section should display as shown in Figure 6–47.

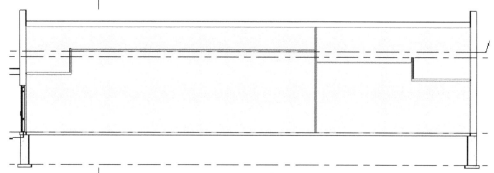

Figure 6–47

13. Save the project.

Task 3 - Correct an issue where spaces overlap.

1. Return to the **01 Space Plan** view.

2. Zoom in on the office area and select the **RECEPTION** space, as shown in Figure 6–48.

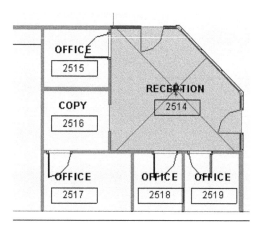

Figure 6–48

This option displays if there is a problem with the selected space.

3. In the *Modify | Spaces* tab>Warnings panel, click  (Show Related Warnings).

4. In the dialog box, expand the warnings as shown in Figure 6–49. The issue is with the reception space on the first floor and the plenum space above.

Autodesk Revit

Messages
 ⊟ Warning (may be ignored)
   ⊟ Space volumes overlap. Adjust the Upper Limit and Limit Offset properties of
      the Spaces.
      ⊟ Warning 1
          ☐ Spaces : Space : RECEPTION 2514 - Number 2514 ; id 227493
          ☐ Spaces : Space : Plenum 3009 - Number 3009 : id 494727

[Show]   [More Info]   [Delete Checked...]

To highlight an element in the graphics window, select it in this tree.

Most standard view commands work without exiting this dialog.

[Export...]   [Close]

Figure 6–49

5. In **Warning 1**, select the plenum space and click **Show**. Read any alerts and continue. The view zooms in and displays the problems, as shown in Figure 6–50.

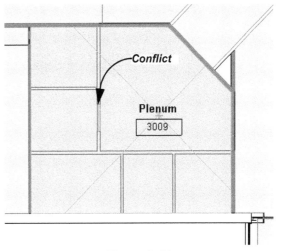

Conflict

Plenum
3009

Figure 6–50

6. Close the Warning dialog box.

7. Draw a short section through this area. Open the section and apply the **Space Section** view template to it.

8. When you select the copy space, you can see how it extends into the plenum area, as shown in Figure 6–51, but you cannot tell why.

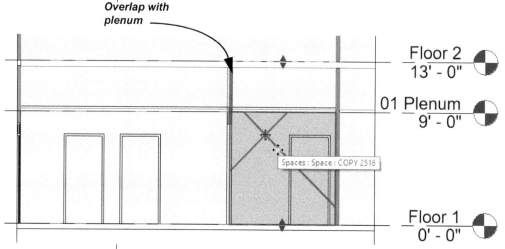

Figure 6–51

9. Open the **01 Space Plan** view.

10. There is an opening rather than a door between the Copy and Reception areas. This is creating an issue with the wall and therefore with the plenum space. To solve this problem you need to add a Space Separator so that the software treats this opening like any other door.

11. In the *Analyze* tab>Spaces and Zones panel, click (Space Separator).

12. In the Options Bar, clear **Chain** and draw two lines on each side of the framed opening as shown in Figure 6–52.

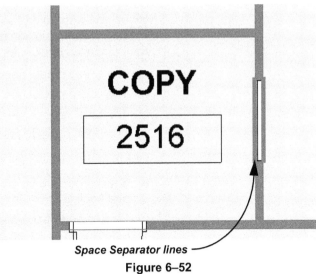

Space Separator lines

Figure 6–52

13. Select the Reception space again. The Warning no longer displays.

14. Display the related section and the **01 Plenum** plan view. None of the overlaps exist.

15. Open the **01 Space Plan** view.

16. Zoom out, save, and close the project.

Chapter Review Questions

1. When you want to add spaces to a project that uses a linked model's room name and number information, what is required for the spaces to work as expected?

   a. The linked model needs to have rooms.

   b. The linked model needs to be set to Room Bounding.

   c. The MEP project needs to be set to Room Bounding.

   d. The MEP project needs to have rooms.

2. Which of the following is true to get an accurate analysis?

   a. Spaces need to be created in all rooms that have heating and cooling.

   b. Spaces need to be created in all rooms that are established in the architectural drawing.

   c. Spaces need to be created in all rooms that span more than one level.

   d. Spaces need to be created in all rooms, as well as shafts, plenums, and other non-occupied spaces.

3. If you do not see spaces in the view you are working in, as shown on the top in Figure 6–53, what is required to display them as shown on the bottom in Figure 6–53?

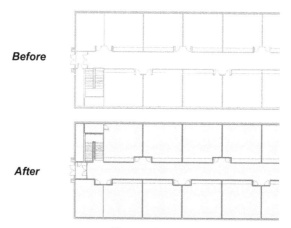

Before

After

Figure 6–53

   a. Open the Visibility/Graphics dialog box and toggle on the **Interior** option under *Spaces*.

   b. Before placing spaces, select **Interior** on the Option Bar.

   c. In Properties, select **Interior**.

   d. In the View Control Bar, toggle on **Spaces**.

4. If a space is not reaching the ceiling, as shown in a section in Figure 6–54, which of the following methods can you use to fix the issue? (Select all that apply.)

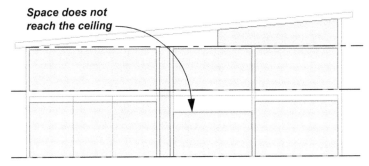

Figure 6–54

a. Change the height of the room because the space reflects room size.

b. Select the space and use the controls to move the top edge above the ceiling.

c. Change the *Space Settings* to **Height by Ceiling**.

d. Verify that the ceiling is set to **Room Bounding**.

5. When you have a space that is not defined entirely by walls, such as a balcony in a 2-story lobby, how do you control the size of the space?

a. Sketch the boundaries of the space.

b. Add space separation lines.

c. Modify the size in Properties.

d. Change the Room Bounding status of the other walls.

Command Summary

Button	Command	Location
	Area and Volume Computations	• **Ribbon:** *Analyze* tab>Spaces & Zones panel>expand the panel title
	Space	• **Ribbon:** *Analyze* tab>Spaces & Zones panel
	Space Naming	• **Ribbon:** *Analyze* tab>Spaces & Zones panel
	Space Separator	• **Ribbon:** *Analyze* tab>Spaces & Zones panel
	Space Tag	• **Ribbon:** *Analyze* tab>Spaces & Zones panel or *Annotate* tab>Tag panel

Chapter 7

Heating and Cooling Loads Analysis

Preparing a project so that you can run a Heating and Cooling Loads analysis involves grouping spaces into zones that are heated and cooled in the same manner. Creating color schemes that graphically indicate the various zones is helpful. When you start the Heating and Cooling Loads tool, you must specify the building type, location, and other options before you can calculate the energy demands of the model. Using the System Browser, you can review existing zones and any spaces that have yet to be assigned to a zone.

Learning Objectives in This Chapter

- Add zones to connect spaces for analysis.
- Use the System Browser with zones.
- Apply color schemes and color fill legends for spaces and zones.
- Prepare a project for a Heating and Cooling Loads analysis.
- Run a Heating and Cooling Loads analysis.

7.1 Creating Zones

After creating spaces, the next step in preparing to compute heating and cooling loads is to divide the building into zones, as shown in Figure 7–1. Each zone consists of similar spaces that would be heated and cooled in the same manner.

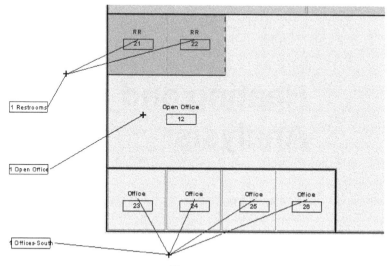

Figure 7–1

- There is always one **Default** zone in a project. All spaces are automatically attached to that zone when they are created.

- While you can add zones into a template, you usually add spaces first, then create zones and add spaces to the zones.

- You can create zones in plan and section views.

How To: Add Zones

1. Open a plan view that contains the spaces you want to work with. If you have a zone that stretches across two levels, open a section view as well.

2. For each view, open the Visibility/Graphic Overrides dialog box, expand **HVAC Zones**, and select all of the options, as shown in Figure 7–2.

You can set up a view template for zones in the same way as you set up one for spaces.

Figure 7–2

3. In the *Analyze* tab>Spaces & Zones panel, click ⊞ (Zone).
4. In Properties, under *Identity Data*, type a name for the Zone for the **Name** value. By default, the zones are numbered incrementally.
5. In the *Edit Zone* tab (shown in Figure 7–3), ensure that ⊞ (Add Space) is automatically selected.

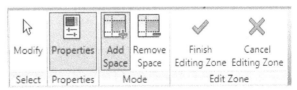

Figure 7–3

6. Select the spaces that you want to add to the zone.

7. Click ✓ (Finish Editing Zone).

- Another quick way to add a zone is to select the spaces first, then in the *Analyze* tab>Spaces & Zones panel, click ⊞ (Zone). The spaces are automatically added to the zone.

- To edit an existing zone, select one of the zone lines, as shown in Figure 7–4, then in the *Modify | HVAC Zones* tab>Zone panel, click ⊞ (Edit Zone). The *Edit Zone* tab displays which enables you to add more spaces.

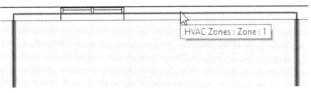

Figure 7–4

- Click ⊞ (Remove Space) to remove a space from the zone or modify the zone properties.

- Zones do not automatically have a tag placed, but it is helpful to display these as you are working. In the *Annotate* tab>Tag panel, click (Tag by Category) and select on the zone(s) that you want to tag, as shown in Figure 7–5.

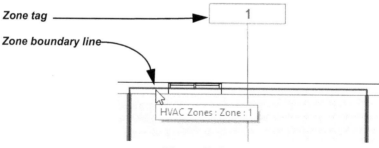

Figure 7–5

- You can change the name of a zone by changing the tag or in Properties. Zone tags are found in the library in the *Annotations>Mechanical* folder.

Using the System Browser with Zones

The System Browser is a useful tool when working with systems, analytical systems, and zones. The System Browser is an effective tool that helps you in finding components that are or are not assigned to a system or zone. When you select a zone or space in the System Browser, it displays in the project, as shown in Figure 7–6. The selected zone or space is automatically made active in the Properties. This enables you to modify names for spaces and zones and assign information, such as electrical loads and mechanical airflow.

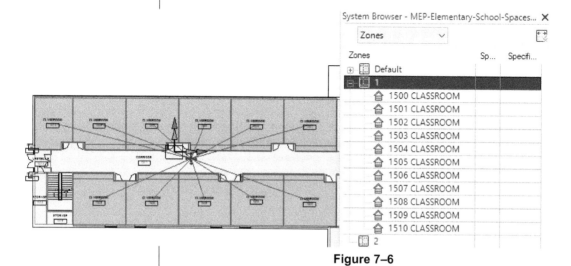

Figure 7–6

- You can open the System Browser using any of the following methods:

    - Press <F9>.
    - In the view, right-click, expand **Browsers**, and select **System Browser**.
    - In the *View* tab>Windows panel, expand (User Interface) and select **System Browser**, as shown in Figure 7–7.

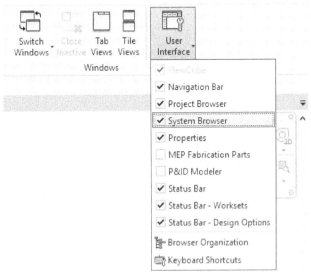

Figure 7–7

- You can float or dock the System Browser to any side of the screen. You can also place it on a second monitor.

- The System Browser can be docked with Properties and the Project Browser to save screen space.

How To: Use the System Browser with Zones

1. In the *Analyze* tab>System Browser panel, click (System Browser) or press <F9>.
2. If the zones are not displayed, expand the View drop-down list and select **Zones**, as shown in Figure 7–8.

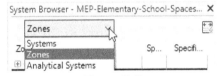

Figure 7–8

3. All of the spaces are listed under the **Default** zone (as shown in Figure 7–9) until they are added to a specific zone.

- Each space displays an icon showing its status:

  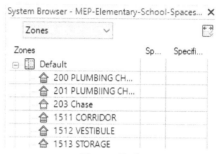 (Occupiable), 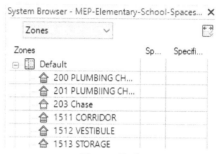 (Not Occupiable), and (Space not placed).

- As new zones are added, the spaces are moved into the new zones.

Figure 7–9

4. Select a space or a zone. It is highlighted in the project and becomes active in the Properties.

- You can select more than one space or zone at a time using <Ctrl> and <Shift>.

- In the System Browser, if you right-click on a space or zone and select **Show**, you may get a message that says there are no open views that show any of the highlighted elements. Click **OK**. The software zooms in on the selected elements.

- If there is more than one view in which the space can be displayed, the Show Element(s) in View dialog box opens, as shown in Figure 7–10.

Figure 7–10

- If you place spaces and then delete them, they remain in the project. To delete a space entirely, in the System Browser, right-click on the space name and select **Delete**.
  - You can also delete spaces in a space schedule view.

7.2 Applying Color Schemes

When working with Zones and Spaces, it is useful to have a view that displays color coding for individual zones, spaces, or rooms, as shown in Figure 7–11. You can include a color fill legend in the same view to clarify the use of the colors.

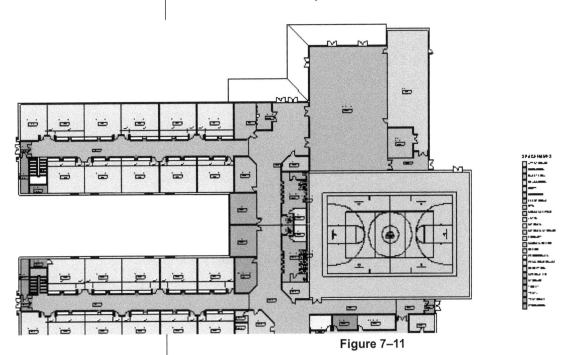

Figure 7–11

- Color schemes are controlled by a view property. Therefore, you should create a view for each color diagram that you want to include.

How To: Set Up a Color Scheme in a View

1. Create or duplicate a view that you want to use for the color scheme.
2. In Properties, click the button next to the **Color Scheme** parameter, as shown in Figure 7–12.

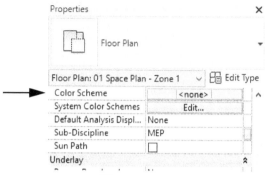

Figure 7–12

3. In the Edit Color Scheme dialog box, in the *Schemes* area, select a **Category**.

4. Select a scheme in the list. In the example shown in Figure 7–13, **Space Names** is selected.

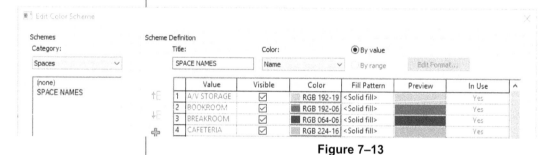

Figure 7–13

For information about creating color schemes see Section A.2 Defining Color Schemes.

5. Click **OK**. The new color scheme displays in the view.

• The color fill of the scheme can display in the background or foreground of the view. In Properties, set the *Color Scheme Location*. This impacts how components display and whether or not the color fill stops at the walls.

- You can add a legend that matches the Color Scheme, as shown in Figure 7–14. In the *Analyze* tab>Color Fill panel, click ▤ (Color Fill Legend), and place the legend where you want it.

The Type Properties for the Color Fill Legend control the appearance of the legend, including the swatch size and text styles.

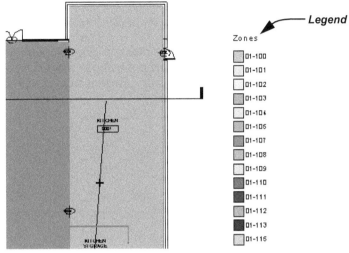

Figure 7–14

- If you change the **Color Scheme** in the View Properties dialog box, it also updates in the associated legend.

Practice 7a | Create Zones

Practice Objectives

- Add zones.
- Use the System Browser to identify and modify zone information.
- Create a color scheme showing the zones.

In this practice, you will add HVAC zones to the project. You will examine the zones and spaces in the System Browser and you set up a view that displays the zone names by color as shown in Figure 7–15 with zone tags. Optionally, you can create additional zones.

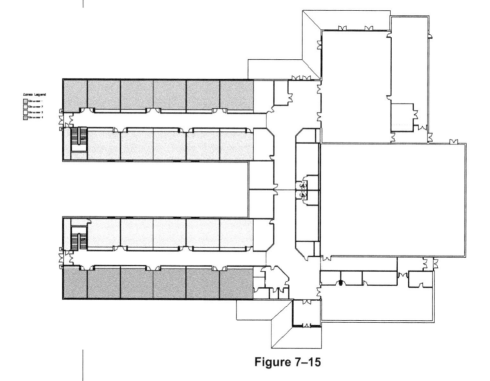

Figure 7–15

Task 1 - Add zones.

1. In the practice files *Analysis* folder, open **Zones-School-MEP.rvt**.

2. Duplicate the **Coordination>MEP>Floor Plans>01 Space Plan** view

3. Rename it to **01 Zones**.

You can still select the spaces, but the interior fill does not display.

4. Select one of the sections in the view and type **VH** to hide the category in the view.

5. Open the Visibility/Graphics Overrides dialog box, set the *Filter List* to **Mechanical** and set the following:
   - **HVAC Zones:** Select **Boundary**, **Interior Fill** and **Reference Lines**
   - **Spaces:** Clear **Interior Fill** and **Color Fill**

6. In the *Analyze* tab>Spaces & Zones panel, click ⊞ (Zone).

7. In the *Edit Zone* tab, verify that ⊞ (Add Space) is selected.

8. Select the spaces across the top group of Classrooms, so the zone displays as shown in Figure 7–16.

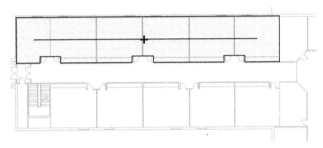

Figure 7–16

9. In Properties, change the *Name* to **Classrooms 1**.

10. In the *Edit Zone* tab>Edit Zone panel, click ✓ (Finish Editing Zone).

11. Add another zone to the Classrooms and Storage Areas on the other side of the hall as shown in Figure 7–17.

The name of the zone automatically increments as each zone is added.

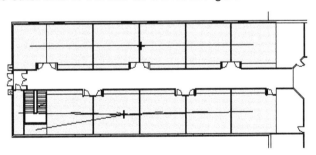

Figure 7–17

12. Add zones to the two classroom groups in the other wing.

13. Save the project.

Task 2 - Use the System Browser.

1. Press <F9> to open the System Browser, if it is not already open.

2. In the System Browser, set the view so it displays **Zones**. It should display as shown in Figure 7–18.

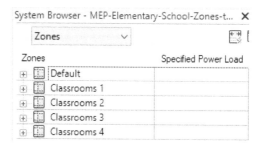

Figure 7–18

3. Expand the **Default** zone. Note that there are a lot of spaces that are not placed in zones. There are also two different types of icons for spaces: occupied (green icon) and unoccupied (orange icon), as shown in Figure 7–19.

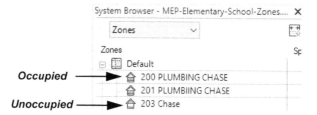

Figure 7–19

4. Some of the spaces that should be unoccupied, such as the Plumbing Chases shown in Figure 7–19, are not set correctly. In the System Browser, hold <Ctrl> and select the two plumbing chases.

5. In Properties, scroll down to the *Energy Analysis* area and clear **Occupiable**. Repeat this for other chases or plenums that might not be correctly identified.

6. As you scroll through the spaces, note that some display

   ⌂ (Space Not Placed). Right-click on them and click **Delete**.

7. In the System Browser, in the default zone, right-click on one of the plenums that has been placed and select **Show** (open additional views as necessary). The view changes to display the location of the plenum, such as the one shown in Figure 7–20. Close the Show Element(s) in View dialog box.

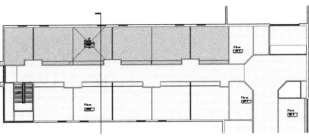

Figure 7–20

8. Click away from any elements to release the selection.

9. Close the System Browser.

10. Save the project.

Task 3 - Add a color scheme.

1. Open the **01 Zones** view. Close any extra view tabs (In the Quick Access Toolbar, click (Close Inactive Windows)).

2. In Properties, in the *Graphics* area, click the button next to *Color Scheme*.

3. In the Edit Color Scheme dialog box, in the *Schemes* area, change the *Category* to **HVAC Zones**.

4. Select the default **Schema 1**. The Scheme Definition automatically populates by zone name as shown in Figure 7–21.

Figure 7–21

5. In the *Schemes* area, rename *Schema 1* to **Zones**.

6. In the *Scheme Definition* area, in the *Title* field, type **Zones Legend**.

7. Click **OK**. The color scheme is applied to the view. The display will be similar to that shown in Figure 7–22.

Your zone colors might vary.

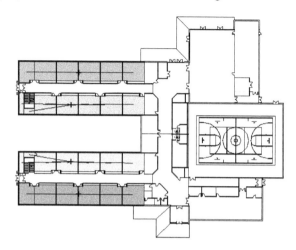

Figure 7–22

- If reference lines are visible, open the Visibility/Graphics dialog box, expand **HVAC Zones** and clear **Reference Lines**. This can make the color fill easier to read.

8. In the *Analyze* tab>Color Fill panel, click (Color Fill Legend) and place the legend near the classrooms, as shown in Figure 7–23.

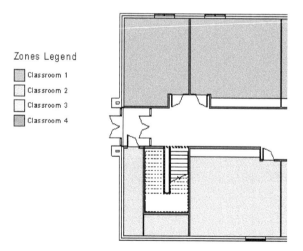

Figure 7–23

9. Save the project.

Task 4 - (Optional) Add additional zones.

1. Add the zones listed below and shown in Figure 7–24.
   - (1) The classroom zones (created in previous steps).
   - (2) All of the corridors plus the Electrical Room.
   - (3) All of the vestibules.
   - (4) Nurse's Office, Bookroom, Special Ed rooms, and Workroom.
   - (5) Reception, Offices, and Copy Room.
   - (6) Library and associated rooms.
   - (7) Gym.
   - (8) Cafeteria.
   - (9) Kitchen and Kitchen Storage.
   - (10) Restrooms.
   - (11) Housekeeping, Janitor, and associated chases.

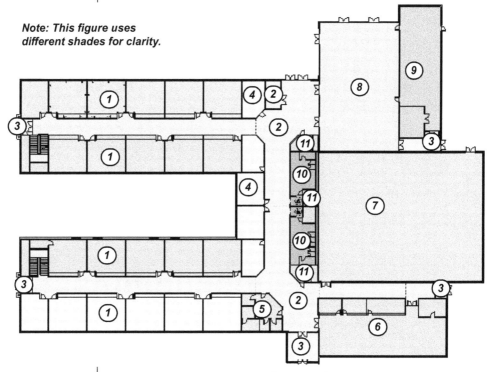

Note: This figure uses different shades for clarity.

Figure 7–24

2. In the *Annotate* tab>Tags panel, click ⌐① (Tag by Category), and select each zone to place a tag.

3. Save the project.

7.3 Analyzing the Heating and Cooling Loads

Additional cloud-based tools for Energy Optimization are included with a subscription.

Using the power of BIM technology in the Autodesk Revit software, the information you set in spaces, zones, and other energy analysis parameters is used as the basis of the loads analysis for the project. Use the **Heating and Cooling Loads** tool to set up important energy settings, including the type and location of the building, as well as to verify the spaces and zones (as shown in Figure 7–25), before calculating a Loads Report.

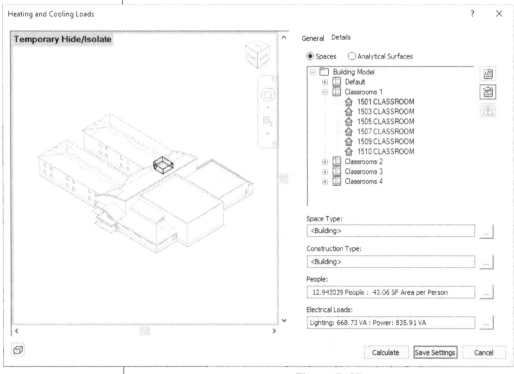

Figure 7–25

For information about managing settings, see Section A.1 Building Type Settings.

- Establishing the building type and location is a critical step because a multi-story office in a tropical climate has different heating and cooling requirements than one in a cold climate.

How To: Set Up a Heating and Cooling Loads Analysis

1. In the *Analyze* tab>Reports & Schedules panel, click
   (Heating and Cooling Loads) or type **LO**.

2. The Heating and Cooling Loads dialog box opens as shown in Figure 7–25. It contains a 3D view of the space volumes and displays information in the *General* and *Details* tabs.

3. In the *General* tab, verify or apply the parameters, as shown in Figure 7–26 and listed in the table below.

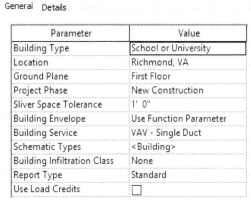

General Details

Parameter	Value
Building Type	School or University
Location	Richmond, VA
Ground Plane	First Floor
Project Phase	New Construction
Sliver Space Tolerance	1' 0"
Building Envelope	Use Function Parameter
Building Service	VAV - Single Duct
Schematic Types	<Building>
Building Infiltration Class	None
Report Type	Standard
Use Load Credits	☐

Figure 7–26

Building Type	Select from a list of building types that are set up in the program. You can also add and modify building types
Location	Specify the geographic location for the building using the Location Weather and Site dialog box.

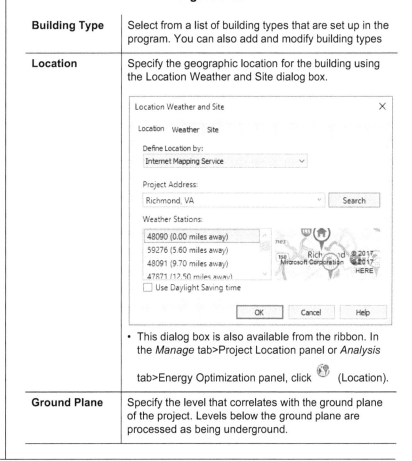

- This dialog box is also available from the ribbon. In the *Manage* tab>Project Location panel or *Analysis* tab>Energy Optimization panel, click 🌐 (Location).

Ground Plane	Specify the level that correlates with the ground plane of the project. Levels below the ground plane are processed as being underground.

Project Phase	Select the phase for the state of the project you are analyzing.
Sliver Space Tolerance	Specify the size for areas considered sliver spaces.
Building Envelope	Specify the method used to calculate the building envelope. • **Use Function Parameter:** The default option, which uses the function parameter of walls, floors, and building pads to determine interior and exterior spaces. • **Identify Exterior Elements:** Uses ray-casting and flood-fill algorithms to determine interior and exterior spaces. An additional parameter, **Analytical Grid Cell Size**, determines the size of 3D grid cubes that divide the building for processing.
Building Service	Specify the type of heating and cooling system used by the building.
Schematic Types	Specify overrides for material and insulation. Select **<Building>** and then click **...** to open the Schematic Types dialog box.

Analysis Properties

By default, analysis properties are generated from information in Conceptual Types.
Properties of Schematic Types are used when override is selected.

Category	Override	Analytic Construction
Roofs	☐	4 in lightweight concrete (U=0.2245)
Exterior Walls	☐	8 in lightweight concrete block (U=0.1428)
Interior Walls	☐	Frame partition with 3/4 in gypsum board (U=0.2595)
Ceilings	☐	8 in lightweight concrete ceiling (U=0.2397)
Floors	☐	Passive floor, no insulation, tile or vinyl (U=0.5210)
Slabs	☐	Un-insulated solid (U=0.1243)
Doors	☐	Metal (U=0.6520)
Exterior Windows	☐	Large double-glazed windows (reflective coating) - industry (U
Interior Windows	☐	Large single-glazed windows (U=0.6498, SHGC=0.86)
Skylights	☐	Large double-glazed windows (reflective coating) - industry (U

All	None	Shading factor for exterior windows: 0

Building Infiltration Class	Select from the list to specify the estimated outdoor air from leaks in the building envelope based on tightly constructed walls. • **Loose:** 0.076 cfm/sqft • **Medium:** 0.038 cfm/sqft • **Tight:** 0.019 cfm/sqft • **None:** Infiltration is excluded from the calculations.
Report Type	Specify the level of information provided by the calculations: **Simple, Standard, Detailed**.

Use Load Credits	Enables negative loads that leaves a zone through a partition into another zone. If you want to include the internal gains such as people, power, and lights, in a heating calculation, use the load credits.

4. Click **Save Settings** to set the energy settings in the General tab.

How To: Review and Update Spaces and Zones

1. Open the Heating and Cooling Loads dialog box.
2. Select the *Details* tab and expand the levels to display the spaces for each level. Icons next to the space name indicate whether the space has been able to be calculated and if it is occupiable or not, as shown in Figure 7–27.

   - Add spaces to zones other than the default zone. The default zone is calculated, but might not work correctly as spaces in the default zone can be far apart.

In this example there are still some spaces left in the Default Zone. You should stop the process and return to the System Browser to establish zones for the spaces and remove extra spaces.

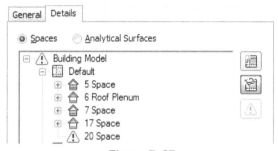

Figure 7–27

3. To display an error, select the room name and click

   ⚠ (Show Related Warnings). The Warning dialog box opens as shown in Figure 7–28, indicating the cause of the warning.

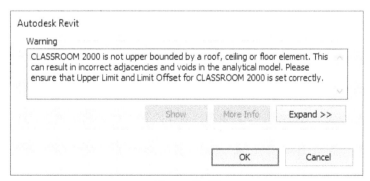

Figure 7–28

4. To display visual information about the space, select the space name and click 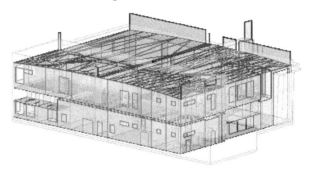 (Highlight) to highlight the space in the 3D view. You can also click (Isolate) to toggle off the display of all of the other spaces in the 3D view.
   - Click the icons again to toggle them off.

5. Select **Analytical Surfaces** to display the surface calculation planes, as shown in Figure 7–29.

Figure 7–29

- You can use the cursor or the ViewCube to zoom, pan, and rotate around the model in the dialog box.

6. If you need to make changes to the model, click **Save Settings** to save any changes you have made and return to the model.

7. When you are ready to run the report, click **Calculate**. The Loads Report displays and is also available in the Project Browser. Expand **Reports>Loads Reports** and select the one you need, as shown in Figure 7–30.

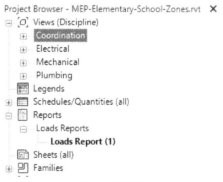

Figure 7–30

- The name of the report can be changed in Properties when the report is selected in the Project Browser.
- The Loads Report includes summaries for the Project, Building, and each Zone.

Practice 7b | Heating and Cooling Analysis

Practice Objectives

- Prepare a project for energy analysis with Energy Settings.
- Review the details of zones and spaces in the Heating and Cooling Loads dialog box and fix any warnings.

In this practice, you will run the Heating and Cooling Loads tool and review the details of the zones and spaces in the project. You will identify problems, as shown in Figure 7–31, solve them in the model, and rerun the software and calculate the analysis.

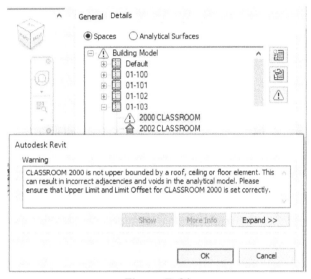

Figure 7–31

Task 1 - Prepare the project for energy analysis.

1. In the practice files *Analysis* folder, open **Analysis-School-MEP.rvt**.

2. In the *Analyze* tab>Reports & Schedules panel, click (Heating and Cooling Loads).

---

3. In the *General* tab, set the following parameter values, and shown in Figure 7–32:

- *Building Type:* **School or University**
- *Location*: Your hometown
- *Building Service:* **VAV - Dual Duct**

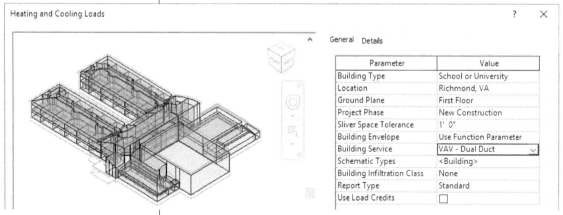

Figure 7–32

4. Click **Save Settings**.

5. Save the project.

Task 2 - Test the project.

1. Reopen the Heating and Cooling Loads dialog box and select the *Details* tab.

2. Several issues need to be resolved before you can calculate the loads starting with a Warning at the top of the building model, as shown in Figure 7–33.

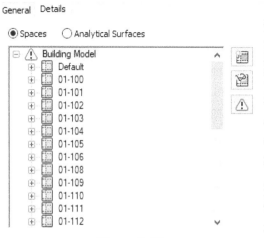

Figure 7–33

If your company includes a space schedule in your templates you can use it as mentioned in the Warning. You can also delete empty spaces in the Zone view of the System Browser.

3. Click ⚠ (Show Related Warnings). The Warning indicates that there are undefined spaces in the model. Click **Cancel**.

4. Expand the **Default** zone. There are several spaces in this zone that need to be modified and moved to other zones, as shown in Figure 7–34.

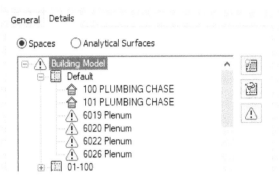

Figure 7–34

5. Select **100 Plumbing Chase**. The information about the space indicates that there are People and Electrical Loads associated with this space when they should not be, as shown in Figure 7–35. This is also indicated by the

🔼 (Occupiable) icon beside the space name.

Figure 7–35

6. Use (Highlight) and/or (Isolate) to identify the plumbing chase locations. For example, you might want to select both chases and isolate them first as shown in Figure 7–36. Then switch to **Highlight** to indicate their location in the building. They are hard to identify because they are very thin.

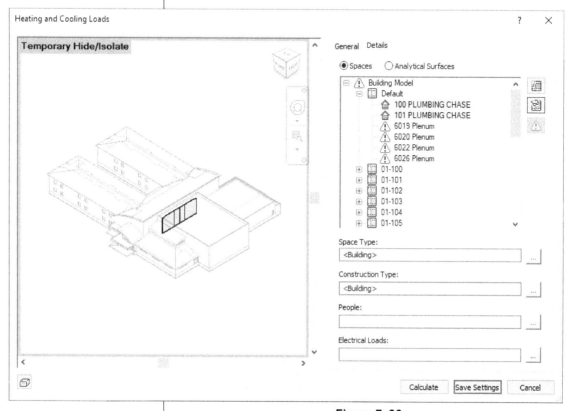

Figure 7–36

7. Toggle off **Highlight** and **Isolate**.

8. Select the four plenum spaces by holding <Ctrl> as you select.

9. Click 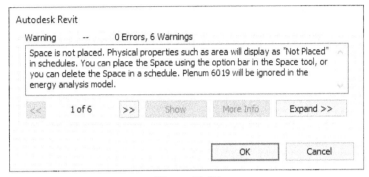 (Show Related Warnings). These spaces have not been placed and are ignored in the energy analysis as shown in Figure 7–37.

Autodesk Revit

Warning -- 0 Errors, 6 Warnings

Space is not placed. Physical properties such as area will display as "Not Placed" in schedules. You can place the Space using the option bar in the Space tool, or you can delete the Space in a schedule. Plenum 6019 will be ignored in the energy analysis model.

<< 1 of 6 >> Show More Info Expand >>

OK Cancel

Figure 7–37

10. Scroll down through the zones to check for other problems, such as the one shown in Figure 7–38. Write down this zone and the space number so you can correct it in the model.

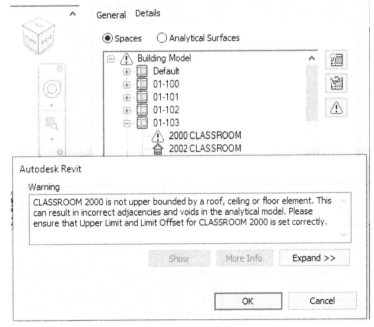

General Details

◉ Spaces ○ Analytical Surfaces

Building Model
 Default
 01-100
 01-101
 01-102
 01-103
  2000 CLASSROOM
  2002 CLASSROOM

Autodesk Revit

Warning

CLASSROOM 2000 is not upper bounded by a roof, ceiling or floor element. This can result in incorrect adjacencies and voids in the analytical model. Please ensure that Upper Limit and Limit Offset for CLASSROOM 2000 is set correctly.

Show More Info Expand >>

OK Cancel

Figure 7–38

11. Click **Save Settings** to close the Heating and Cooling Loads dialog box and return to the model so that it can be modified.

Task 3 - Modify the model.

1. Open the System Browser (press <F9>) in the Zones view.

2. Expand the **Default** zone to see the four unplaced plenum spaces. Right-click on one at a time and select **Delete**, as shown in Figure 7–39.

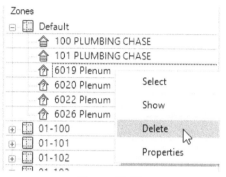

Figure 7–39

3. When prompted to delete the space, click **OK**.

4. In the System Browser in the *Default* zone, select both of the plumbing chase spaces.

5. In Properties, scroll down to the *Energy Analysis* area, clear **Occupiable** and click **Apply**. The icons in the System Browser change as shown in Figure 7–40.

Figure 7–40

6. These two chases need to be added to the same zone as the other chases nearby. In the view, hover the cursor over **Chase 104** and press <Tab> until the Zone lines highlight, as shown in Figure 7–41, with lines going to each of the individual spaces. Click to select the zone.

*If you want see it is in the project, right-click and select **Show**. The view zooms in to the location with the space selected.*

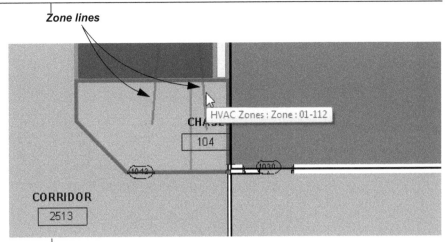

Zone lines

CORRIDOR
2513

Figure 7–41

7. In the *Modify | HVAC Zones* tab>Zone panel, click (Edit Zone).

8. In the *Edit Zone* tab>Mode panel, click (Add Space).

9. Zoom in as needed and select the two plumbing chase spaces. They should change to the color of the selected zone. Click (Finish Editing Zone).

10. In the System Browser, there should no longer be any spaces in the default zone.

Task 4 - Fix a space.

1. In the System Browser, find Zone **01-103** Space **2000 Classroom**. This had a problem with HVAC Loads, but does not display any warnings in the System Browser.

2. Right-click on the space and select **Show**. The view zooms in on the space but there are no warnings that anything is wrong. Close the Show Element(s) in View dialog box.

3. Double-click on the nearby section marker to open the section. The space does not extend up to the ceiling as it should, as shown in Figure 7–42.

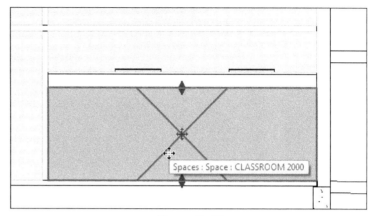

Figure 7–42

4. In the section view, select the space. In Properties, change the *Limit Offset* to **10'-0"**. The space now extends up to touch the ceiling as shown in Figure 7–43.

You can also use the drag controls to modify the height of the space.

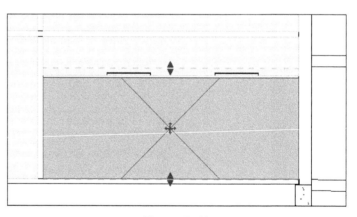

Figure 7–43

5. Return to the **01 Zones** plan view.

6. Zoom out to display the entire plan.

7. Save the project.

Task 5 - Run the heating and cooling loads.

1. Type **LO** (the shortcut key) or in the *Analyze* tab>Reports & Schedules panel, click ▦ (Heating and Cooling Loads).

2. In the Heating and Cooling Loads dialog box, in the *Details* tab, expand the zones. The problems have been taken care of as shown in Figure 7–44.

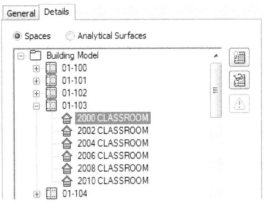

Figure 7–44

3. Click **Calculate**. The progress displays in the Status bar as shown in Figure 7–45. This takes time.

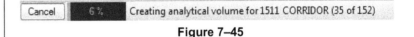

Figure 7–45

4. Review the Loads analysis document as shown in part in Figure 7–46.

Building Summary

Inputs	
Building Type	School or University
Area (SF)	97,464
Volume (CF)	1,196,855.87
Calculated Results	
Peak Cooling Total Load (Btu/h)	2,212,094.1
Peak Cooling Month and Hour	July 2:00 PM
Peak Cooling Sensible Load (Btu/h)	1,849,905.9
Peak Cooling Latent Load (Btu/h)	362,188.2
Maximum Cooling Capacity (Btu/h)	2,254,597.8
Peak Cooling Airflow (CFM)	90,474
Peak Heating Load (Btu/h)	922,739.6
Peak Heating Airflow (CFM)	32,941

Figure 7–46

5. Save the project.

Chapter Review Questions

1. You want to modify a view so that colors for the various zones display as shown in Figure 7–47. How do you apply the colors to the view?

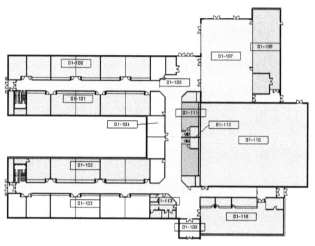

Figure 7–47

   a. Modify the color scheme in Visibility/Graphics.

   b. Assign a color scheme in Properties.

   c. Toggle on **Color Schemes** in the View Control Bar.

   d. Add a Color Fill Legend.

2. Zones (shown in Figure 7–48) are formed of spaces that can be heated and cooled in the same manner.

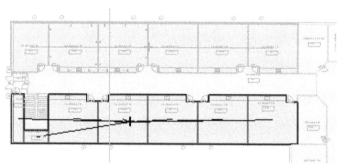

Figure 7–48

   a. True

   b. False

3. Which of the following are Energy Settings that impact Energy Analysis? (Select all that apply.)

   a. Geographic location of the building.

   b. Exterior wall construction.

   c. Number of spaces in the model.

   d. Plenum heights.

4. In the System Browser, in the Zones view, 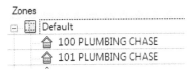 displays next to the name of the space. It indicates that the space...

   a. occupancy has not been defined.

   b. does not have an upper boundary.

   c. has not been placed.

   d. is not part of a zone.

5. When running the Heating and Cooling Loads analysis, the *Details* tab indicates that there are still spaces listed under Default, as shown in Figure 7–49. What needs to be done?

Zones
- Default
  - 100 PLUMBING CHASE
  - 101 PLUMBING CHASE

Figure 7–49

   a. Delete those spaces from the model.

   b. Verify the height of the spaces.

   c. Move the spaces to a zone.

   d. Change the status of the spaces to unoccupied.

6. To get an accurate energy analysis, all areas in the project need to be set up with...

   a. Light fixtures

   b. Spaces

   c. Heating equipment

   d. Sun shade devices

Command Summary

Button	Command	Location
	Color Fill Legend	• **Ribbon:** *Analyze* tab>Color Fill panel
	Heating and Cooling Loads	• **Ribbon:** *Analyze* tab>Reports & Schedules panel
	System Browser	• **Ribbon:** *View* tab>Windows panel, expand User Interface • **Shortcut:** <F9>
	Zone	• **Ribbon:** *Analyze* tab>Spaces & Zones panel

Chapter

8

Basic Systems Tools

Systems can be created by connecting elements such as air terminals and plumbing fixtures using ducts and pipes. You can also create systems without connecting the elements. Use placeholders early on in the design phase for ducts and pipes. You can use the System Browser to review the systems.

Learning Objectives in This Chapter

- Connect components using ducts, pipes, cable trays, and conduits.
- Create MEP systems.
- Review MEP systems in the System Browser.

8.1 Connecting Components

The process of creating MEP systems in Autodesk Revit is simple. All you need to do is insert components such as air terminals, plumbing fixtures, or lighting fixtures and then connect them using ducts (as shown in Figure 8–1), pipes, cable trays, and conduits. For electrical systems, wiring can also be generated, but these elements are only symbolic and annotative.

In-depth steps for creating these connections are covered later in this guide.

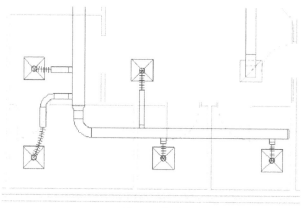

Figure 8–1

• When you draw the connecting elements, the Autodesk® Revit® software calculates the height and size of the opening and applies the appropriate fittings.

There are several ways of drawing connections between components:

• Select a component and click on the connector icon, shown in Figure 8–2.

• Select a component and right-click on a connector to select one of the options, as shown for a plumbing fixture in Figure 8–2.

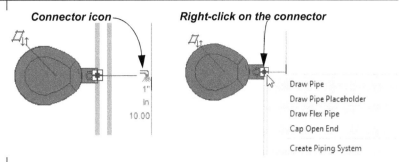

Figure 8–2

- You can also type in the associated shortcut key that displays when you hover over the tool in the ribbon, as shown in Figure 8–3.

Cable trays and conduits are typically placed separately from the components.

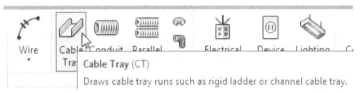

Figure 8–3

- Start the commands from the *Systems* tab>HVAC, Plumbing & Piping, and Electrical panels. Primary tools include:

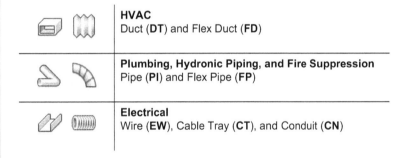

	HVAC Duct (**DT**) and Flex Duct (**FD**)
	Plumbing, Hydronic Piping, and Fire Suppression Pipe (**PI**) and Flex Pipe (**FP**)
	Electrical Wire (**EW**), Cable Tray (**CT**), and Conduit (**CN**)

- When in plan view, in order to draw segments vertically, you can use **Middle Elevation** from the Options Bar. For the example shown in Figure 8–4, the pipe from the lavatory is drawn to the middle of the wall. Then, from the Options Bar, **Middle Elevation** is set to **9'-0"**, which draws the pipe **9'-0"** up, then the pipe is continued down the wall.

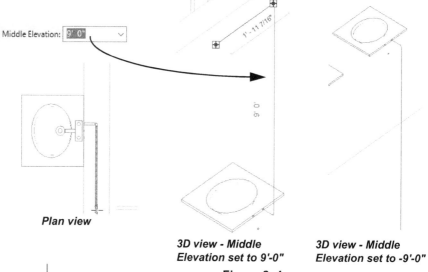

Plan view

3D view - Middle Elevation set to 9'-0"   *3D view - Middle Elevation set to -9'-0"*

Figure 8–4

How To: Connect Components

1. Select a component and click on the connector icon.
2. In the Type Selector, select the type, as shown in Figure 8–5. For example, you would select a pipe that matches the kind of system you are creating.

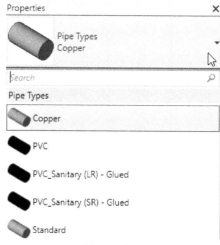

Figure 8–5

3. In the contextual tab, Options Bar, and Properties, specify the required options, as shown in Figure 8–6. The options that are available depend on the type of elements you are using.

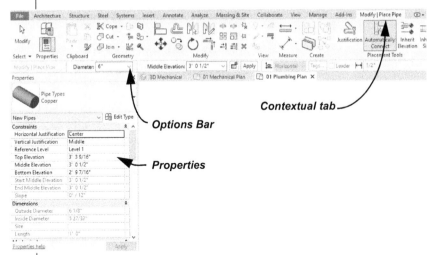

Figure 8–6

4. Draw the objects using temporary dimensions and snaps, as shown in Figure 8–7. Ensure that you are selecting the correct connector or related element. Fittings are automatically applied.

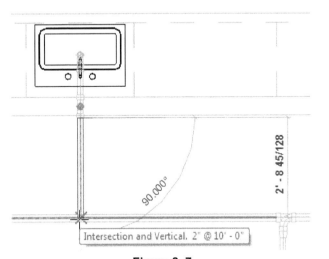

Figure 8–7

Hint: Placeholders

Placeholders can be used in the early stage of design to give approximate locations of duct or pipe layouts. These are represented as single-line layouts without fittings. Later in the design phase, you can convert the placeholders to two-line duct or pipe layouts with fittings.

- To place placeholders, from the *System* tab>HVAC panel, click (Duct Placeholder) or from the *System* tab> Plumbing & Piping panel, click (Pipe Placeholder).

  - Specify a type and size for the duct or pipe, then specify other settings as needed.

- To convert a placeholder, select the pipe or duct system, and from the *Modify | Pipe Placeholders* or *Modify | Duct Placeholders* tabs, select (Convert Placeholder).

  - Once converted, you cannot return a system back to a placeholder.

Connecting Into

A quick way to generate connections is to use the **Connect Into** tool. To use this tool, you must already have some duct, pipe, conduit, or cable trays in the project, as well as have the components you need to connect. When you select a component, the **Connect Into** option is available in the contextual tab.

- Check your project in a 3D view to ensure that the path is acceptable.

How To: Connect a Component to Existing Connectors

1. Select the component that you want to connect to an existing connector.
2. In the *Modify | <contextual>* tab>Layout panel, click (Connect Into).
3. If the fixture has more than one connector, in the Select Connector dialog box click on the system type and click **OK**.

4. Select the connector, such as the pipe shown in Figure 8–8.

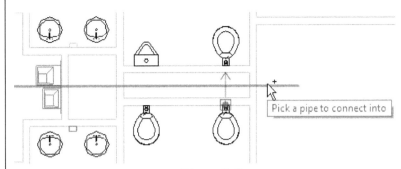

Figure 8–8

- This process automatically connects the component into a system.

- If you select a connector that cannot work with the component, an error is displayed, as shown in Figure 8–9. Click **Cancel** and then try a different connector, or add the connectors separately.

  - This error most often occurs because the offset between two elements is too close for the software to create the connection based on the default fittings.

  - Another cause of this error is that the connector is the wrong system type. The *System Type* can be changed in the Properties of the element, as required.

Figure 8–9

Modifying Fittings

Fittings are added automatically when connectors touch each other, turn, or change size. Fittings can be modified using the Type Selector, Properties, Options Bar, or a variety of connectors and controls. For example, when using ducts, an elbow can be changed to a tee connection by clicking a control, as shown in Figure 8–10. You can then add another duct to the newly-opened connector.

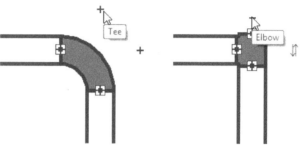

Figure 8–10

Testing Connections

A quick way to test the continuity of connectors is to hover the cursor over a linear connection and press <Tab> until the entire system is highlighted. For example, one of the ducts shown in Figure 8–11 is not highlighted because it is not attached to the fitting.

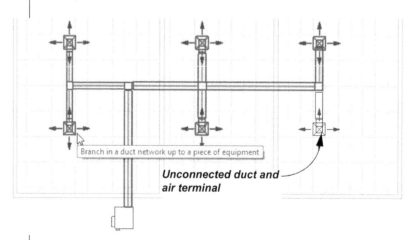

Unconnected duct and air terminal

Figure 8–11

Alternatively, you can also display the disconnects using the **Show Disconnects** tool.

How To: Show Disconnects

1. In the *Analyze* tab>Check Systems panel, click 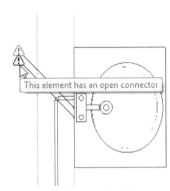 (Show Disconnects).
2. In the Show Disconnects Options dialog box, select the types of systems you want to display (as shown in Figure 8–12) and click **OK.**

3. Any disconnects display ⚠ (Warning), as shown in Figure 8–13.

Figure 8–12

Figure 8–13

- The disconnects continue to display until you either correct the situation or run **Show Disconnects** again and clear all of the selections.
- Hover the cursor over the warning icon to display a tooltip with the warning. You can also click on the icon to open the Warning dialog box.

Practice 8a	# Connect Components - Mechanical

Practice Objectives

- Draw a duct.
- Connect fixtures to the duct.

In this practice, you will create a duct using controls and commands. You will also use the **Connect Into** command to connect air terminals.

1. In the practice files *Basics* folder, open **Simple-Building-Connect.rvt**.

2. Open the Mechanical>HVAC>Floor Plans>**1 - Mech** view.

3. Tile the 3D view and 1-Mech view by type **WT**. Type **ZA** to zoom both views.

4. In the **Mech/Elec 106** room, select the Air Handling Unit. Note that it has connectors for ducts, pipes, and electrical, as shown in Figure 8–14. Select the Return Air **Create Duct** icon to create the duct.

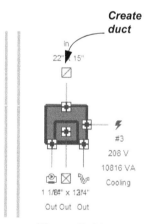

Figure 8–14

5. Move the cursor up and note that the duct is connected to the cursor. Using the temporary dimensions, type **2'** and press <Enter>. In the Options Bar, set the *Middle Elevation* to **10'-0"**. This creates a duct that goes up, as shown in Figure 8–15. You are still in the Duct command. Click a point in the middle of the hall, then down the hall to the left, as shown in Figure 8–16.

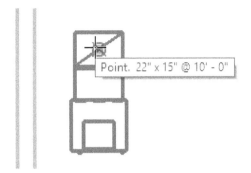

Point. 22" x 15" @ 10' - 0"

Figure 8–15

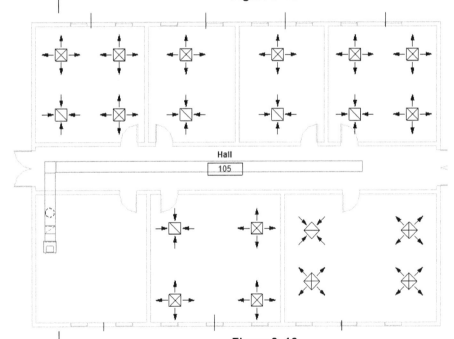

Hall
105

Figure 8–16

6. Click � (Modify) to end the command.

7. In **Lab 107**, select the return diffuser.

8. In the *Modify | Air Terminals* tab>Layout panel, click

   (Connect Into) and select the horizontal duct. Your model should look similar to that shown in Figure 8–17.

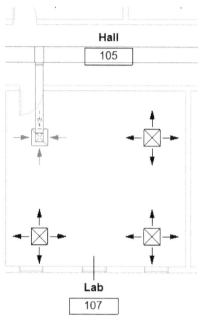

Figure 8–17

9. Repeat the process with the other Return diffusers, as shown in Figure 8–18. Note that the Connect Into tool does not necessarily create ducts as expected when you have an angled diffuser. You can either draw the duct from this diffuser or modify the duct to get a useful connection.

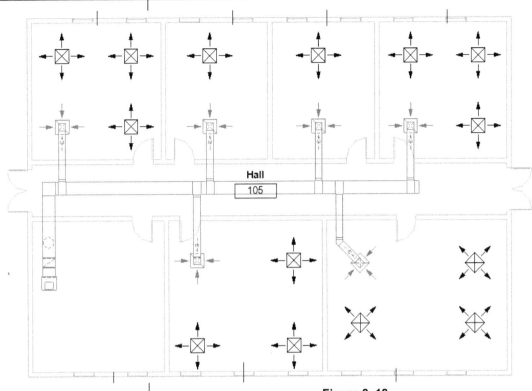

Hall

105

Figure 8–18

10. All of the elements connected are shown in magenta, which indicates that they are all part of a return air system.

11. Save and close the project.

Practice 8b

Connect Components - Electrical

Practice Objective

- Draw a cable tray.

In this practice, you will create a cable tray and connect cable trays from each of the rooms.

1. In the practice files *Basics* folder, open **Simple-Building-Connect.rvt**.

2. Open the Electrical>Power>Floor Plans>**1 - Power** view.

Note: Cable Tray and Conduit are placed separately from the components.

3. In the *Systems* tab>Electrical panel, click (Cable Tray).

4. In the Options Bar, set the *Middle Elevation* to **8'-6"**.

5. Draw a length of cable tray down the center of the hallway. It is place above the lighting fixtures. Then, add other cable trays coming out from each end and into each room, as shown in Figure 8–19.

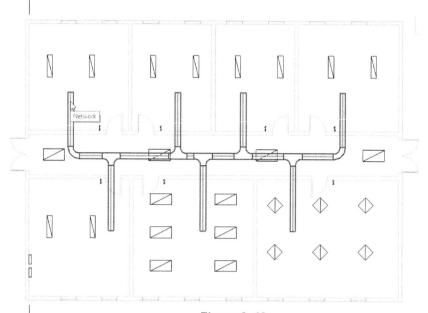

Figure 8–19

6. Save and close the project.

Practice 8c

Connect Components - Plumbing

Practice Objectives

- Draw piping.
- Connect equipment to the piping.

In this practice, you will create piping using controls and commands. You will also use the **Connect Into** command.

1. In the practice files *Basics* folder, open **Simple-Building-Connect.rvt**.

2. Open the Plumbing>Plumbing>Floor Plans>**1 - Plumbing** view.

3. Pan and zoom in on the **Women's 103** room.

4. Select the lavatory closest to the window. Zoom in so that the three connectors display and click on the Hot Water connector.

5. In the Options Bar, note that *Diameter* and *Middle Elevation* are automatically set to the height of the fixture connector, as shown in Figure 8–20.

Modify | Place Pipe | Diameter: 1/2" ∨ | Middle Elevation: 2' 9 161/256 ∨ | Apply

Figure 8–20

6. In the Type Selector, select **Pipe Types: Standard**.

7. Draw the pipe horizontally into the wall. Note that the sink turns red, indicating that it is now part of the Domestic Hot Water system, as shown in Figure 8–21.

8. In the Options Bar, change the *Middle Elevation* to **9'-0"** and click **Apply**. This sends the pipe directly up.

9. The *Detail Level* of the view is set to **Medium**. In the View Control Bar set the *Detail Level* to ⊠ (Fine). The pipe now displays full scale (as shown in Figure 8–22), rather than in schematic. Stay in the Pipe command.

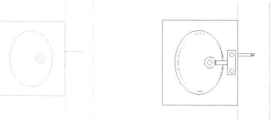

Figure 8–21   Figure 8–22

10. Draw the pipe down the wall, into the hall, and then down past the hot water heater to the far left of the building, as shown in Figure 8–23.

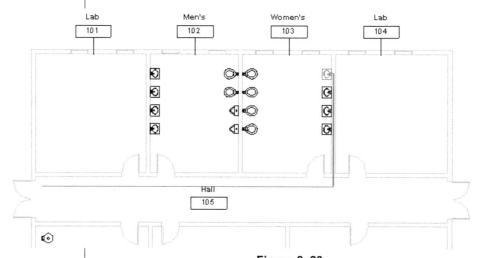

Figure 8–23

11. Click ☌ (Modify) and select the hot water heater.

12. In the *Modify | Mechanical Equipment* tab>Layout panel, click ⊩ (Connect Into).

13. In the Select Connector dialog box, select **Connector 2: Domestic Hot Water** (as shown in Figure 8–24) and click **OK**.

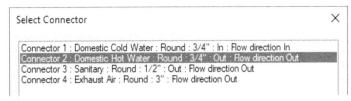

Figure 8–24

14. Select the pipe in the hall. The correct pipe is automatically added.

15. Change the Detail Level to **Fine** and zoom in on the intersection of pipe, as shown in Figure 8–25.

Figure 8–25

16. Delete the extra pipe and transition fitting, then select the pipe fitting and select the Elbow control, as shown in Figure 8–26.

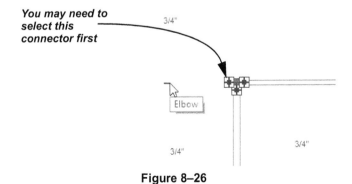

You may need to select this connector first

3/4"

Elbow

3/4"

3/4"

Figure 8–26

17. Open the Plumbing>Plumbing>3D Views>**3D Plumbing** view.

18. Select one of the other lavatories in the Women's room.

19. In the *Modify | Plumbing Fixtures* tab>Layout panel, click (Connect Into).

20. In the Select Connector dialog box, select the **Domestic Hot Water** connector and click **OK**. Select the pipe above the lavatory.

21. Repeat with the other two lavatories. They are added to the Hot Water system, as shown in Figure 8–27.

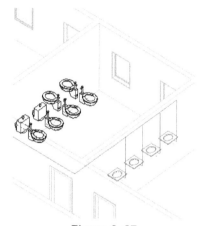

Figure 8–27

22. Save and close the project.

8.2 Creating Systems - Overview

When you connect components, such as air terminals with ducts or plumbing fixtures with pipes, systems are automatically created. These systems frequently overlap. For example, as part of an HVAC installation, an air handling unit is connected to supply and return duct systems, as well as hydronic supply and return systems. It is also connected to an electrical system (circuit), as shown in Figure 8–28.

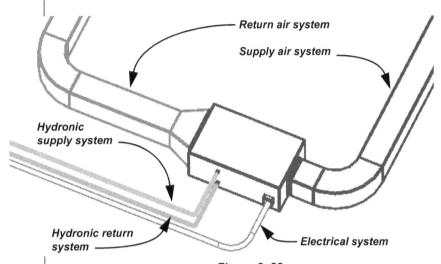

Figure 8–28

- Creating systems correctly is critical for the Autodesk Revit software to understand and calculate flow, pressure, etc.

- While most systems are created automatically as you connect components with duct or pipe, you can create the system first and then connect the components later.

- Electrical systems (such as switches and data) do not have connecting elements and therefore need to be created.

How To: Create a System

1. Select one or more related components. Do not select source equipment at this point.
2. In the *Modify | contextual* tab>Create Systems panel, click

   (Duct), (Power), (Piping), (Data), (Fire Alarm, (Controls), or other system types.

The type of systems available depends on the component you select.

3. For duct and piping systems, you are prompted to select the *System type* and assign a *System name,* as shown in Figure 8–29. Click **OK**.

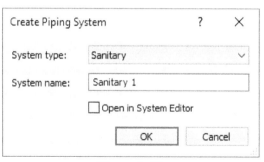

Figure 8–29

4. In the contextual *Modify* tab>System Tools panel, click  (Select Equipment) as shown in Figure 8–30, or for

electrical circuits, click (Select Panel). Select the equipment or panel.

Figure 8–30

- The number of options that display in the *Modify* tab depends on where you are in the system creation.

5. To add additional end components, in the contextual *Modify* tab>System Tools panel, click the **Edit Systems/Circuit** tool. The related contextual tab displays, as shown in Figure 8–31.

Figure 8–31

- While the icon and name for each system type is different, the processes and locations are still the same.

6. The related **Add to System/Circuit** tool is automatically selected. Click on other components in the model to add them to the system. Remove components from the system using the **Remove from System/Circuit** tool.

7. To add mechanical equipment or an electrical panel to a system, you can use the related **Select Equipment/Select Panel** tool or in the Options Bar, select the equipment from a list.

8. When you have completed your selection, click ✓ (Finish Editing System/Circuit).

Selecting Systems

You can select systems by hovering over one component and pressing <Tab> until the system displays, as shown in Figure 8–32. If duct and pipe are in place, the system outline follows the linear elements. If not, there is a bounding box around all of the system elements.

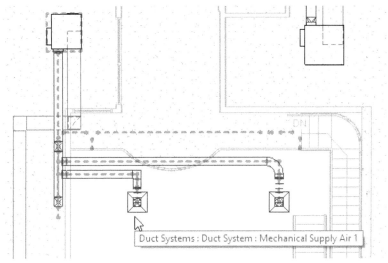

Figure 8–32

- Whenever you select a component that is assigned to a system, you can return to editing the system by clicking on the contextual tabs, as shown for an air handling unit in Figure 8–33.

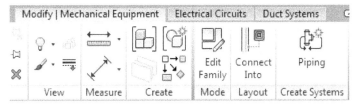

Figure 8–33

Using the System Browser with Systems

The System Browser, as shown in Figure 8–34, is an important part of determining the relationships between components and the systems they are a part of. It also enables you to identify and select the components, especially those not assigned to a system.

Switch systems do not display in the System Browser as they only denote which fixtures are connected to the switch.

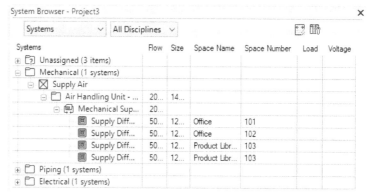

Figure 8–34

- At the top of the System Browser, you can select **Systems**, **Zones** (used in HVAC analysis), or **Analytical Systems** to display the appropriate options.

- When working with **Systems**, select the discipline in which you want to work, as shown in Figure 8–35.

Selecting a discipline limits the display of elements to that specific discipline.

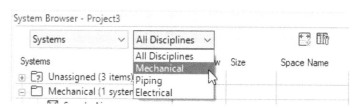

Figure 8–35

- Components that are not in a system, display in the Unassigned list.

- In the System Browser, when you hover the cursor over the system name or select it, or select an individual component, it gets selected in the model as shown in Figure 8–36. It also works the other way when you select the element in the model.

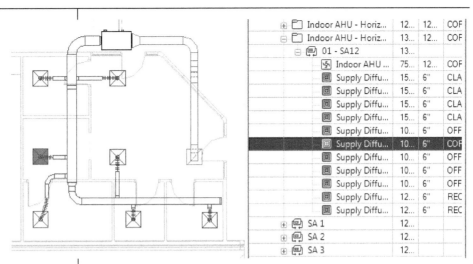

Figure 8–36

- Properties also updates to match the selection, enabling you to modify parameters associated with the elements.

- Hold <Ctrl> or <Shift> to select multiple items in the System Browser.

- If you select a component that is referenced to multiple systems, it is highlighted in each of those systems as shown in Figure 8–37.

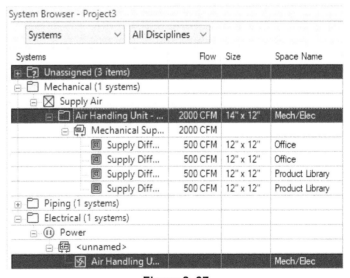

Figure 8–37

- To get a close-up view of a component, select it in the System Browser, right-click and select **Show**. If a view with the component is already open, it zooms into that view. In the Show Element(s) In View dialog box, as shown in Figure 8–38, click **Show** to search for other views.

Figure 8–38

- To delete a component through the System Browser, right-click on it and select **Delete**. This deletes it from the project.

Hint: Changing the Display in the System Browser

Two buttons in the System Browser help display what you need to see.

- Click 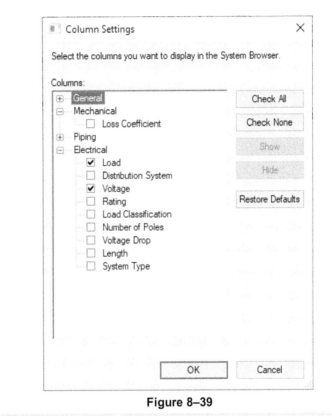 (Autofit all Columns) to change the width of the columns so that the contents fit exactly in the column.

- Click (Column Settings) to open the Column Settings dialog box (shown in Figure 8–39), in which you can select the parameters to display for the various system types.

Figure 8–39

Practice 8d

View and Create Systems - Mechanical

Practice Objectives

- Create systems.
- Review and update systems.

In this practice, you will create systems and use the System Browser to find elements in the system. You will then change the name of the system within Properties.

Task 1 - Create a system.

1. In the practice files *Basics* folder, open **Simple-Building-Systems.rvt**.

2. Open the Mechanical>HVAC>Floor Plans>**1 - Mech** view.

3. In the **Lab 101** room, select one of the supply diffusers.

4. In the *Modify | Air Terminals* tab>Create Systems panel, click 🖑 (Duct).

5. In the Create Duct System dialog box, verify that the *System* type is set to **Supply Air**. Accept the default name and select **Open in System Editor**, and then click **OK**.

6. The *Edit Duct System* tab displays with **Add to System** already selected, as shown in Figure 8–40.

Figure 8–40

7. Hold <Ctrl> and select the other supply air terminals in the rooms on the same side of the hall. If you select the return air terminal, a warning displays that you cannot connect to this system.

8. Click 🖑 (Select Equipment) and select the Air Handling Unit in the **Mech/Elec 106** room. Note that it turns black because there are now two systems connected to it.

9. Click 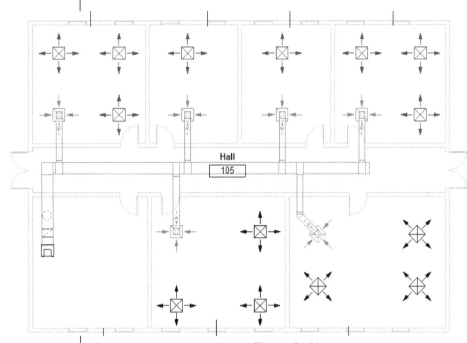 (Finish Editing System). The air terminals are added to the system and turn blue to indicate that it is a supply air system, as shown in Figure 8–41.

Hall

105

Figure 8–41

10. Save the project.

Task 2 - Review systems in the System Browser.

1. Open the Mechanical>HVAC>3D views>{3D} view.

2. Open the System Browser by pressing <F9>. Verify that the System Browser has the **Systems** options selected and that the discipline is set to **Mechanical**, as shown in Figure 8–42.

3. Expand the Mechanical (2 systems)>Return Air>Mechanical Return Air 1 nodes to display the systems, as shown in Figure 8–42.

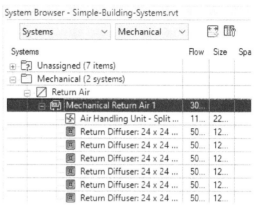

Figure 8–42

4. In the view, select one of the return diffusers and note how it relates to the system in the System Browser.

5. In the System Browser, hover your cursor over the system name, as shown in Figure 8–43.

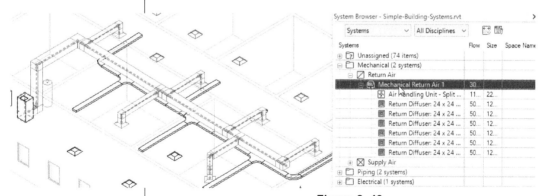

Figure 8–43

6. Select the system name and note that the *Modify | Duct System* tab displays in the ribbon. Keep the system selected.

7. In Properties, change the *System Name* to **Return Air**, as shown in Figure 8–44.

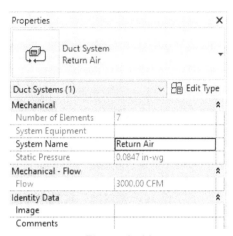

Figure 8–44

8. Click **Apply** or move the cursor over in the view. The name updates in the System Browser.

9. Save and close the project.

Practice 8e

View and Create Systems - Electrical

Practice Objectives

- Create systems.
- Review and update systems.

In this practice, you will create systems and use the System Browser to find elements in the system. You will then modify the system by selecting the system and modifying it within the ribbon.

Task 1 - Create a system.

1. In the practice files *Basics* folder, open **Simple-Building-Systems.rvt**.

2. Open the Electrical>Lighting>Floor Plans>**1 - Lighting** view.

3. Select one of the light fixtures in **Office 108** (with the rotated lights).

- Lighting fixtures can be connected to Switch and Power systems. In the *Modify | Lighting Fixtures* tab>Create Systems panel (shown in Figure 8–45), **Power** and **Switch** are the two choices for related systems.

Figure 8–45

4. In the *Modify | Lighting Fixtures* tab>Create Systems panel, click ⬜ (Switch).

5. In the *Modify | Switch Systems* tab>System Tools panel, click ⬜₊ (Select Switch).

6. Select the switch near the door in the same room. A line connecting the lighting fixture to the switch displays, as shown in Figure 8–46.

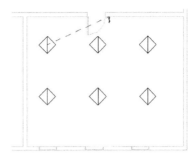

Figure 8–46

7. The new switch system is still selected. In the *Modify | Switch System* tab>System Tools panel, click (Edit Switch System). (Add to System) is automatically selected.

8. Click on the other lighting fixtures in the same room and click (Finish Editing System).

9. Hover over one of the lighting fixtures and press <Tab> until the Switch System displays, as shown in Figure 8–47.

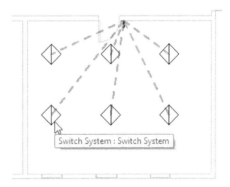

Figure 8–47

10. Move the cursor away from the selection.

11. Select the same light fixtures. From the *Modify | Lighting Fixtures* tab, select (Power).

12. From the *Modify | Electrical Circuits* tab>System Tools panel,

select 📷 (Select Panel) and select one of the panels in the **Mech/Elec 106** room, as shown in Figure 8–48.

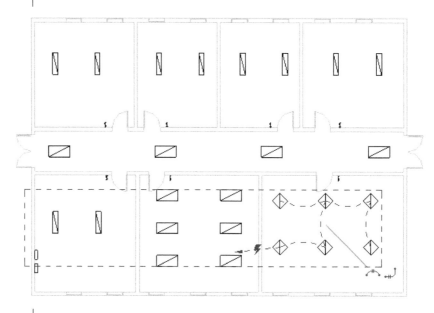

Figure 8–48

13. Save and close the project.

Task 2 - Review systems in the System Browser.

1. Open the Electrical>Lighting>Floor Plans>**1 - Lighting** view.

2. Open the System Browser by pressing <F9>. Verify that the System Browser has the **Systems** options selected and that the discipline is set to **Electrical**, as shown in Figure 8–49.

3. Expand the nodes to display the systems, as shown in Figure 8–49.

Switch systems are not included in the System Browser.

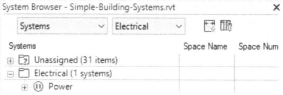

Figure 8–49

4. In the view, select one of the light fixtures in **Office 108** and note how the related information displays in the System Browser.

5. Expand the related nodes in the System Browser and hover your cursor over the system name, as shown in Figure 8–50.

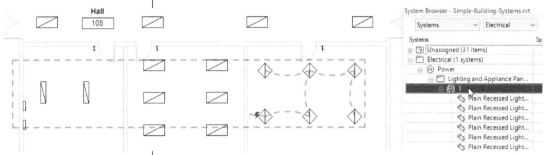

Figure 8–50

6. Select the system name. The related Modify | System tab displays in the ribbon.

7. Edit the system and add other related elements to the system, then click (Finish Editing System). Note that if you try to add a hall light to the system, you get a warning message about the voltage being out of range.

8. Save and close the project.

Practice 8f

View and Create Systems - Plumbing

Practice Objectives

- Create systems.
- Review and update systems.

In this practice, you will create a system and use the System Browser to find elements in the system. You will modify the system by selecting the system in the view and editing the system from the ribbon.

Task 1 - Create a system.

1. In the practice files *Basics* folder, open **Simple-Building-Systems.rvt**.

2. Open the Plumbing>Plubming>Floor Plans>**1 - Plumbing** view.

3. Select one of the lavatories that is not connected to the hot water system.

4. In the *Modify | Plumbing Fixtures* tab>Create Systems panel, click (Piping System).

5. In the Create Piping System dialog box, expand the System type list and select **Sanitary**. Then, click **OK**.

6. In the *Modify | Piping Systems* tab>System Tools panel, select (Edit System). Note that (Add to System) is automatically selected.

7. Click on the other plumbing fixtures in the same room and click ✓ (Finish Editing System). Note that the fixtures all turn green to indicate a sanitary system, as shown in Figure 8–51.

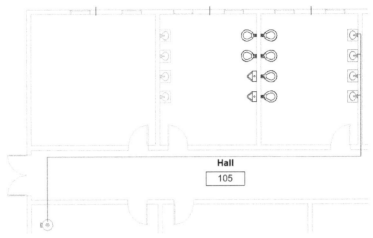

Figure 8–51

8. Save the project.

Task 2 - Review systems in the System Browser.

1. Open the Plumbing>Plumbing>Floor Plans>**1 - Plumbing** view.

2. Open the System Browser by pressing <F9>.

3. Expand the following System Browser nodes:

    *   Unassigned>Piping>Domestic Cold Water
    *   Piping (2 Systems)>Sanitary>Sanitary 1

4. In the view, select the lavatory in **Room 102** closest to the window, as shown in Figure 8–52. Note that in the System Browser, it is highlighted under the *Unassigned*, *Domestic Hot Water*, and *Sanitary* sections.

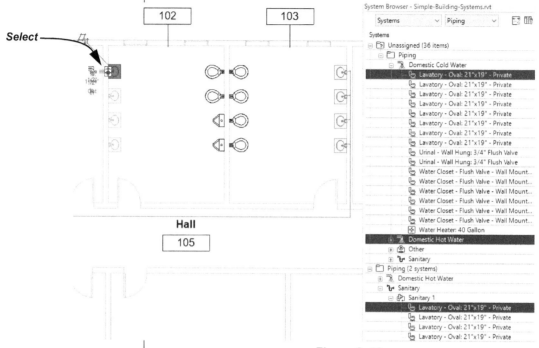

Figure 8–52

5. Open the default 3D view that displays all of the system elements. Select the elements that you do not need to see in this view, such as light fixtures, terminals, ducts, etc., and type **VH**.

6. In the System Browser, select Sanitary1. The group of lavatories highlights in the view, as shown in Figure 8–53.

Figure 8–53

7. Select the system name. The related Modify | System tab displays in the ribbon.

8. Edit the system and add other related elements to the system, then click ✓ (Finish Editing System).

9. Save and close the project.

Chapter Review Questions

1. When you select a Mechanical Equipment component, several icons display. What is the purpose of these icons?

   a. They are where ducts, pipes, or electrical circuits connect to the equipment.

   b. You can draw ducts, pipes, or circuits from them.

   c. They establish the size or power of the connection.

   d. All the above.

2. When you draw connecting elements (such as duct or pipe) directly from a component, the connector you select controls the size and elevation.

   a. True

   b. False

3. Which of the following happens when you select components in the System Browser, as shown in Figure 8–54?

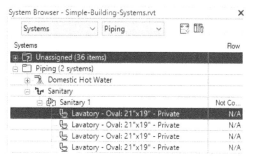

Figure 8–54

   a. The components highlight in the current view.

   b. The component changes to a different system.

   c. You are put into edit mode.

   d. Nothing happens.

Command Summary

Button	Command	Location
Connectors		
	Cable Tray	• **Ribbon:** *Systems* tab>Electrical panel • **Shortcut:** CT • Right-click on a control; **Draw Cable Tray**
	Conduit	• **Ribbon:** *Systems* tab>Electrical panel • **Shortcut:** CN • Right-click on a control; **Draw Conduit**
	Connect Into	• **Ribbon:** *Modify* | *<contextual>* tab> Layout panel
	Duct	• **Ribbon:** *Systems* tab>HVAC panel • **Shortcut:** DT • Right-click on a control: **Draw Duct**
	Flex Duct	• **Ribbon:** *Systems* tab>HVAC panel • **Shortcut:** FD • Right-click on a control: **Draw Flex Duct**
	Flex Pipe	• **Ribbon:** *Systems* tab>Plumbing & Piping panel • **Shortcut:** FP • Right-click on a control: **Draw Flex Pipe**
	Pipe	• **Ribbon:** *Systems* tab>Plumbing & Piping panel • **Shortcut:** PI • Right-click on a control: **Draw Pipe**
	Show Disconnects	• **Ribbon:** *Analyze* tab>Check Systems panel
	Wire (Arc)	• **Ribbon:** *Systems* tab>Electrical panel • **Shortcut:** EW
Systems		
(varies)	Add to System	• **Ribbon:** **Edit System/Circuit tab**>Edit System/Circuit panel
	Data	• **Ribbon:** *Modify* | *<contextual>* tab> Create Systems panel • Right-click on a control; **Create Data Circuit**
	Duct	• **Ribbon:** *Modify* | *<contextual>* tab> Create Systems panel • Right-click on a control; **Create Duct System**

	Fire Alarm	• **Ribbon:** *Modify | <contextual>* tab> Create Systems panel • Right-click on a control; **Create Fire Alarm Circuit**
	Piping	• **Ribbon:** *Modify | <contextual>* tab> Create Systems panel • Right-click on a control; **Create Piping System**
	Power	• **Ribbon:** *Modify | <contextual>* tab> Create Systems panel • Right-click on a control; **Create Power Circuit**
	Switch	• **Ribbon:** *Modify | <contextual>* tab> Create Systems panel • Right-click on a control; **Create Switch Circuit**
	Select Equipment	• **Ribbon:** *Modify | <contextual>* tab> System Tools panel • **Ribbon:** *Edit <contextual> System* tab> Edit <contextual> System panel
	Select Panel	• **Ribbon:** *Modify | <contextual>* tab> System Tools panel • **Ribbon:** *Edit Circuit* tab>Edit Circuit panel
N/A	**System Browser**	• **Ribbon:** *View* tab>Window panel, expand (User Interface) • **Shortcut:** <F9>

HVAC Systems

HVAC systems consist of components that include mechanical equipment, air terminals, ducts, and pipes. The process of combining these components and ensuring they work correctly is a significant part of developing an HVAC project.

Learning Objectives in This Chapter

- Add HVAC components, including mechanical equipment and air terminals.
- Add ducts and pipes to connect HVAC components.
- Modify ducts and pipes.

9.1 Adding Mechanical Equipment and Air Terminals

When beginning an HVAC system in a project, you typically start with mechanical equipment and air terminals, and then network them together using ducts, as shown in Figure 9–1. You also add hydronic piping connecting mechanical equipment.

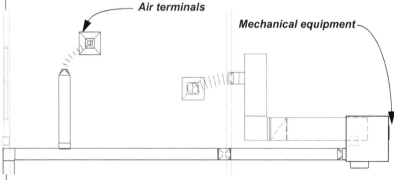

Air terminals

Mechanical equipment

Figure 9–1

Mechanical Equipment

Mechanical equipment includes various air handling units, such as fan coil units or variable air volume units. Mechanical equipment families are managed in Properties, as shown in Figure 9–2, and have connectors, as shown in Figure 9–3.

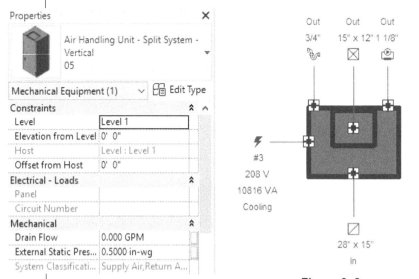

Figure 9–2

Figure 9–3

- Mechanical equipment might also include connections for hydronic piping and electrical power.

- Depending on the component, mechanical equipment can be placed in plan, elevation, and 3D views.

How To: Place Mechanical Equipment

1. In the *Systems* tab>Mechanical panel, click (Mechanical Equipment), or type **ME**.
2. In the Type Selector, select a mechanical equipment type.
3. In Properties, set any other values, such as the *Level* and *Offset from Host,* if it is not hosted.
4. In the Options Bar, specify if you want to be able to rotate the equipment after placement.
5. Place the equipment in the model by clicking at the required location in the model view.

- You can use other objects in the model to align the element and press <Spacebar> to rotate it before placing it.

- Additional boilers, radiators, VAV units and more can be loaded from the Autodesk® Revit® library in the *Mechanical> MEP* subfolders.

Hint: Tagging Mechanical Equipment and Air Terminals

Both air terminals and mechanical equipment can be tagged, as shown in Figure 9–4.

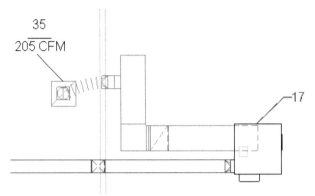

Figure 9–4

- When you are adding the elements, in the *Modify |*

  contextual tab>Tag panel, toggle ⌐①⌐ (Tag on Placement) on or off as needed.

- To add tags later, in the *Annotate* tab>Tag panel, click

  ⌐①⌐ (Tag by Category) and select the elements to tag.

  - You can modify a terminal's flow by changing the CFM in the tag.

Air Terminals

Air terminals can be used in supply, return, or exhaust air systems, as shown in Figure 9–5. You can place individual air terminals or batch copy them from a linked model.

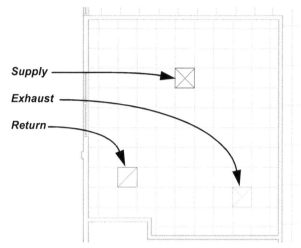

Figure 9–5

- Often, air terminals are placed on a host, such as a ceiling. Therefore when placing an air terminal, use a reflected ceiling plan view.
- Some air terminal types can also be placed directly on ducts.
- Air terminals display regardless of the cut plane of the view.
- The flow of each air terminal in a space is summed, so that total air flow in a space can be easily checked against the Specified Airflow and Calculated Airflow in a schedule.

How To: Place an Air Terminal

1. In the *Systems* tab>HVAC panel, click 🔲 (Air Terminal) or type **AT**.
2. In the Type Selector, select an air terminal type.
   - If the Air terminal is not hosted, in Properties, set the *Level* and *Offset from Host*.
   - If the air terminal type is hosted, in the *Modify | Place Air Terminal* tab>Placement panel, select the type of placement to a face or a plane.

	Place on Vertical Face	Places air terminal on a vertical face, such as a wall.
	Place on Face	Places the air terminal on a defined face, such as the ceiling grid.
	Place on Work Plane	Places the air terminal on a defined plane such as a level or ceiling in a linked architectural model.

3. In Properties, set the *Flow* and other parameters.
4. Place the air terminal in the model by clicking at the required location in the model view.
5. Continue to place additional air terminals, as shown in Figure 9–6, or click ▷ (Modify) to exit the command.

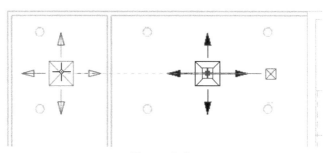

Figure 9–6

Use other objects in the model, such as the ceiling grid or previously placed air terminals, to line up the air terminal.

- After any air terminal is initially placed, you can modify it in any view and use the standard modify tools to move, align, and rotate it.

- You can modify the flow of an air terminal by selecting it and setting the **Flow** from the Options Bar.

In the Load Family dialog box, click on Imperial Libraries from the Places panel.

- If the air terminal you want does not exist in your project, you can load one from the default Revit library>*Mechanical> MEP>Air-Side Components>Air Terminals* folder. Some air terminal types prompt you to select sizes, as shown in Figure 9–7.

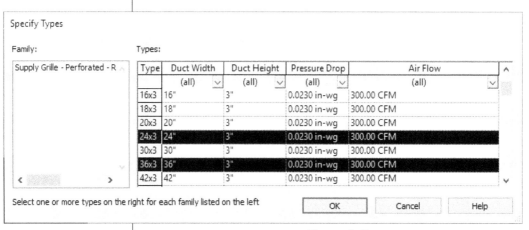

Figure 9–7

- Air terminals that are hosted by a ceiling in a linked model (as shown in Figure 9–8), move automatically with any changes that the architects make to the ceiling height. This can be an advantage of using hosted fixtures.

- When using a non-hosted air terminal, it is placed at a specified height above the level of the current view, as shown in Figure 9–9. The height above the level is not modified when changes are made to the linked architectural model.

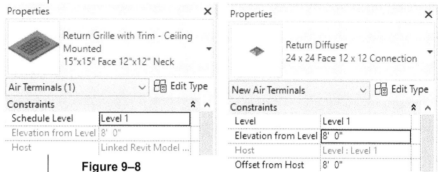

Figure 9–8   Figure 9–9

- If the architect deletes the ceiling and puts a new one in the linked model, the hosted air terminals are orphaned and do not move with changes in the ceiling height. A Warning dialog box opens when you reload the linked model or reopen the MEP project, as shown in Figure 9–10. Use the **Coordination Monitoring** tools to address the issue.

Figure 9–10

- Some firms add reference planes and place the hosted families on them instead of in the ceiling. This gives them control over the height of the families. If the architect moves the ceilings up or down, the engineer adjusts the height of the reference plane to match.

How To: Place an Air Terminal on a Duct

1. Have a duct in place. If it is a round or oval duct, verify the diameter before selecting the air terminal.
2. Start the **Air Terminal** command.
3. In the Type Selector, select the required air terminal. There are different types for curved and rectangular duct faces. Curved face air terminals are created by duct diameter, as shown in Figure 9–11.

Ensure that you are selecting an air terminal that matches the system type of the duct.

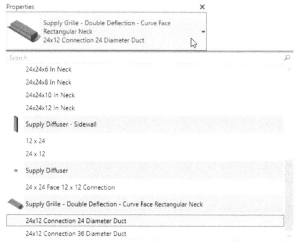

Figure 9–11

4. In the *Modify | Place Air Terminal* tab>Layout panel, verify that ![icon] (Air Terminal on Duct) is toggled on.
5. Move the cursor over to the duct where you want to place the air terminal. The air terminal automatically rotates to the face you are closest to, as shown in Figure 9–12.

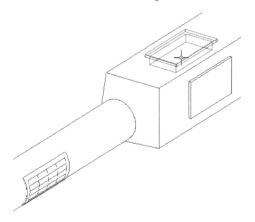

Figure 9–12

6. Click to place the air terminal.

Copying Air Terminals

If you have air terminals in a project with similar parameters including the type, elevation, and flow, you can place one and then copy it to the other locations. This works with independently placed air terminals and those placed directly on ducts, as shown in Figure 9–13.

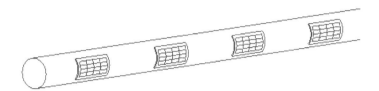

Figure 9–13

Rehosting Air Terminals

While working with linked models, if air terminals are copied from one ceiling to other ceilings of the same height, the copied air terminals are hosted by their respective new ceilings. However, if the ceilings are a different height than the ceiling that hosts the original air terminal, the copied fixtures are not associated with the ceiling. They end up at the same elevation as the original air terminal, as shown in Figure 9–14. Therefore, you need to rehost the air terminal.

If the ceilings are in the host project you are not permitted to copy a hosted air terminal from one ceiling to another.

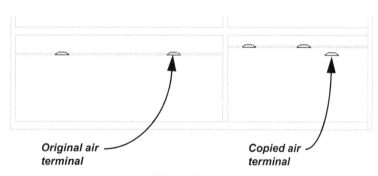

Original air terminal — Copied air terminal

Figure 9–14

How To: Rehost an Air Terminal

1. Copy the air terminals as needed.
2. Select the one(s) that need to be rehosted to a different ceiling.
3. In the *Modify | Air Terminals* tab>Work Plane panel, click

    (Pick New).

4. In the Placement panel, click 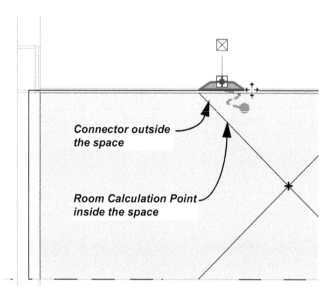 (Face).
5. Select the ceiling to which you want the air terminal(s) hosted.

- This needs to be done in the reflected ceiling plan view for ceiling hosted fixtures.

- Occasionally, the location of a light fixture or air terminal is such that the software assigns its electrical/mechanical values to the wrong space. This results in faulty heating and cooling load calculations and incorrect space values. To correct this, use a family that has the **Room Calculation Point** toggled on. The point is displayed in the project when a fixture is selected, as shown in Figure 9–15. However, the point cannot be manipulated and its visibility is only for review purposes.

Not all air terminals or light fixtures have this feature toggled on by default. It must be added in the Family Parameters of the component.

Connector outside
the space

Room Calculation Point
inside the space

Figure 9–15

Practice 9a | Add Mechanical Equipment and Air Terminals

Practice Objectives

- Place mechanical equipment.
- Place air terminals.
- Place air terminals on ducts.

In this practice, you will add Air Handling Units (AHUs) in the hallway at a specified height. You will then place supply and return air terminals on the face of a ceiling. You will align the air terminals to the ceiling grid and copy the air terminals as needed to create the layout shown in Figure 9–16. You will also add air terminals directly to round ducts in the gym.

Figure 9–16

Task 1 - Add mechanical equipment.

1. In the practice files *HVAC* folder, open **HVAC-School-MEP.rvt**.

2. Open the Mechanical>HVAC>Floor Plans>**01 Mechanical Plan** view and zoom in on the north wing. There are some existing HVAC systems and open locations where you will add components, as shown in Figure 9–17.

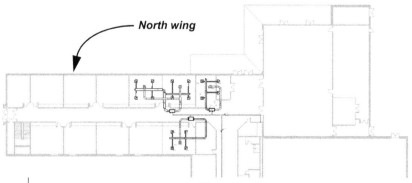

Figure 9–17

3. In the *Systems* tab>Mechanical panel, click 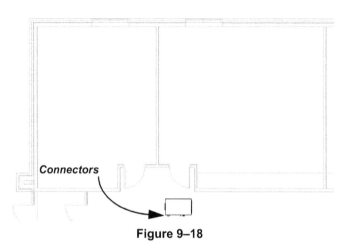 (Mechanical Equipment).

4. In the Type Selector, select **Indoor AHU - Horizontal - Chilled Water Coil: Unit Size 24** and then set the *Offset from Host* to **9'-3"**.

5. Place the AHU so that the connectors are facing the hallway, as shown in Figure 9–18.

Figure 9–18

6. While still in placement mode, press <Spacebar> until the equipment is rotated 180 degrees. Place another AHU outside of the classroom doors on the opposite side of the hall, as shown in Figure 9–19.

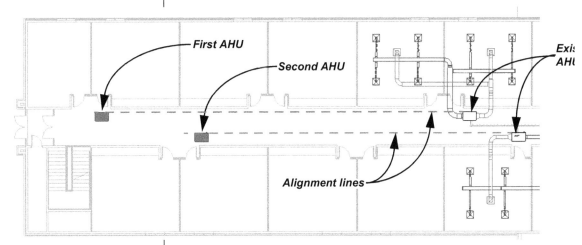

Figure 9–19

7. Click **Modify**.

8. In the *Modify* tab>Modify panel, click ⬚ (Align).

9. Select the inside edge of the existing AHU and then the first AHU placed, as shown in Figure 9–19. Repeat this on the second AHU placed.

10. Save the project.

Task 2 - Add air terminals.

---

1. Open the Mechanical>HVAC>Ceiling Plans> **01 Mechanical - Ceiling** view. In this view, you can see the locations of the ceiling grid and light fixtures provided in the architectural project.

2. In the *Systems* tab>HVAC panel, click ▣ (Air Terminal).

3. In the Type Selector, select **Supply Diffuser - Round Neck - Ceiling Mounted: 24x24x6 In Neck,** as shown in Figure 9–20.

Figure 9–20

4. In Properties, set *Flow* to **150 CFM**.

5. In the *Modify | Place Component* tab>Placement panel, click (Place on Face).

6. In the upper left corner of the north wing, move the cursor over the ceiling so the ceiling highlights. Place the air terminal near one of the lighting fixtures, as shown in Figure 9–21. (Hint: It may be easier to place the air terminal at the intersection of the ceiling grid and snap to a point, then move as needed.)

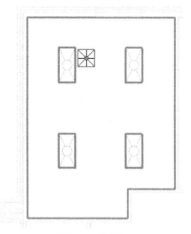

Figure 9–21

7. Type **AL** to start the **Align** command. Align the air terminal to the grid.

8. Type **CO** to start the **Copy** command. Select the air terminal and press <Enter>.

9. In the Options Bar, select **Multiple**.

10. Place copies beside each of the other lighting fixtures in the same room and the room beside it, as shown in Figure 9–22.

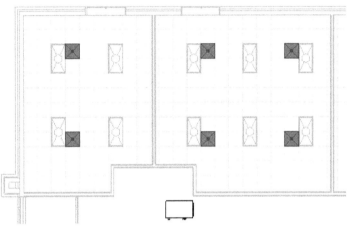

Figure 9–22

11. Zoom out so that one of the existing systems to the far right of the north wing displays, as shown in Figure 9–23.

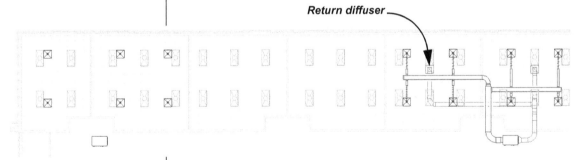

Figure 9–23

12. Select one of the return diffusers, right-click and select **Create Similar**. The Air Terminal command is started with the correct type and properties automatically applied.

13. In the *Modify | Place Component* tab>Placement panel, click (Place on Face).

14. Place a return diffuser in each of the rooms, as shown in Figure 9–24. Align them to the ceiling grid.

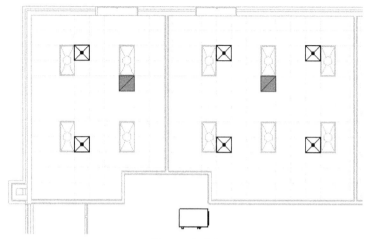

Figure 9–24

15. Copy the air terminals and diffusers to the two rooms across the hall. Align them to the ceiling grid.

16. Save the project.

Task 3 - Add air terminals directly on duct.

---

1. Open the Mechanical>HVAC>3D Views>**3D Mechanical** view.

2. Zoom in on the ductwork in the gym.

3. Start the **Air Terminal** command.

4. In the Type Selector, select **Supply Grille - Double Deflection - Curve Face Rectangular Neck: 24x12 Connection 36 Diameter Duct.**

5. In the *Modify | Place Air Terminal* tab>Layout panel, click

    (Air Terminal on Duct).

6. Add several air terminals along the larger part of one of the ducts, as shown in Figure 9–25

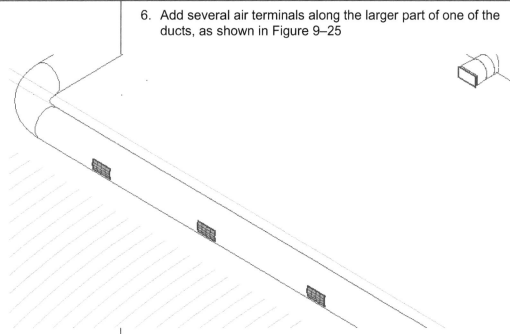

Figure 9–25

7. In the Type Selector, change the type to the ...**24 Diameter Duct** and add air terminals to the smaller diameter duct.

8. Click **Modify** and select one of the new air terminals.

9. Right-click and select **Select all Instances>Visible in View**.

10. Mirror the selected air terminals to the opposite duct.
Hint: Use the center duct as the mirroring axis point. Rotate the view around to see the mirrored supply grille.

11. Save and close the project.

9.2 Adding Ducts and Pipes

Ducts connect mechanical equipment to air terminals and pipes connect mechanical equipment to the hydronic supply, as shown in Figure 9–26. There are various shapes and sizes that can be used both for regular and flex duct and pipe. By using connectors in the equipment and the air terminals, you can quickly attach the ducts and pipes and have the software automatically calculate any differences in height.

Fittings are automatically added in some cases. You can also modify fittings and add others.

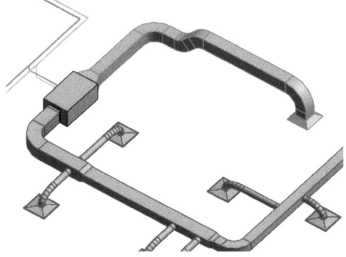

Figure 9–26

• Ducts and pipes can be drawn in plan, elevation/section, and 3D views.

• To get the ducts and pipes at the right height, it is recommended to start it from the Mechanical Equipment.

• Fittings between changes of height or size are automatically applied as you model the elements, as shown in Figure 9–27.

Figure 9–27

• If you need to lay the runs, but the type and size has not yet been determined, create Duct or Pipe Placeholders and convert them to standard ducts or pipes at a later stage.

Mechanical Settings

Before you add ducts or pipes, review and modify the Mechanical Settings to suit your project or office standards. These settings control the angles at which the ducts and pipes can be drawn (as shown in Figure 9–28), and the default types, offsets, sizes, and Pressure Drop calculation method.

- In the *Systems* tab>Mechanical panel, click ⅈ (Mechanical Settings), or type **MS**, to open the Mechanical Settings dialog box.

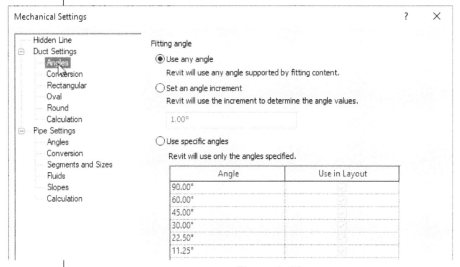

Figure 9–28

Hidden Line	Specify the size and type of hidden lines that show when ducts or pipe cross over each other.
Duct Settings	Specifies a set of common duct system parameters.
Pipe Settings	Displays all parameters common to piping, plumbing, and fire protection systems.
Angles	Specify at what angles fittings are applied for both duct and pipe.
Conversion	Specify how the ducts or pipe work when using the Generate Layout tool. (These are also available in that command.)
Rectangular, Oval, and Round	Specify the sizes that can be used when placing ducts. (Duct only.)
Segments and Sizes	Specify the sizes and other properties for piping by material type. (Pipe only.)
Fluids	Specify the temperature, viscosity, and density of fluids by fluid type. (Pipe only.)

| **Slopes** | Specify slope values for piping runs. (Pipe only.) |
| **Calculation** | Specify the duct or pipe pressure drop for straight sections. You can select from a variety of calculation methods. |

- Duct and Pipe Settings are set by project and can be included in templates or imported into a project from another project using **Transfer Project Standards**.

- If you are working with hydronic piping, you need to set up the analysis process in **Mechanical Settings** on the *Pipe Settings>Calculation >Hydronic Networks* tab. Select **Enable analysis for closed loop hydronic piping networks**.

Adding Ducts and Pipes

The process of adding various types of duct or pipe is essentially the same whether you are drawing standard, flex, or placeholder elements.

There are several ways to start the commands:

1. In the *Systems* tab>HVAC or Plumbing & Piping panels, click the required command:

Duct (DT)	Pipe (PI)
Duct Placeholder	Pipe Placeholder
Flex Duct (FD)	Flex Pipe (FP)

2. Select the element, hover the cursor over a connector icon, and then select the command, as shown in Figure 9–29.

3. Select the element, right-click on a connector, and then select the command name, as shown in Figure 9–30.

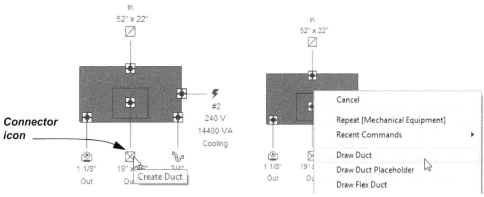

Connector icon

Create Duct

Figure 9–29

Cancel

Repeat [Mechanical Equipment]

Recent Commands

Draw Duct

Draw Duct Placeholder

Draw Flex Duct

Figure 9–30

How To: Draw Duct and Pipe

1. Start the command using one of the options outlined above.
2. In the Type Selector, select a type as shown for ducts in Figure 9–31.
    *   Drawing from existing connectors automatically applies the System Type.

You can limit the number of options that display by typing part of the name in the search box.

Figure 9–31

3. If you are drawing ducts or pipes without selecting an existing connector, in Properties, specify the *System Type* (as shown in Figure 9–32) before you start drawing the elements. You can also adjust the horizontal and vertical justifications, as well as the top, middle, and bottom elevations.

Figure 9–32

- For information about creating duct and pipe types, see *Section A.3 Custom Duct and Piping Types.*

4. In the Options Bar, set the *Width*, *Height* (or *Diameter* for round ducts and pipes), and *Middle Elevation,* as shown in Figure 9–33. If you started from a connector, the default sizes and middle elevation match the parameters of the selected connector.

Figure 9–33

5. In the ribbon, set up the various placement tools, as outlined in the next section.
6. Draw the elements using temporary dimensions, snaps, and alignments to locate each point along the path as shown in Figure 9–34.

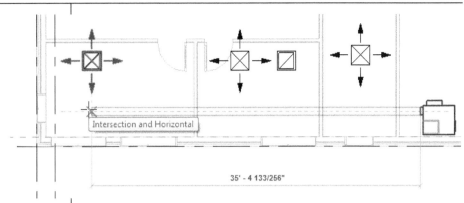

Intersection and Horizontal

35' - 4 133/256"

Figure 9–34

7. Press <Esc> once to stay in the command, but have a new start location.

You can also press <Spacebar> to inherit the elevation and the size of the duct or pipe you snap to.

- When snapping to another element with connectors, ensure that you select the point snap on the end of the other element to create the connection, as shown in Figure 9–35.

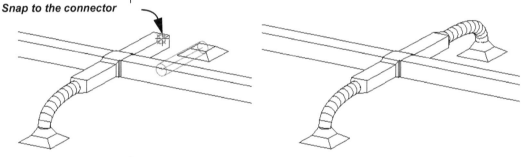

Snap to the connector

Figure 9–35

Duct and Pipe Placement Tools

	Automatically Connect (on/off)	On by default. Ducts and pipes connect to other ones and automatically place all of the required fittings. To draw a duct or pipe that remains at the original elevation, toggle this option off. • Even if **Automatically Connect** is not toggled on, when you snap to a connector any changes in height and size are applied with the appropriate fittings.
	Justification	Opens the Justification Setting dialog box, which enables you to set the default settings for the *Horizontal Justification, Horizontal Offset,* and *Vertical Justification.*

	Inherit Elevation (on/off)	If the tool is toggled on and you start modeling a duct or pipe by snapping to an existing one, the new duct or pipe takes on the elevation of the existing one regardless of what is specified, as shown in Figure 9–36.
	Inherit Size (on/off)	If the tool is toggled on and you start modeling duct or pipe by snapping to an existing one, the new duct or pipe takes on the size of the existing one regardless of what is specified, as shown in Figure 9–36.

Offset lower   **Inherit Elevation on**   **Size smaller**   **Inherit Size on**

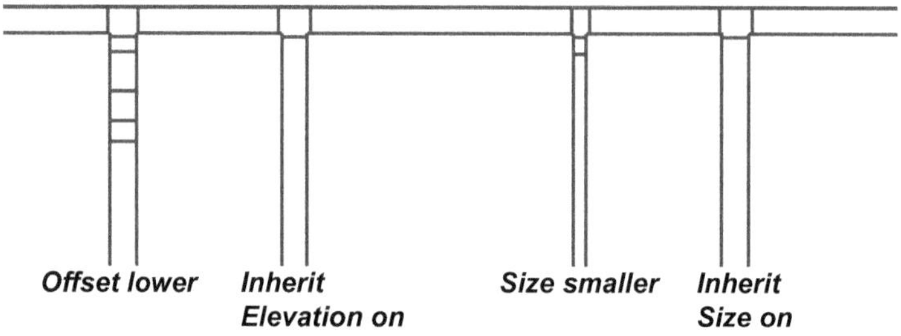

Figure 9–36

- If you already have some ducts or pipes in the project, you can use (Connect Into). This option displays in the contextual tab when you select a component.

- To display centerlines for round ducts or pipe, in the Visibility/ Graphics Overrides dialog box, toggle on the *Centerline* subcategory for duct and duct fittings, as shown in Figure 9–37.

*Centerlines display in plan and elevation views set to the **Wireframe** or **Hidden Line** visual style.*

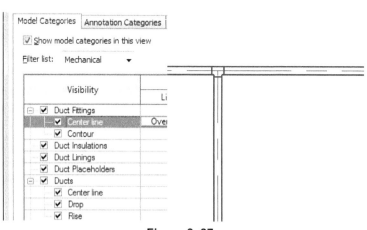

Figure 9–37

Creating Parallel Pipes

The **Parallel Pipes** tool facilitates the creation of piping runs parallel to an existing run, as shown in Figure 9–38. This can save time because only one run needs to be laid out, and the tool generates parallel runs for you.

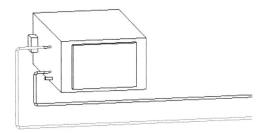

Figure 9–38

- The **Parallel Pipes** tool creates an exact duplicate of the selected pipe, including the *System Type*. You can change the *System Type* in Properties before connecting other pipes into it.

- It might be easier to draw the parallel pipes directly from the fixtures so that they use the correct system type. Also, you might have to modify connectors to get the pipe in the correct place.

- Parallel pipes can be created in plan, section, elevation, and 3D views.

How To: Create Parallel Pipe Runs

1. Create an initial single run of pipe or use an existing pipe run, as required.
2. In the *Systems* tab>Plumbing & Piping panel, click

   ▤ (Parallel Pipes).
3. In the *Modify | Place Parallel Pipes* tab>Parallel Pipes panel, set the *Horizontal Number, Vertical Number, Horizontal Offset,* and/or *Vertical Offset* options, as shown in Figure 9–39.

Figure 9–39

If you do not select the entire run, parallel pipes are only created for the single piece of existing pipe.

4. Hover the cursor over the existing piping (as shown in Figure 9–40) and press <Tab> to select the existing run.

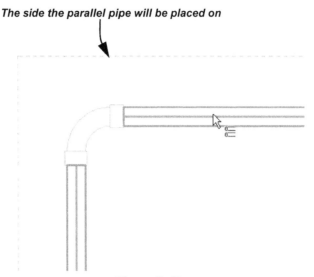

The side the parallel pipe will be placed on

Figure 9–40

5. When the preview displays, click to create the parallel runs. The preview varies depending on which side of the existing run you hover the cursor.

Parallel Pipe Creation Options

Horizontal Number	The total number of parallel pipe runs in the horizontal direction.
Horizontal Offset	The distance between parallel pipe runs in the horizontal direction.
Vertical Number	The total number of parallel pipe runs in the vertical direction.
Vertical Offset	The distance between parallel pipe runs in the vertical direction.

• In section and elevation views, horizontal refers to parallel to the view (visually up, down, left, or right from the original conduit). Vertical creates parallel conduit runs perpendicular to the view, in the direction of the user.

Hint: Analytical Hydronic Piping

In the early stages of a project you might not want to create all of the exact connections between hydronic piping and mechanical equipment, but you still want to be able to calculate flow and pressure drop. To do this, you can add analytical connections, as shown in Figure 9–41.

Select mechanical equipment or hydronic piping, and then in the *Modify* contextual tab>Create panel, click 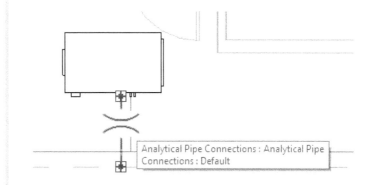 (Analytical Connections). Then, select the pipe or equipment you want to connect into.

Figure 9–41

- After the element is placed, you can assign the **Pressure Drop** (which is 0 by default) in the Type Properties of the analytical connection element.

Practice 9b | Add Ducts and Pipes

Practice Objectives

- Add ductwork.
- Add hydronic piping.

In this practice, you will draw ducts from mechanical equipment connectors and from air terminals using flex duct. You will also add hydronic piping from the mechanical equipment using connectors and the **Connect Into** tool. The completed project is shown in Figure 9–42.

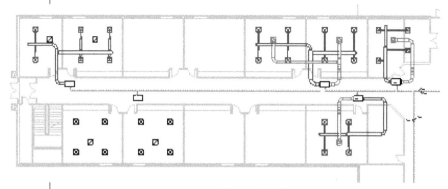

Figure 9–42

Task 1 - Add ducts.

1. In the practice files *HVAC* folder, open the project **Ducts-School-MEP.rvt**.

2. Open the Mechanical>HVAC>Floor Plans>**01 Mechanical Plan** view and zoom in on the upper left rooms of the north wing.

3. Select the Air Handling Unit (AHU) in the hallway. On the **Out** side, click **Create Duct**, as shown in Figure 9–43.

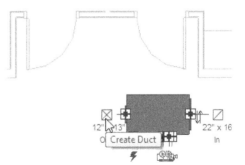

Figure 9–43

4. In the Type Selector, select **Rectangular Duct: Radius Elbow / Taps**.

5. Draw the duct into the room on the left, as shown in Figure 9–44. Press <Esc> once and then draw duct from the main vertical line over into the other room.

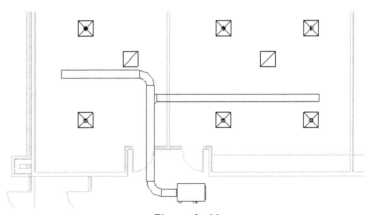

Figure 9–44

6. In the *Systems* tab>HVAC panel, click 🖼 (Duct).

7. In the Type Selector, select R**ound Duct: Taps / Long Radius.**

8. In the *Modify | Place Duct* tab>Placement Tools panel, click 🖼 (Inherit Elevation).

9. In the Options Bar, set *Diameter* to **6"**.

10. Select a point on the duct where it is aligned to the air terminal (as shown in Figure 9–45), and draw it about halfway to the air terminal (as shown in Figure 9–46).

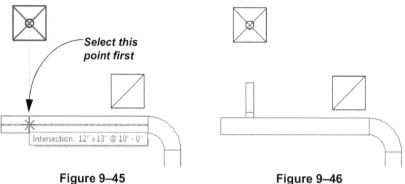

Figure 9–45   Figure 9–46

11. Click **Modify**.

12. Select the Air Terminal, right-click on the connector, and select **Draw Flex Duct**, as shown in Figure 9–47.

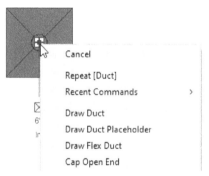

Figure 9–47

13. Draw the flex duct from the air terminal to the new duct, ensuring that you select the point connectors shown in Figure 9–48. As soon as you connect the duct, the air terminal turns blue. It is now attached to the supply air system.

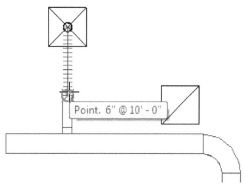

Figure 9–48

14. Repeat the process to connect the other air terminals to the ducts. The final system should look similar to Figure 9–49.

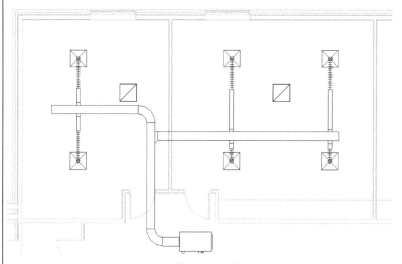

Figure 9–49

15. Save the project.

Task 2 - Draw pipe.

1. Select the AHU and zoom in so that the three pipe outlets clearly display, as shown in Figure 9–50.

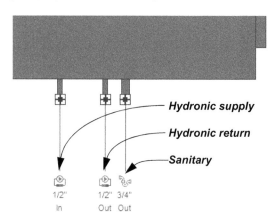

Figure 9–50

2. Select the **Hydronic Supply** icon to start the **Draw Pipe** command.

3. In the Type Selector, select **Pipe Types: Standard**.

4. Draw the pipe down from the AHU, and continue drawing the pipe down the hallway until it is near but not touching existing pipe (as shown in Figure 9–51), zooming out as needed.

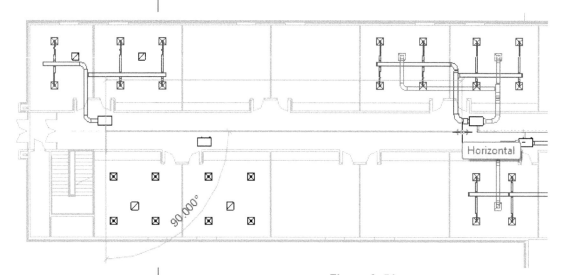

Figure 9–51

5. Press <Esc> and use the **Align** command to align the pipe with existing hydronic supply pipe. (You will modify the connections in the next practice.)

6. Repeat the process with the Hydronic Return pipe, which displays with a dashed line style.

7. Zoom in on and select the other AHU in the hallway, as shown in Figure 9–52.

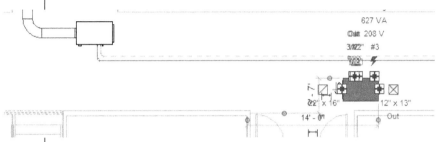

Figure 9–52

8. In the *Modify | Mechanical Equipment* tab>Layout panel, click (Connect Into).

9. In the Select Connector dialog box, select the **Hydronic Return** connector and click **OK**.

10. Select the Hydronic Return pipe (the dashed line).

11. Repeat the process with the Hydronic Supply connector and pipe, as shown in Figure 9–53.

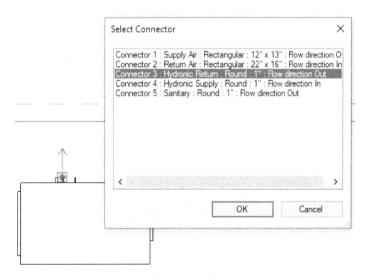

Figure 9–53

12. Zoom out to fit the model in the view.

13. Save and close the project.

Task 3 - (Optional) Add return air ducts.

Add return air ducts to the same area where you added the supply air ducts. You can also add ducts to the air terminals across the hall.

9.3 Modifying Ducts and Pipes

Ducts and pipes can be modified using a variety of standard modifying tools and other specialty tools, such as duct/pipe sizing, converting placeholders, changing rigid ducts/pipes to flexible ones, adding insulation and lining, and modifying the justification of ducts/pipes.

For example, the elbow fitting in Figure 9–54 is too large. In Figure 9–55, the size has changed, a fitting automatically applied, and another fitting added to create the appropriate layout.

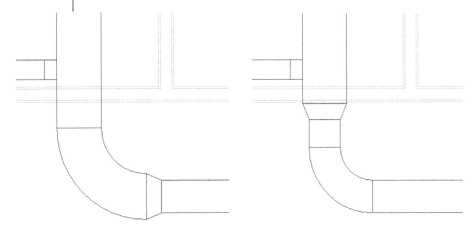

Figure 9–54   Figure 9–55

Using Standard Modify Tools

- You can modify ducts and pipes using universal methods by making changes in:
    - Properties
    - Options Bar
    - Temporary Dimensions
    - Controls
    - Connectors
- You can also use modify tools (e.g., **Move**, **Rotate**, **Split**, **Trim/Extend**, and **Align**) to help you place the ducts and pipes at the correct locations.

Adding Fittings and Accessories

Many fittings are automatically applied as you draw ducts and pipes. However, you might want to modify or add new fittings or accessories, such as a Butterfly Valve (shown in Figure 9–56), fire damper, filter, or smoke detector, and place it at an appropriate connector.

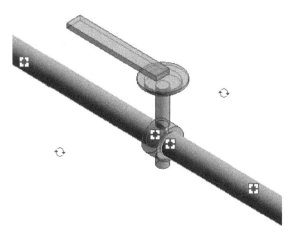

Figure 9–56

How To: Add Fittings and Accessories

1. In the *Systems* tab>HVAC or Plumbing & Piping panel, select the appropriate command:

   - Duct Fitting (DF)

   - Duct Accessory (DA)

   - Pipe Fitting (PF)

   - Pipe Accessory (PA)

2. In the Type Selector, select the type of fitting or accessory you want to use.
3. Hover the cursor over the duct or pipe. Only usable locations are highlighted.
4. Click on the required location. The fitting or accessory resizes to fit the element on which it is placed.

   - Additional fittings and accessories can be loaded from the library. Ensure that you start the correct command for the element you want to load. You can load fittings when you have started the **Accessories** command.

Modifying Fittings

Whether added automatically or manually, fittings can be modified using the Type Selector, Properties, the Options Bar, and a variety of connectors and controls. For example, an Elbow can be changed to a Tee by clicking a control, as shown in Figure 9–57.

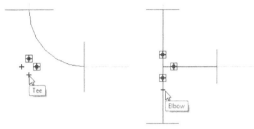

Figure 9–57

Capping Open Ends

You can cap the open end of a duct or pipe by right-clicking on the end control and selecting **Cap Open End**, as shown in Figure 9–58.

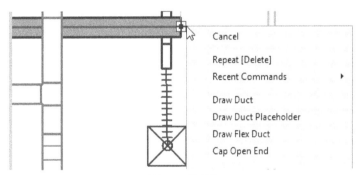

Figure 9–58

Alternatively, if you have more than one opening on the ends of a run, in the *Modify* contextual tab>Edit panel, click ⌐ (Cap Open Ends). The caps are applied (as shown in Figure 9–59) and a warning displays telling you the number of caps applied.

Figure 9–59

Duct and Pipe Sizing

It is easiest to draw ducts or pipes using the default sizes provided by the opening sizes of the equipment, or as preset in the Mechanical Settings. However, these sizes are often incorrect for the system being used. The **Duct/Pipe Sizing** tool uses a specified sizing method and constraints to determine how to correctly size the pipes or ducts, as shown in Figure 9–60.

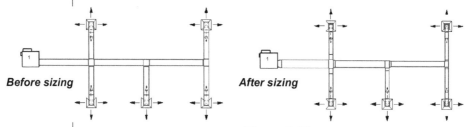

Before sizing   After sizing

Figure 9–60

- If you select only one duct or pipe, it analyzes just that one set of connections. Select the entire system to ensure that all of the connections are analyzed.

How To: Size Ducts and Pipes

1. Select all of the components in a duct or pipe system.
2. In the *Modify | Multi-Select* tab>Analysis panel, click

   (Duct/Pipe Sizing).
3. In the Duct Sizing dialog box, set the *Sizing Method* and *Constraints* as required, as shown in Figure 9–61.

*The most common method for low pressure duct work is **Friction**. Ducts and pipes should be sized according to company design standards.*

Figure 9–61

4. Click **OK**.

- Once you make a change to the system, you need to run the software again. For example, the CFM was changed on two the air terminals shown in Figure 9–62.

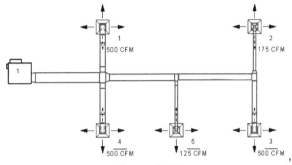

Figure 9–62

- You can also modify duct or pipe sizes on your own to create the most appropriate layout for your methodology. A helpful tool to separate lengths of duct or pipe before you change the size is ⊕ (Split Element).

Converting Ducts and Pipes

After placing ducts or pipes, you can change the type of the entire run (including fittings). If the definition of a type has been changed, you can reapply the type to existing runs. You can also convert placeholders to standard ducts/pipes and, (for ducts only) rigid duct to flex duct when connected to an air terminal.

How To: Change the Type of Duct/Pipe Runs

1. Select the duct/pipe run and filter out everything except the related duct/pipe, accessories, and fittings.
2. In the *Modify | Multi-Select* tab>Edit panel, click ⊞ (Change Type).
3. In the Type Selector, select a new type of run. For the example shown in Figure 9–63, the type **Rectangular Duct: Radius Elbows / Tees** was changed to the type **Round Duct: Taps**.

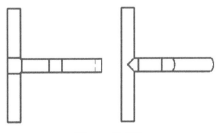

Figure 9–63

How To: Reapply the Type to Runs

1. Select a single duct/pipe run. You can select different runs, but they must be all of the same type and same system. If you select runs in different systems, the software prompts you to select one system to which to reapply the type.
2. Filter out everything except ducts/pipes, fittings, and accessories.
3. In the *Modify | Multi-Select* tab>Edit panel, click 🖱 (Reapply Type).

How To: Convert Placeholders to Duct/Pipe

1. Select the duct/pipe placeholder(s).
2. In the *Modify | contextual* tab>Edit panel, click 🖱 (Convert Placeholder).
3. The placeholders are changed into the duct/pipe type, including the appropriate fittings, as shown for pipes in Figure 9–64.

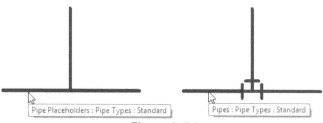

Pipe Placeholders : Pipe Types : Standard   Pipes : Pipe Types : Standard

Figure 9–64

How To: Convert Rigid Duct to Flex Duct

1. In the *Systems* tab>HVAC panel, click 🖱 (Convert to Flex Duct) or type **CV**.
2. In the Options Bar set the *Max Length*. The default is **6'-0"**, a standard code requirement.
3. Select the air terminal connected to the rigid duct. The duct is converted as shown in Figure 9–65.

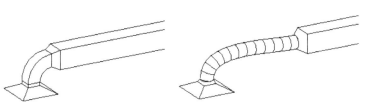

Figure 9–65

- This command only works if the rigid duct is connected to an air terminal.

Adding Insulation and Lining

You can add insulation to ducts and pipes and add lining to ducts. This information displays as a thin line outside of the duct/pipe for insulation and a dashed line inside the duct for lining, as shown in Figure 9–66.

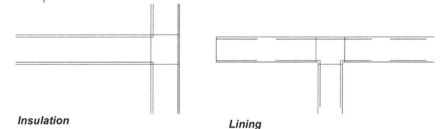

Insulation   *Lining*

Figure 9–66

- Accessories can also be insulated, as shown in Figure 9–67.

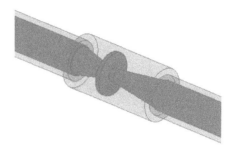

Figure 9–67

How To: Add Insulation or Lining

1. Select the duct/pipe run that you want to insulate, or the duct run you want to line. You can select more than one system at a time for these commands.

2. Use ▽ (Filter) to select only the ducts/pipes, fittings, and accessories.

3. In the *Modify | contextual* tab>Duct or Pipe Insulation panel or Duct Lining panel, select the appropriate command:

   - 🔲 Add Insulation (Duct)

   - 🔲 Add Lining (Duct)

   - 🔲 Add Insulation (Pipe)

4. In the associated dialog box, select a *Insulation Type* and set the *Thickness,* as shown for Duct Insulation in Figure 9–68. Click **OK**.

Figure 9–68

- To modify the insulation, select the insulated duct or pipe and, in the contextual ribbon, select one of the following commands. When editing, change the *Type* in the Type Selector and/or change the *Thickness* in Properties.

    - Edit Insulation (Duct)

    - Edit Lining (Duct)

    - Remove Insulation (Duct)

    - Remove Lining (Duct)

    - Edit Insulation (Pipe)

    - Remove Insulation (Pipe)

Modifying the Justification

If a duct/pipe run has different sized duct/pipe, you can modify the justification, as shown in Figure 9–69.

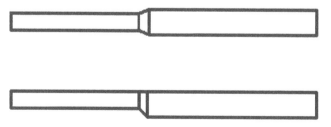

Figure 9–69

How To: Modify Justifications

1. Select the duct/pipe run.
2. In the *Modify | Multi-Select* tab>Edit panel, click 📐 (Justify).
3. To specify the point on the duct that you want to justify around, in the *Justification Editor* tab>Justify panel, click

   🔍 (Control Point) to cycle between the end point references.

   • The alignment location displays as an arrow, as shown in Figure 9–70.

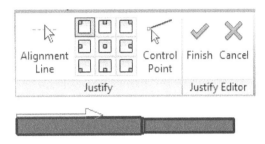

Figure 9–70

4. To indicate the required alignment, either click one of the nine alignment buttons in the Justify panel, or in a 3D view, use

   🔍 (Alignment Line) to select the required dashed line, as shown in Figure 9–71.

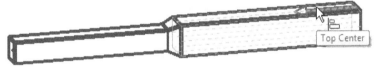

Figure 9–71

Hint: Using Thin Lines

Line thickness can negatively impact the display of elements, such as insulation or lining. To toggle lineweight on or off, in the

Quick Access Toolbar, click 📏 (Thin Lines) or type **TL**.

Practice 9c | Modify Ducts and Pipes

Practice Objectives

- Change pipe types.
- Modify pipe fittings.
- Cap open duct ends.
- Use the Duct/Pipe Sizing tool.
- Add lining to ducts.

In this practice, you will change a run of pipes from one type to another. You will view the pipes in 3D, modify fittings, and make revisions to the pipes to match existing pipes. You will also modify ducts by capping open ends, using the **Duct/Pipe Sizing** tool, and modifying the duct fittings, as shown in Figure 9–72. Finally you will add lining to all of the duct networks in the project.

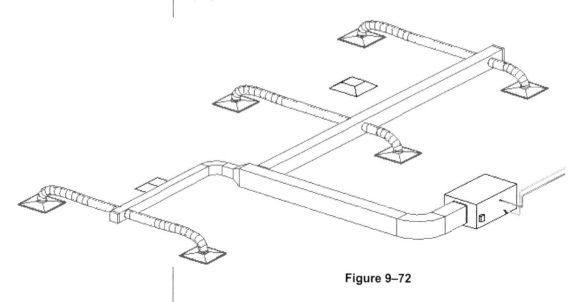

Figure 9–72

Task 1 - Modify the type of pipes.

1. In the practice files *HVAC* folder, open
   Modify-Ducts-School-MEP.rvt.

2. In the **01 Mechanical Plan** view, zoom in on the area near
   AHU 3, as shown in Figure 9–73. Note that the pipes are not
   connected.

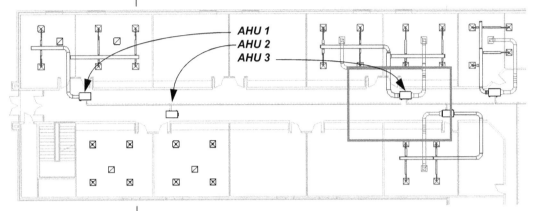

Figure 9–73

3. Hover the cursor over one of the pipes on the left and then
   over one of the pipes on the right. Note that they are two
   different types, as shown in Figure 9–74.

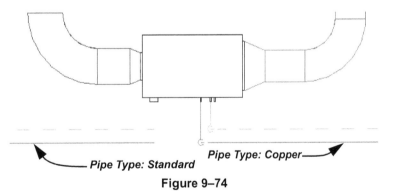

Figure 9–74

4. Zoom out to see the entire piping layout.

5. Hover the cursor over one of the pipes on the left and press <Tab> until the entire pipe run is highlighted (as shown in Figure 9–75) and then select it.

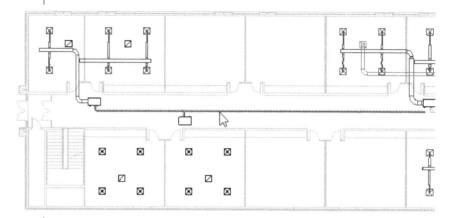

Figure 9–75

6. In the *Modify | Multi-Select* tab>Edit panel, click (Change Type).

7. In the Type Selector, change the type to **Pipe Types: Copper**.

8. Repeat the process with the pipes running parallel.

9. Save the project.

Task 2 - Modify fittings.

1. Open the Mechancial>HVAC>3D Views: **3D Mechanical** view.

   • The Hydroncial Return system color has been changed for clarity in this view.

2. Select the linked model, in the View Control Bar, click (Temporary Hide/Isolate) and then select **Hide Element**.

If you align the pipes while they are connected to the mechanical equipment the AHUs will also move.

3. Zoom in on **AHU 3**. Note that the pipes are not connected and are at different heights, as shown in Figure 9–76.

4. Delete the pipes shown in Figure 9–76.

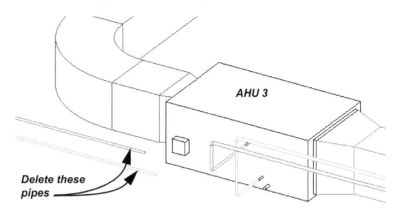

Figure 9–76

5. Select the elbow connector on each of the top pipes and click the **Tee** icon, as shown in Figure 9–77.

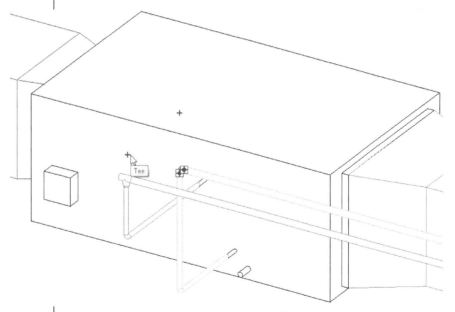

Figure 9–77

6. Switch back to the plan view.

7. Delete the rest of the horizontal pipes created earlier. Zoom in on **AHU 1** and **AHU 2** and delete the orphaned fittings but retain the pipes coming from the AHUs, as shown in Figure 9–78.

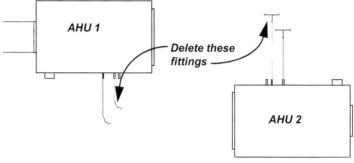

Figure 9–78

8. Zoom or pan back over to **AHU3**.

9. Change the *Display Level* to **Fine** to improve the display of the connectors.

10. Select the Tee fitting, right-click on the open connector, and then select **Draw Pipe**.

11. Draw the pipe down the hall past **AHU 1**.

12. Repeat the process with the other pipe.

13. Zoom in on **AHU 1**.

14. In the *Modify* tab>Modify panel, click (Trim/Extend to Corner). Select the pipe coming from the **AHU 1** and then the horizontal pipe. Repeat with the second pipe, as shown in Figure 9–79.

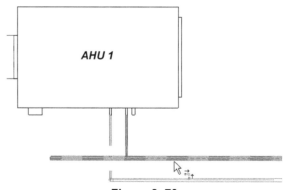

Figure 9–79

15. Pan over to **AHU 2** and use the 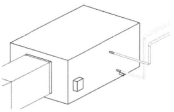 (Trim/Extend Single) command to clean up the intersection between the horizontal and vertical pipes.

16. Return to the 3D Mechanical view to see the revised pipe layout, as shown in Figure 9–80.

Figure 9–80

17. Save the project.

Task 3 - Cap open duct ends.

1. Continue working in the **3D Mechanical** view.

2. Zoom in on the supply duct system connected to **AHU 1**.

3. In the *Analyze* tab>Check Systems panel, click (Show Disconnects).

4. In the Show Disconnects Options dialog box, select **Duct** and click **OK**.

5. Warning icons display indicating the end of the duct where there is an open connector, as shown in Figure 9–81. The warning icons will also display if there are elements not connected to anything.

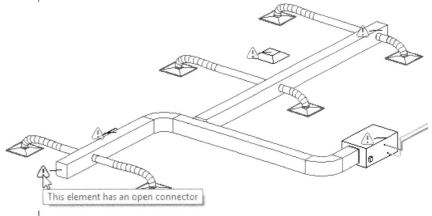

This element has an open connector

Figure 9–81

6. Select the duct, then right-click on the end connector and select **Cap Open End**.

7. The duct is capped and the warning icon no longer displays.

8. Repeat the process on the end of the other open duct.

9. Open the Show Disconnects Options dialog box. Toggle off the **Duct** option and click **OK**.

10. Save the project.

Task 4 - Resize the ducts.

1. Continue working in the **3D Mechanical** view.

2. Hover the cursor over one duct and press <Tab> until the full network displays, then select it.

3. In the **Modify | Multi-Select** tab>Analysis panel, click

   (Duct/Pipe Sizing).

4. In the Duct Sizing dialog box, accept the defaults and click **OK**. The ducts resize, as shown in Figure 9–82.

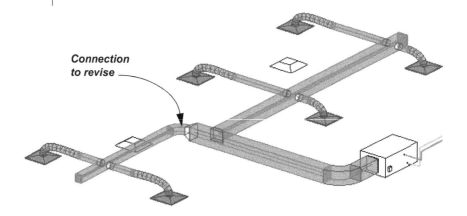

Connection
to revise

Figure 9–82

5. One of the connections needs to be revised, as shown in Figure 9–82.

6. Open the **01 Mechanical Plan** view and zoom in on the supply duct network.

7. Delete the fitting shown in Figure 9–83.

8. Select the open end of the vertical duct and drag it closer to the intersection with the horizontal duct on the right.

9. Right-click on the open end of the elbow and select **Draw Duct**. Draw the duct until it connects to the vertical duct. The appropriate fitting is reapplied, as shown in Figure 9–84.

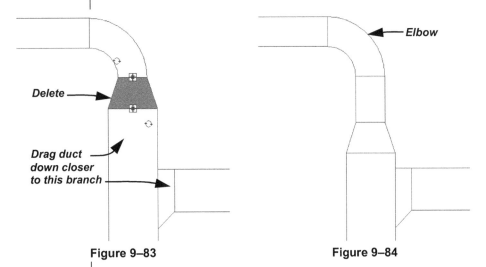

Figure 9–83   Figure 9–84

10. (Optional) Make additional adjustments to the ducts, including shortening the horizontal ducts past the final air terminals.

11. Zoom to fit everything in the view.

12. Save the project.

Task 5 - Add duct lining.

1. Continue working in the **01 Mechanical Plan** view.

2. Draw a window around all of the elements in the view.

3. In the Status Bar or in the *Modify | Multi-Select* tab>Selection panel, click ▽ (Filter).

4. In the Filter dialog box, clear everything except **Ducts, Duct Fittings**, and **Flex Ducts**. Click **OK**.

5. In the *Modify | Multi-Select* tab>Duct Lining panel, click

 (Add Lining).

6. In the Add Duct Lining dialog box, set the *Thickness* to **1/2"** and click **OK**.

If required, in the Quick Access Toolbar, click

(Thin Lines).

7. Zoom in and see the lining applied to the ducts, as shown in Figure 9–85.

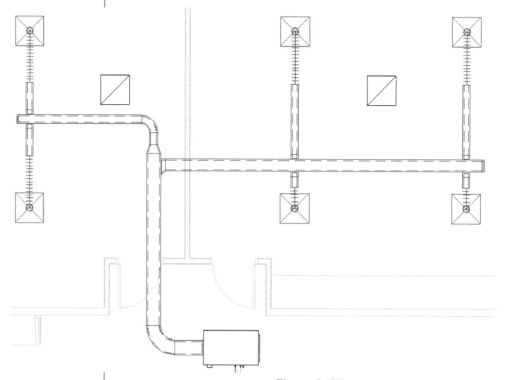

Figure 9–85

8. Zoom out.

9. Reset the **Temporary Hide/Isolate**.

10. Save and close the project.

Chapter Review Questions

1. Where do you specify the *Flow* of an air terminal, such as that shown in Figure 9–86? (Select all that apply.)

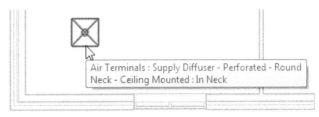

Figure 9–86

   a. In the Ribbon

   b. In the Options Bar

   c. In the Air Flow Dialog Box

   d. In the Properties

   e. In the Air Terminal tag

2. Which method enables you to move an air terminal hosted by a ceiling that has been copied, as shown in Figure 9–87, up to a different ceiling height?

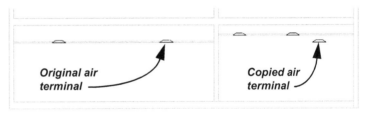

Figure 9–87

   a. Move the air terminal.

   b. Pick New Host.

   c. Change the elevation in Properties.

   d. Copied air terminals cannot be moved off the original plane.

3. The size of the duct drawn from a control on mechanical equipment must remain the same size as the opening on the equipment until it intersects with another duct.

   a. True

   b. False

4. How do you change an elbow fitting to a tee fitting?

   a. Delete the elbow and place a tee instead.

   b. Select the elbow and use the Type Selector to select a tee fitting instead.

   c. Select the elbow and click **+** (Plus).

   d. Select the elbow and click **Convert to Tee** in the ribbon.

5. When adding pipe accessories, such as the Butterfly Valve shown in Figure 9–88, you are first required to:

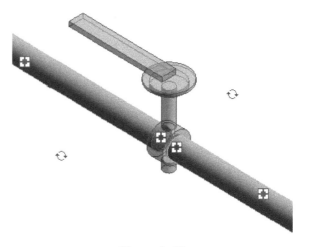

Figure 9–88

   a. Split the pipe using ⊞ (Split Element).

   b. Split the pipe using ⊡ (Split with Gap).

   c. Place the accessory near the pipe and then move it in place.

   d. Do nothing extra, just place the accessory on the pipe.

6. When can you convert a rigid duct to a flexible duct, such as that shown in Figure 9–89?

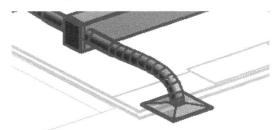

Figure 9–89

a. When the rigid duct is round.

b. When the air terminal is already connected by a rigid duct.

c. When creating a system and sizing the ducting.

d. When the **Allow Conversion** parameter is selected in the rigid duct's instance properties.

7. Which of the following commands can be used when modifying pipe? (Select all that apply.)

a. **Change Type**

b. **Reapply Type**

c. **Add Insulation**

d. **Edit Lining**

e. **Modify Justification**

f. **Modify Material**

g. **Change Offset**

8. Parallel pipe runs are created automatically at the correct distance from equipment, as shown in Figure 9–90.

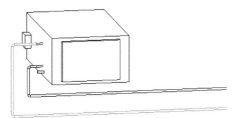

Figure 9–90

a. True

b. False

Command Summary

Button	Command	Location
HVAC Tools		
	Air Terminal	• **Ribbon:** *Systems* tab>HVAC panel • **Shortcut:** AT
	Air Terminal on Duct	• **Ribbon:** *Modify	Place Air Terminal* tab>Layout panel
	Analytical Connections	• **Ribbon:** *Modify	Mechanical Equipment* (or *Modify | Pipes*) tab>Create panel
	Cap Open Ends	• **Ribbon:** *Modify	contextual* tab>Edit panel
	Duct	• **Ribbon:** *Systems* tab>HVAC panel • **Shortcut:** DT
	Duct Accessory	• **Ribbon:** *Systems* tab>HVAC panel • **Shortcut:** DA
	Duct Fitting	• **Ribbon:** *Systems* tab>HVAC panel • **Shortcut:** DF
	Duct Placeholder	• **Ribbon:** *Systems* tab>HVAC panel
	Flex Duct	• **Ribbon:** *Systems* tab>HVAC panel • **Shortcut:** FD
	Flex Pipe	• **Ribbon:** *Systems* tab>Plumbing & Piping panel • **Shortcut:** FP
	Pipe	• **Ribbon:** *Systems* tab>Plumbing & Piping panel • **Shortcut:** PI
	Pipe Accessory	• **Ribbon:** *Systems* tab>Plumbing & Piping panel • **Shortcut:** PA
	Pipe Fitting	• **Ribbon:** *Systems* tab>Plumbing & Piping panel • **Shortcut:** PF
	Pipe Placeholder	• **Ribbon:** *Systems* tab>Plumbing & Piping panel
	Mechanical Equipment	• **Ribbon:** *Systems* tab>Mechanical panel • **Shortcut:** ME

	Mechanical Settings	• **Ribbon:** *Systems* tab>HVAC or Mechanical panel title • **Shortcut:** MS

Duct Modification

	Add Insulation	• **Ribbon:** (*with Ducts and Duct Fittings selected*) *Modify | Multi-Select* tab>Duct Insulation panel
	Add Lining	• **Ribbon:** (*with Ducts and Duct Fittings selected*) *Modify | Multi-Select* tab> Duct Lining panel
	Change Type	• **Ribbon:** (*with Ducts and Duct Fittings selected*) *Modify | Multi-Select* tab>Edit panel
	Convert to Flex Duct	• **Ribbon:** *Systems* tab>HVAC panel • **Shortcut:** CV
	Edit Insulation	• **Ribbon:** (*with Ducts and Duct Fittings that have Insulation selected*) *Modify | Multi-Select* tab>Duct Insulation panel
	Edit Lining	• **Ribbon:** (*with Ducts and Duct Fittings that have Lining selected*) *Modify | Multi-Select* tab>Duct Lining panel
	Inherit Elevation	• **Ribbon:** *Modify | Place Duct* tab>Placement Tools panel
	Inherit Size	• **Ribbon:** *Modify | Place Duct* tab>Placement Tools panel
	Justification (Settings)	• **Ribbon:** *Modify | Place Duct* tab>Placement Tools panel
	Justify	• **Ribbon:** (*with Ducts and Duct Fittings selected*) *Modify | Multi-Select* tab> Edit panel
	Remove Insulation	• **Ribbon:** (*with Ducts and Duct Fittings that have Insulation selected*) *Modify | Multi-Select* tab>Duct Insulation panel
	Remove Lining	• **Ribbon:** (*with Ducts and Duct Fittings that have Lining selected*) *Modify | Multi-Select* tab>Duct Lining panel

Pipe Modification

	Add Insulation	• **Ribbon:** (*with one or more Pipes selected*) *Modify | Pipe* tab>Edit panel or (*with Pipes and Pipe Fittings selected*) *Modify | Multi-Select* tab>Edit panel
	Change Type	• **Ribbon:** (*with one or more Pipes selected*) *Modify | Pipe* tab>Edit panel or (*with Pipes and Pipe Fittings selected*) *Modify | Multi-Select* tab>Edit panel

	Convert Placeholder	• **Ribbon:** *Modify	Pipe Placeholders* tab>Edit panel
	Edit Insulation	• **Ribbon:** (*with one or more Pipes selected*) *Modify	Pipe* tab>Edit panel or (*with Pipes and Pipe Fittings selected*) *Modify	Multi-Select* tab>Edit panel
	Inherit Elevation	• **Ribbon:** *Modify	Place Pipe* tab>Placement Tools panel
	Inherit Size	• **Ribbon:** *Modify	Place Pipe* tab>Placement Tools panel
	Justification (Settings)	• **Ribbon:** *Modify	Place Pipe* tab>Placement Tools panel
	Justify	• **Ribbon:** (*with one or more Pipes selected*) *Modify	Pipe* tab>Edit panel or (*with Pipes and Pipe Fittings selected*) *Modify	Multi-Select* tab>Edit panel
	Remove Insulation	• **Ribbon:** (*with one or more Pipes selected*) *Modify	Pipe* tab>Edit panel or (*with Pipes and Pipe Fittings selected*) *Modify	Multi-Select* tab>Edit panel

Plumbing Systems

Plumbing systems consist of pipes that connect plumbing fixtures and mechanical equipment. The process of putting these together and ensuring they work correctly is a significant part of developing a plumbing project. Frequently, fire protection is included in the plumbing design. Fire protection networks include wet and dry sprinklers with the associated piping.

Learning Objectives in This Chapter

- Add plumbing fixtures and mechanical equipment.
- Add pipes to connect plumbing fixtures and equipment.
- Modify pipes and fittings.
- Add sprinklers and piping for fire protection systems.

10.1 Adding Plumbing Fixtures and Equipment

When you start to create plumbing systems in a project, you typically start by adding plumbing fixtures and mechanical equipment as needed, then network them together using pipes, as shown in Figure 10–1.

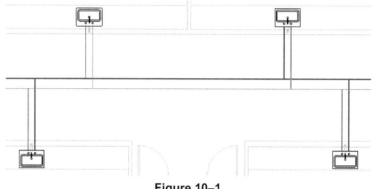

Figure 10–1

Mechanical Equipment

Mechanical equipment for plumbing includes various water heaters, pumps, and water filters. Mechanical equipment specifications are set up through Properties (as shown in Figure 10–2) and have connectors (as shown in Figure 10–3).

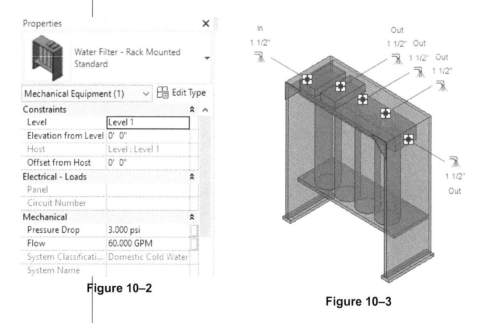

Figure 10–2

Figure 10–3

- Depending on the component, mechanical equipment can be placed in plan, elevation, and 3D views.

How To: Place Mechanical Equipment

1. In the *Systems* tab>Mechanical panel, click 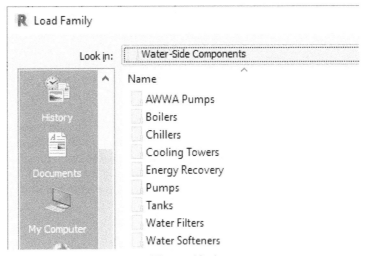 (Mechanical Equipment) or type **ME**.
2. In the Type Selector, select a mechanical equipment type.
3. In Properties, set any other values such as the *Level* and *Offset from Host* if the equipment is not hosted.
4. In the Options Bar, specify if you want to be able to rotate the equipment after placement.
5. Place the mechanical equipment in the model by clicking at the required location in the model view.

- You can use other objects in the model to align the element, or press <Spacebar> to rotate it before or after placing it.

- Plumbing-based mechanical equipment can be loaded from the Autodesk® Revit® library in the *Mechanical>MEP> Water-side Components* folder (as shown in Figure 10–4) and the *Mechanical>MEP>Equipment* folder.

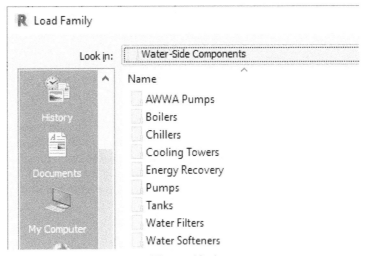

Figure 10–4

Hint: Tagging Equipment and Fixtures

You can tag both plumbing fixtures and mechanical equipment, as shown in Figure 10–5.

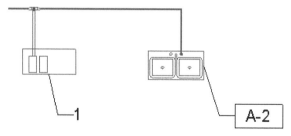

Figure 10–5

- When you are adding plumbing elements, in the *Modify |*

  contextual tab>Tag panel, toggle 🔲 (Tag on Placement) on or off as required.

- To add a tag to an existing element, in the *Annotate* tab>

  Tag panel, click 🔲 (Tag by Category) and select the elements to tag.

- If you change anything in the tag, it will modify the element and update it in Properties (i.e., changing a fixture's name in the tag will change it in Properties and potentially affect other fixtures of the same type).

Plumbing Fixtures

Plumbing fixtures include water closets, sinks, lavatories, bathtubs, drains, drinking fountains and many more. Some examples of plumbing fixtures are shown in Figure 10–6. Depending on the type of fixture, there are connectors for sanitary and domestic hot and cold water pipes.

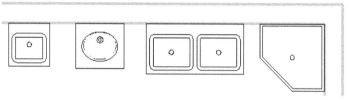

Figure 10–6

- Plumbing fixtures can also be copy/monitored into projects from linked architectural models.

How To: Place Plumbing Fixtures

1. In the *Systems* tab>Plumbing & Piping panel, click

   (Plumbing Fixture) or type **PX**.
2. In the Type Selector, select a plumbing fixture type.
3. Proceed as follows:

If the fixture is...	Then...
Not hosted	In Properties, set any required values (e.g., *Level*, etc.).
Hosted	In the *Modify	Place Plumbing Fixture* tab>Placement panel, select the type of placement for the specific fixture. The default placement type is (Place on Vertical Face), as shown in Figure 10–7.

Figure 10–7

4. Place the fixture in the model by clicking on the required location in the model view.

- Press <Spacebar> to rotate the fixture before or after placing it.

- Additional plumbing fixtures can be loaded from the Autodesk Revit library in the *Plumbing>MEP>Fixtures* subfolder.

- If you have plumbing fixtures in a project with similar parameters, you can place one and then copy or array it to the other locations, as shown in Figure 10–8.

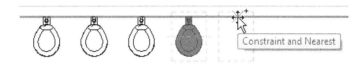

Figure 10–8

- When mirroring fixtures, note that the location of hot and cold water taps in lavatories and sinks can change.

Rehosting Fixtures

If you want to move a wall or face-based fixture to a different location, you might need to rehost the fixture, as shown in Figure 10–9.

Original

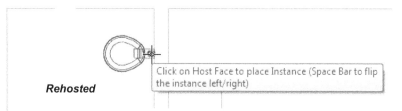

Rehosted

Figure 10–9

How To: Rehost Plumbing Fixtures

1. Select the fixture that needs to be rehosted.
2. In the *Modify | Plumbing Fixtures* tab>Work Plane panel, click

    (Pick New).
3. In the Placement panel, select the type of placement required by the fixture:
    - **Vertical Face**
    - **Face**
    - **Work Plane**
4. Select the element to which you want the fixture hosted.

Practice 10a | Add Plumbing Fixtures and Equipment

Practice Objective

- Add plumbing fixtures and equipment.

In this practice, you will copy/monitor lavatories from a linked model. You will also load and place a plumbing fixture and hot water heaters, as shown in Figure 10–10. Optionally, you can also place floor drains in the restrooms and kitchen area.

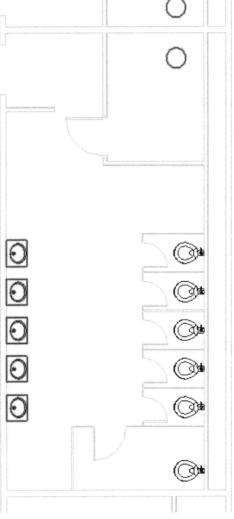

Figure 10–10

Task 1 - Copy/monitor plumbing fixtures.

1. In the practice files *Plumbing* folder, open
   Plumbing-School-MEP.rvt.

2. In the **Plumbing>Floor Plans:1 - Plumbing** view, note that
   some of the water closets have already been placed in the
   project through copy/monitor, while the lavatories have not,
   as shown in Figure 10–11.

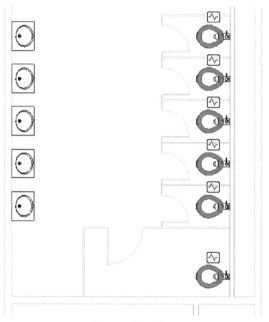

Figure 10–11

3. In the *Collaborate* tab>Coordinate panel, expand
   (Copy/Monitor) and click (Select Link).

4. Select the linked model.

5. In the *Copy/Monitor* tab>Tools panel, click (Coordination
   Settings).

6. In the Coordination Settings dialog box, expand **Plumbing
   Fixtures** and select **Type Mapping**. Several elements were
   set so that they did not get copied in, as shown in
   Figure 10–12.

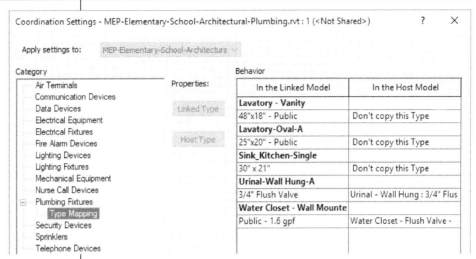

	In the Linked Model	In the Host Model
Lavatory - Vanity		
	48"x18" - Public	Don't copy this Type
Lavatory-Oval-A		
	25"x20" - Public	Don't copy this Type
Sink_Kitchen-Single		
	30" x 21"	Don't copy this Type
Urinal-Wall Hung-A		
	3/4" Flush Valve	Urinal - Wall Hung : 3/4" Flus
Water Closet - Wall Mounte		
	Public - 1.6 gpf	Water Closet - Flush Valve -

Figure 10–12

7. Beside the option for *Lavatory-Oval-A*, select **Lavatory-Oval: 25" x 20" - Public**. This is an MEP-based fixture with connectors for pipes included.

8. Click **Copy**.

9. In the *Copy/Monitor* tab>Copy/Monitor panel, click

   (Finish).

10. The lavatories in the restrooms have now been copied and monitored into the project (as shown in Figure 10–13), but the sinks in the classrooms have not.

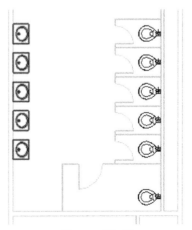

Figure 10–13

11. Save the project.

Task 2 - Load and add a plumbing fixture.

1. Pan to the classroom shown in Figure 10–14 and zoom in on the sink.

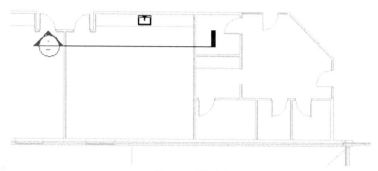

Figure 10–14

2. In the *Systems* tab>Plumbing & Piping panel, click (Plumbing Fixture).

3. Expand the Type Selector list and in the search box type **kit**. A short list of plumbing fixtures display that have Kitchen in the name, as shown in Figure 10–15.

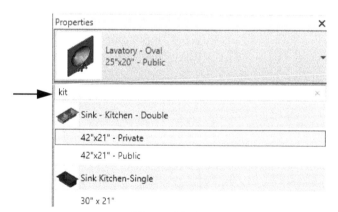

Figure 10–15

4. Select **Sink Kitchen-Single: 30" x 21"** and place it directly on top of the sink in the linked model.

5. Click **Modify** and select the new sink. Note that the sink does not include connectors for piping, as shown in Figure 10–16.

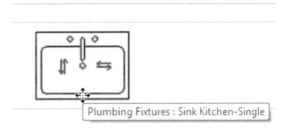

Figure 10–16

This is a method of loading families without starting a command.

6. In the *Insert* tab>Load from Library panel, click (Load Family).

7. In the Load Family dialog box, navigate to the practice files *Plumbing* folder (not the Autodesk Revit library folder) and select **Sink_Kitchen-Single-MEP.rfa**. This is a custom sink that matches the architectural sink, but includes MEP connectors.

8. In the view, select the sink. In the Type Selector, change the type to **Sink_Kitchen-Single-MEP: 30" x 21"**. The fixture updates with connectors, as shown in Figure 10–17.

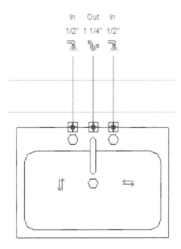

Figure 10–17

9. With the sink still selected, right-click and select **Create Similar**.

10. Place a copy of the sink across the hall, as shown in Figure 10–18. Press <Spacebar> to rotate the sink to the correct orientation before placing it so that it is aligned with the fixture in the linked architectural model.

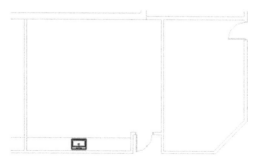

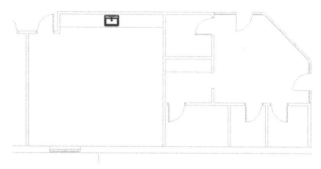

Figure 10–18

11. Click **Modify** and select both of the sinks.

12. In the *Modify | Plumbing Fixtures* tab>Clipboard panel, click (Copy to Clipboard).

13. In the Clipboard panel, expand (Paste) and select (Paste Aligned to Selected Levels).

14. In the Select Levels dialog box, select **Level 2** and then click **OK**.

15. Open the **2 - Plumbing** view. Note that copies of the sinks are placed on Level 2 directly above the selected sinks.

16. Return to the **1 - Plumbing** view and zoom out to see the entire building.

17. Save the project.

Task 3 - Add water heaters.

1. In the **1 - Plumbing** view, zoom in on the janitor's closets between the restrooms.

2. In the *Systems* Tab>Mechanical panel, click ⊛ (Mechanical Equipment).

3. In the *Modify | Place Mechanical Equipment* tab>Mode panel, click 🔽 (Load Family).

Click on the Imperial Libraries folder in the Places panel to quickly get to the Revit library folder location.

4. In the Autodesk Revit library, navigate to the *Plumbing> MEP>Equipment>Water Heaters* folder and load the family **Water Heater.rfa**.

5. In the Type Selector, select **Water Heater: 40 Gallon**.

6. Place a water heater in the janitor's closet in each restroom. Rotate the components so that the Sanitary connector faces the wall, as shown in Figure 10–19. After placing the water heaters, you can select them again and press <Spacebar> to rotate them.

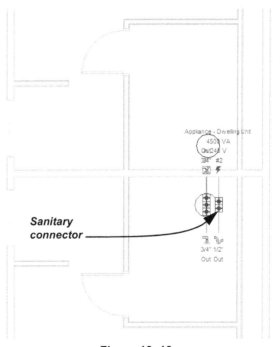

Figure 10–19

7. Zoom out to fit the view.

8. Save the project.

Task 4 - Add floor drains.

1. For additional practice, add drains to the restrooms and kitchen, as shown in Figure 10–20.

   - Work in the **Plumbing>Drainage>Floor Plans> 1 - Drainage** view.
   - Use the plumbing fixture **Floor Drain - Round: 5" Strainer - 3" Drain**.
   - Place the drain on the work plane.

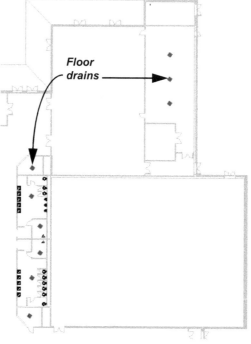

Floor drains

Figure 10–20

2. Save and close the project.

10.2 Adding Plumbing Pipes

Plumbing Systems include sanitary, domestic hot water, and domestic cold water, as shown in Figure 10–21. The pipes in a system connect plumbing fixtures together and indicate how the network is laid out. You can draw the pipes independently or using connectors in the fixtures.

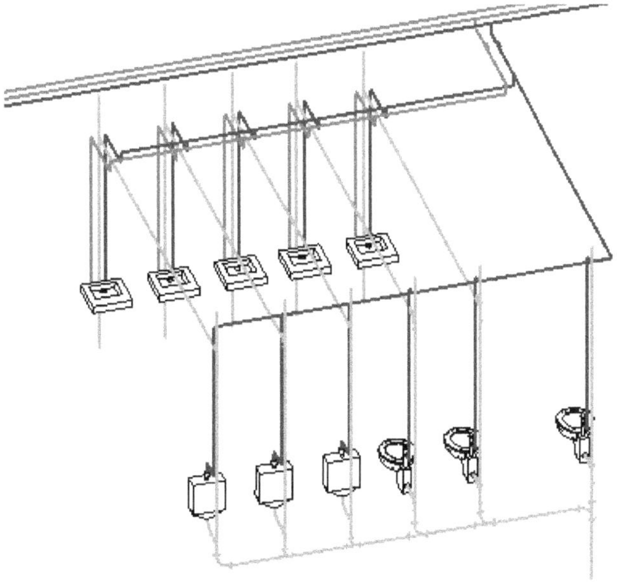

Fittings are automatically added in some cases, but you can also add and modify fittings.

Check sanitary pipe fittings in particular to ensure that they are pointing the right way.

Figure 10–21

- Pipes can be drawn in plan, elevation/section, and 3D views.

- To get the pipes at the right height, it is recommended to start from the connectors in the plumbing fixtures.

- Fittings between changes of height or size are automatically applied as you model the elements, as shown in Figure 10–22.

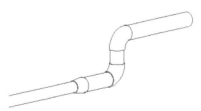

Figure 10–22

- If you need to lay the runs, but the type and size has not yet been determined, create Placeholders and convert them to standard pipes at a later stage.

Mechanical Settings

Before you add pipes, review and modify the Mechanical Settings to suit your project or office standards. These settings control the angles at which the pipes can be drawn (as shown in Figure 10–23), the default types, offsets, sizes, slopes, and the Pressure Drop calculation method.

- In the *Systems* tab>Mechanical panel, click ⁑ (Mechanical Settings) or type **MS** to open the Mechanical Settings dialog box.

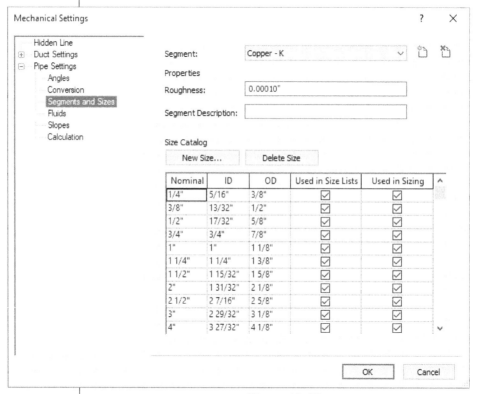

Figure 10–23

Hidden Line	Specify the size and type of hidden lines that show when pipes cross over each other.
Pipe Settings	Displays all parameters common to piping, plumbing, and fire protection systems.
Angles	Specify at what angles fittings are applied for pipe runs.
Conversion	Specify how the pipes work when using the Generate Layout tool. (These are also available in that command.)
Segments and Sizes	Specify the sizes and other properties for piping by material type.

Fluids	Specify the temperature, viscosity, and density of fluids by fluid type.
Slopes	Specify slope values for piping runs.
Calculation	Specify the pipe pressure drop for straight sections. You can select from a variety of calculation methods.

- Mechanical Settings are set by project and can be included in templates or imported into a project from another one using **Transfer Project Standards**.

Adding Pipes

The process of adding standard, flex, or placeholder pipes is essentially the same. There are several ways to start the commands:

1. In the *Systems* tab>Plumbing & Piping panel, click the appropriate command or type the shortcut:

   - Pipe (PI)

   - Pipe Placeholder

   - Flex Pipe (FP)

2. Select the element, hover the cursor over a connector icon, and then select the command, as shown in Figure 10–24.

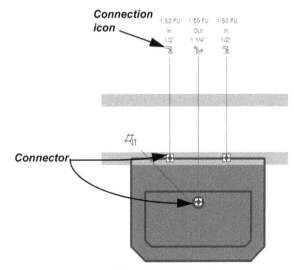

Figure 10–24

3. Select the element, right-click on a connector, and then select the command name.

How To: Add Pipe

1. Start the ⌁ (Pipe), ⌁ (Pipe Placeholder), or ⌁ (Flex Pipe) command.
2. In the Type Selector, select a pipe type, as shown in Figure 10–25.
3. If you are drawing pipes without selecting an existing connector, in Properties, specify the *System Type* (as shown in Figure 10–26) before you start drawing the elements.
    - Drawing from existing connectors automatically applies the System Type.

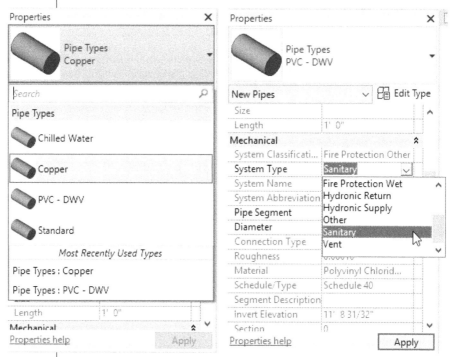

Figure 10–25   Figure 10–26

4. In the Options Bar, set the *Diameter* and *Middle Elevation*, as shown in Figure 10–27. If you started from a connector, the default size and offset match the parameters of the selected connector.

Figure 10–27

5. In the ribbon, set up the various placement tools, as outlined below.

- For information about creating pipe types, see *Section A.3 Custom Duct and Piping Types*.

Pipe Placement Tools

	Automatically Connect (on/off)	On by default. Pipes connect to other pipes and automatically place all of the required fittings. Toggle this option off, if you want to draw a pipe that remains at the original elevation. • Even if **Automatically Connect** is not toggled on, when you snap to a connector any changes in height and size are applied with the appropriate fittings.
	Justification	Opens the Justification Setting dialog box, which enables you to set the default settings for the *Horizontal Justification, Horizontal Offset,* and *Vertical Justification.*
	Inherit Elevation (on/off)	If the tool is toggled on and you start modeling a pipe by snapping to an existing one, the new pipe takes on the elevation of the existing one regardless of what is specified, as shown in Figure 10–28.
	Inherit Size (on/off)	If the tool is toggled on and you start modeling pipe by snapping to an existing one, the new pipe takes on the size of the existing one regardless of what is specified, as shown in Figure 10–28.

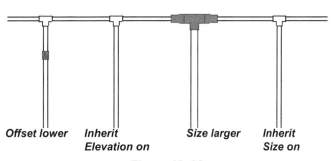

Offset lower *Inherit*   *Size larger* *Inherit*
       Elevation on   *Size on*

Figure 10–28

• If you already have some pipes in the project, you can use

(Connect Into). This option displays in the contextual tab when you select a component.

- To display centerlines for pipe, in the Visibility/Graphics Overrides dialog box, toggle on the *Centerline* subcategory for pipes and pipe fittings, as shown in Figure 10–29.

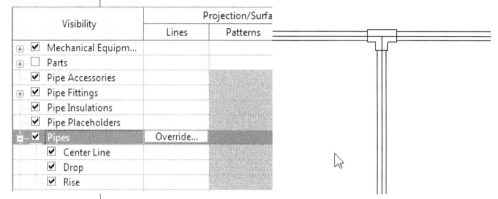

Figure 10–29

- Centerlines display in plan and elevation views set to the **Wireframe** or **Hidden Line** visual style.

Sloped Piping

When drawing pipes with a slope, it helps to identify the direction that *drains to daylight* (the point in the system where it attaches to the exterior drainage pipes). Then, start drawing the pipes from the top most fixture in the system as shown in Figure 10–30.

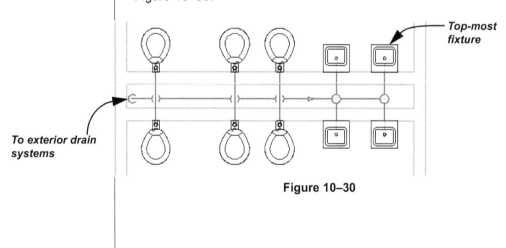

Figure 10–30

- As you are drawing pipes with slopes, you can set the information in the *Modify | Place Pipe* tab>Sloped Piping panel as shown in Figure 10–31. You can change the direction of the slope, the slope value, and toggle the slope off or specify that it be ignored when connecting.

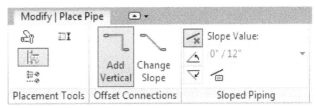

Figure 10–31

- In the Sloped Piping panel, toggle on  (Show Slope Tooltip) to see the exact information of the offsets and slope as you draw, as shown in Figure 10–32.

Start Offset   0' 0"
Current Offset -0' 3 1/8"
Slope   1/4" / 12" Down

Horizontal and Nearest

Figure 10–32

Creating Parallel Pipes

The **Parallel Pipes** tool helps you create piping runs that are parallel to an existing run, as shown in Figure 10–33. This can save time because only one run needs to be laid out, and the tool generates the parallel runs for you.

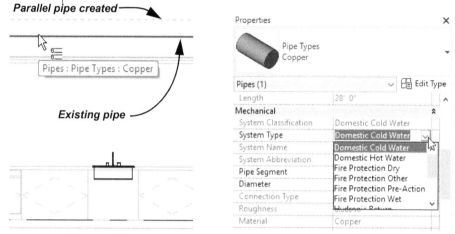

Figure 10–33   Figure 10–34

- The **Parallel Pipes** tool creates an exact duplicate of the selected pipe, including the system type. You can change the System Type in Properties (as shown in Figure 10–34) before connecting other pipes into it.

- It might be easier to draw the parallel pipes directly from the fixtures so that the pipe takes on the correct system type. Also, you might have to modify connectors to get the pipe in the correct place.

- Parallel pipes can be created in plan, section, elevation, and 3D views.

How To: Create Parallel Pipe Runs

1. Create an initial pipe run, or use an existing pipe run.
2. In the *Systems* tab>Plumbing & Piping panel, click (Parallel Pipes).
3. In the *Modify | Place Parallel Pipes* tab>Parallel Pipes panel, set the required options, as shown in Figure 10–35.

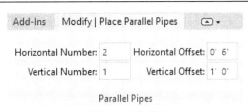

Parallel Pipes

Figure 10–35

4. Hover the cursor over the existing piping (as shown in Figure 10–36) and press <Tab> to select the existing run.

If you do not press <Tab>, parallel pipes are only created for the single piece of existing pipe.

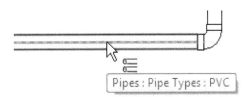

Figure 10–36

5. When the preview displays, click to create the parallel runs. The preview varies depending on which side of the existing run you hover the cursor.

Parallel Pipe Creation Options

Horizontal Number	The total number of parallel pipe runs, in the horizontal direction.
Horizontal Offset	The distance between parallel pipe runs, in the horizontal direction.
Vertical Number	The total number of parallel pipe runs, in the vertical direction.
Vertical Offset	The distance between parallel pipe runs, in the vertical direction.

• In section and elevation views, horizontal refers to parallel to the view (visually up, down, left, or right from the original conduit). Vertical creates parallel conduit runs perpendicular to the view, in the direction of the user.

Practice 10b | Add Plumbing Pipes

Practice Objectives

- Set mechanical settings.
- Add pipes.
- Change the size and height of the pipes as you draw them.
- Create sloped pipes.

In this practice, you will draw cold water mains from the origin point to the classroom wing, changing the diameter and offset of the pipes as you draw them. You will connect water heaters into the mains and then draw hot water pipes from the water heater to the classroom wing. Finally, you will draw sloped sanitary piping from floor drains, as shown in Figure 10–37.

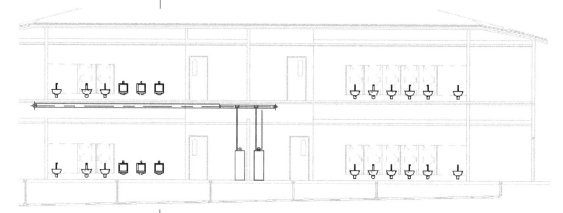

Figure 10–37

Task 1 - Set mechanical settings.

1. In the practice files *Plumbing* folder, open the project **Piping-School-MEP.rvt**.

2. In the *Systems* tab>Mechanical panel title bar, click ꙮ (Mechanical Settings).

3. In the Mechanical Settings dialog box, in *Pipe Settings,* select **Angles**.

4. In the right pane, select **Use specific angles** and clear the checks for 22.50° and 11.25°, as shown in Figure 10–38. Then, click **OK**. This limits the angles you can use to draw the piping to industry specific fittings.

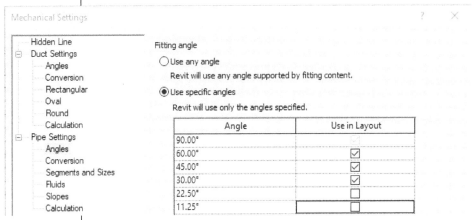

Figure 10–38

Task 2 - Run cold water mains.

In this task, you will model cold water mains following the path shown in Figure 10–39. You will change the diameter and offset of the pipes as you progress.

The piping lines in this graphics is enhanced for clarity.

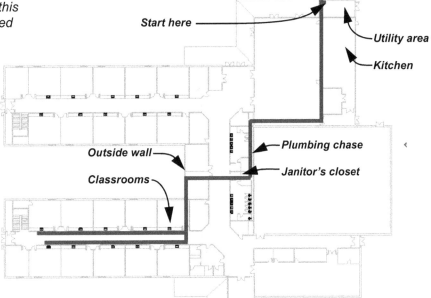

Figure 10–39

1. Open the Plumbing>Plumbing>Floor Plans>**1 - Plumbing** view.

2. Review the path of the piping shown in Figure 10–39.

3. In Properties, in the *Underlay* area, set the *Range: Base Level* to **Level 2**. This will display the piping as it is being drawn above the first level.

4. Zoom in on the utility area outside the kitchen. There is a water main connector available, as shown in Figure 10–40.

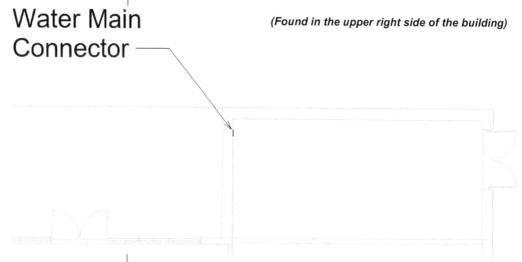

Water Main Connector

(Found in the upper right side of the building)

Figure 10–40

5. Right-click on the connector and select **Draw Pipe**.

6. In the Type Selector, select **Pipe Types: Copper**.

7. Note that the following is automatically set based on the information stored in the connector:
   - In Properties, *System Type* is set to **Domestic Cold Water.**
   - In the Options Bar, *Diameter* is set to **8"** and *Middle Elevation* to **2'-6"**.

8. Draw the pipe to the right a short distance. In the Options Bar, change the *Middle Elevation* to **12'-0"** and click **Apply**.

9. Continue drawing the pipe down the side of the kitchen, as shown in Figure 10–41.

Figure 10–41

10. Draw the pipe close to the gym and then turn left to draw towards the restrooms.

11. Refer to the image in Figure 10–42. Draw the pipe around the restrooms in the plumbing chase, and then across the hall to the exterior wall of the building. In the Options Bar, change the *Diameter* and *Middle Elevation* at the points shown in Figure 10–42.

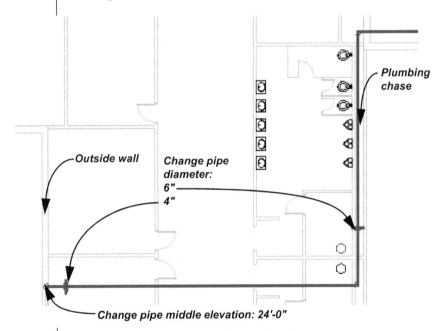

Figure 10–42

12. Continue drawing the pipe down to the hallway of the classroom wing, then down the hall to the left until it is past the last sink.

13. Press <Esc> once to stop the pipe run but stay in the command.

14. Draw a pipe run starting from the last sink on the other side of the hall until it ties into the vertical pipe, as shown in Figure 10–43.

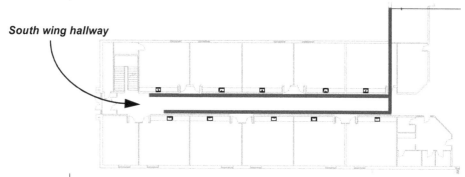

South wing hallway

Figure 10–43

15. Click **Modify**.

16. Switch to the **South-Plumbing** elevation to see that the pipe is at the second level. (More work will be done later on.)

17. Zoom in on the water heaters in the Janitor's closets in the restrooms.

18. Select one of the water heaters. In the *Modify | Mechanical Equipment* tab>Layout panel, click (Connect Into).

19. In the Select Connector dialog box, select the Cold Water connector and click **OK**.

20. Select the cold water main.

21. Repeat Steps 16 and 17 with the other water heater. The pipes are connected as shown in Figure 10–44

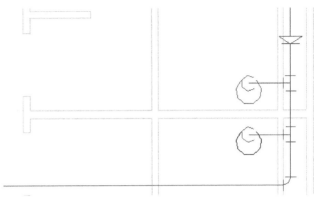

Figure 10–44

22. Save the project.

Task 3 - Add hot water lines.

1. Continue working zoomed in to the water heaters.

2. Select the water heater closest to the south wing of the building.

3. Click on the hot water connector to start the **Create Pipe** command.

4. In the Options Bar, change *Middle Elevation* to **11'-6"** and press <Enter>.

5. Continue drawing the pipe following the path of the cold water pipes, changing the *Middle Elevation* to **23'-6"** at the point shown in Figure 10–45.

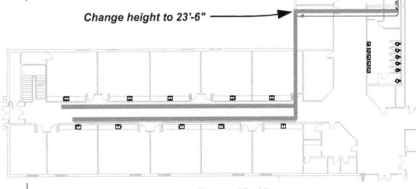

Figure 10–45

- When you draw the second horizontal pipe, ensure that the extra pipe connects to the hot water pipe and not the cold water pipe. Press <Tab> to cycle through the options. In the Status Bar, you want to see Pipe Type Copper 3/4" @23'-6".
- If you need to make changes to the pipe on the second floor, open the **2 - Plumbing** view.

6. Save the project.

Task 4 - Draw sloped pipes for drains.

1. Open the Plumbing>Plumbing>Sections (Building Section)> **Restroom Section** view. Note that the floor drains display.

2. Select the floor drain on the far right and click the Sanitary connector to start the **Create Pipe** command.

3. In the Type Selector, select **Pipe Types: Standard**. (This type acts as a placeholder until a later practice.)

4. In the *Modify | Place Pipe* tab>Sloped Piping panel, select (Slope Down) and set the *Slope Value* to **1/4" / 12"**.

5. Draw the pipe down and then over to the left, as shown in Figure 10–46.

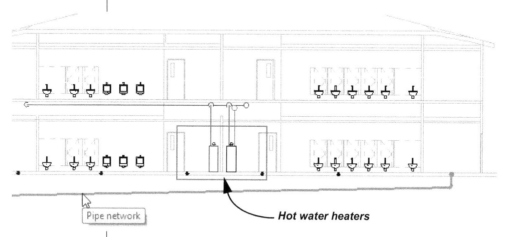

Figure 10–46

6. Click **Show Crop Region** and draw a pipe from each of the other floor drains into the sloped pipe.

7. Click **Modify** and select the two floor drains and related piping near the hot water heaters. (Hint: You may have to select a bit more to get the visual that you want to see in Figure 10–46.)

8. In the *Modify | Multi-Select* tab>View panel, click (Selection Box). A 3D view opens with the selected elements displaying as shown in Figure 10–47.

Figure 10–47

9. Select one of the lateral pipes and in the *Modify | Pipes* tab> Edit panel, click (Slope).

10. In the Slope Editor change the *Slope Value* to **1/4" / 12"** and click (Finish). The pipe is now sloped as shown in Figure 10–48. Repeat with the other pipe.

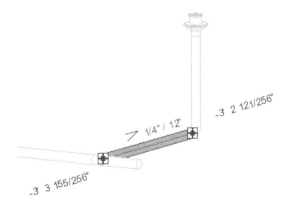

Figure 10–48

11. Open the Plumbing>3D Views>**3D Plumbing** view and review all of the piping.

12. Save and close the project.

10.3 Modifying Plumbing Pipes

Plumbing pipes can be modified using a variety of standard and specialty tools, such as converting placeholders, changing rigid pipes to flexible ones, adding insulation, and modifying the justification of pipes.

For the example shown in Figure 10–49, the fittings are incorrect for sanitary systems. In Figure 10–50, these have been changed to create the appropriate layout.

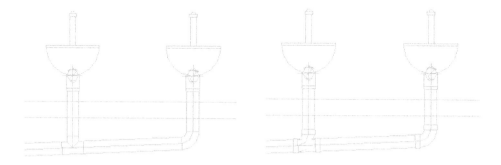

Figure 10–49   Figure 10–50

Using Standard Modify Tools

You can modify pipes using universal methods by making changes in:

- Properties
- Options Bar
- Temporary Dimensions
- Controls
- Connectors
- You can also use modify tools, such as **Move**, **Rotate**, **Split Trim/Extend**, and **Align**, to help you place the pipes at the required locations.

Pipe Fittings & Accessories

One of the challenges about working with plumbing is specifying the correct pipe fitting or accessory and verifying that it is working as expected. For example, if a fitting is facing the wrong direction, you can use ⟨⟩ (Flip) to switch it, as shown in Figure 10–51.

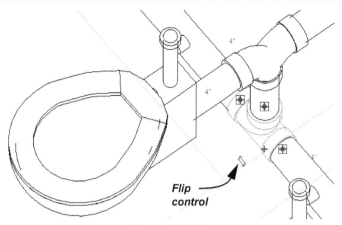

Figure 10–51

- Check various views to verify that you have correctly attached the plumbing fittings to the pipes.

- Some pipe fittings are specified in the Routing Preferences in the Type Properties of the pipe but others have to be added separately. Accessories are always added later.

- Additional fittings and accessories can be loaded from the library. Ensure you start the correct command for the element you want to load. You can load fittings when you have started the accessories command.

In the Load Family dialog box, click on Imperial Libraries from the Places panel.

- Pipe fittings can be loaded from the library in the *Pipe> Fittings* subfolder. Select the folder for the type of pipe you are using, such as **PVC**, as shown in Figure 10–52. Pipe accessories are in the *Pipe>Accessories* subfolder.

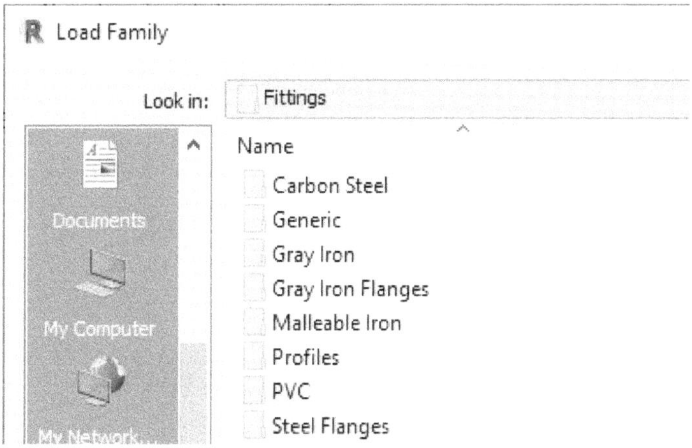

Figure 10–52

How To: Add a Pipe Fitting or Accessory

1. In the *Systems* tab>Plumbing & Piping panel, select the appropriate command:

   🔧 Pipe Fitting (PF)

   🔧 Pipe Accessory (PA)

2. In the Type Selector, select the fitting or accessory you want to use.
3. Click on the pipe where you want the fitting.
4. In some cases, the fitting might be pointing in the wrong direction, as shown in the left in Figure 10–53. Click

   ↻ (Rotate) until it points in the required direction.

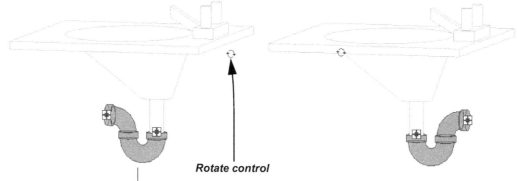

Rotate control

Figure 10–53

Capping Open Ends

You can cap the open end of a pipe by right-clicking on the end control and selecting **Cap Open End**. Alternatively, if you have more than one opening on the ends of a run, in the *Modify*

contextual tab>Edit panel, click 🔧 (Cap Open Ends). The caps are applied (as shown in Figure 10–54) and a warning displays telling you the number of caps applied.

Figure 10–54

Changing the Slope

To change the slope of a pipe, select it and modify the *Edit Slope* control, as shown in Figure 10–55. You can also click

✎ (Slope) to open the Slope Editor. The controls are available in plan or section/elevation views.

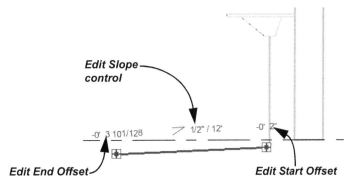

Figure 10–55

- You can change the diameter of the pipe in the Options Bar or Properties. The offset of the pipe ends can be changed using Properties or the *Edit Start/End Offset* controls.

Converting Pipes

After placing pipes, you can change the type of the entire run (including fittings). If the definition of a type has been changed, you can reapply the type to existing runs. You can also convert placeholders to standard pipes.

How To: Change the Type of Pipe Runs

1. Select the pipe run and filter out everything except the related pipe, accessories, and fittings.
2. In the *Modify | Multi-Select* tab>Edit panel, click 🔲 (Change Type).
3. In the Type Selector, select a new type of run. For the example shown in Figure 10–56, the type **Standard** was changed to **PVC - DWV**.

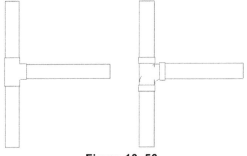

Figure 10–56

How To: Reapply a Type to Pipe Runs

1. Select a single pipe run.

    • You can select different runs, but they must all be of the same type and system. If you select runs in different systems, the software prompts you to select one system to which to reapply the type.

2. Filter out everything except pipes, fittings, and accessories.

3. In the *Modify | Multi-Select* tab>Edit panel, click 🔲 (Reapply Type).

How To: Convert Placeholders to Pipe

1. Select the pipe placeholder(s).

2. In the *Modify | contextual* tab>Edit panel, click 🔲 (Convert Placeholder).

3. The placeholders are changed into the pipe type and includes the appropriate fittings, as shown in Figure 10–57.

Pipe placeholder   **Standard pipe**

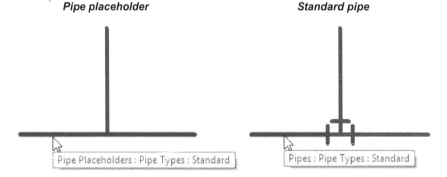

Pipe Placeholders : Pipe Types : Standard   Pipes : Pipe Types : Standard

Figure 10–57

Adding Insulation

You can add insulation to pipes which displays in plan as a thin line outside of the pipe. Accessories can also be insulated, as shown in Figure 10–58.

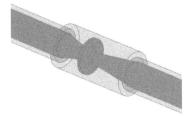

Figure 10–58

How To: Add Insulation

1. Select the pipe run that you want to insulate. You can select more than one system at a time for this command.

2. Use  (Filter) to select only the pipes, pipe fittings, and pipe accessories.

3. In the *Modify | contextual* tab>Pipe Insulation panel, click

    (Add Insulation).

4. In the Add Pipe Insulation dialog box, select a *Insulation Type* and set the *Thickness,* as shown in Figure 10–59. Click **OK**.

Add Pipe Insulation	? ✕
Insulation Type:	Fiberglass ⌄ ▦ Edit Type
Thickness:	1"
	OK Cancel

Figure 10–59

- To modify the insulation, select the insulated pipe and, in the contextual ribbon, select one of the following commands.

    - Edit Insulation (Pipe)

    - Remove Insulation (Pipe)

    When editing, change the type in the Type Selector and/or change the thickness in Properties.

Modifying the Justification

If a pipe run has different sized pipe, you can modify the justification, as shown in Figure 10–60.

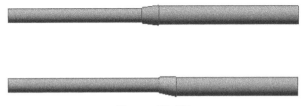

Figure 10–60

How To: Modify Justifications

1. Select the pipe run.
2. In the *Modify | Multi-Select* tab>Edit panel, click  (Justify).
3. To specify the point on the pipe that you want to justify around, in the *Justification Editor* tab>Justify panel, click

   (Control Point) to cycle between the end point references.

   - The alignment location displays as an arrow, as shown in Figure 10–61.

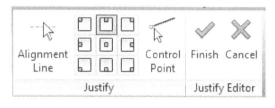

Figure 10–61

4. To indicate the required alignment, either click one of the nine alignment buttons in the Justify panel, or in a 3D view, use

   (Alignment Line) to select the required dashed line, as shown in Figure 10–62.

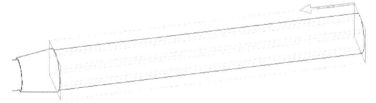

Figure 10–62

Hint: Using Thin Lines

Line thickness can negatively impact the display of elements, such as insulation or lining. To toggle lineweight on or off, in the

Quick Access Toolbar, click (Thin Lines) or type **TL**.

Practice 10c | Modify Plumbing Pipes

Practice Objectives

- Change the type of pipe runs.
- Modify locations and sizes of pipes.
- Connect fixtures to pipes.
- Modify pipe fittings.

In this practice, you will change the type of a piping run to the correct sanitary type. You will modify the size and location of pipes. You will connect two classroom sinks to the cold and hot water mains and then copy the sinks and piping along the hall. Finally, you will modify connections where the copies did not clean up automatically, as shown in Figure 10–63.

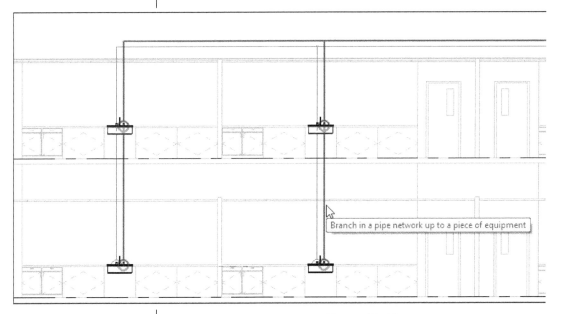

Figure 10–63

Task 1 - Change the type of pipe and verify fittings.

1. In the practice files *Plumbing* folder, open
   Modify-Piping-School-MEP.rvt.

2. Open the Plumbing>Plumbing>Sections (Building Section)>
   Restroom Section view.

3. Zoom in on one of the piping intersections and highlight the
   fitting. As shown in Figure 10–64, this is not the correct type
   of fitting for a sanitary system.

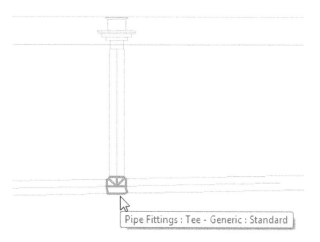

Pipe Fittings : Tee - Generic : Standard

Figure 10–64

4. Zoom out to see the full view.

5. Hover the cursor over one of the sanitary sloped pipes and
   press <Tab> until everything in the line is selected (do not
   select the system.

6. In the *Modify | Multi-Select* tab>Selection panel, click
   (Filter).

7. In the Filter dialog box, clear the check beside **Plumbing
   Fixtures** and then click **OK**. Note that:

   • The ribbon tabs have now changed because only pipes
     and pipe fittings are selected.

   • The Type Selector is grayed out. You cannot make
     changes to the pipe type here.

8. In the *Modify | Multi-Select tab*>Edit panel, click 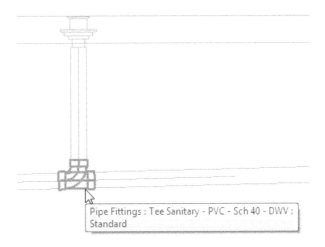 (Change Type).

9. In the Type Selector, select **Pipe Types: PVC - DWV**.

10. Zoom back in and check the fitting. It is now the correct type, as shown in Figure 10–65.

Pipe Fittings : Tee Sanitary - PVC - Sch 40 - DWV : Standard

Figure 10–65

11. Save the project.

Task 2 - Modify location and size of piping.

---

1. Open the Plumbing>Plumbing>Floor Plans>**2 - Plumbing** view.

2. Zoom in on the sinks at the beginning of the hall in the south classroom wing.

3. Change the *Detail Level* to **Fine** to display the pipe sizes clearly.

4. Select one of the hot water pipes (zoom in) and drag slightly to the left, as shown in Figure 10–66.

5. Select the cold water horizontal pipes in the classroom wing. Note that they are larger in diameter than they need to be, as shown in Figure 10–66.

6. In the Options Bar, change the *Diameter* to **1"**. New step down fittings are applied, as shown in Figure 10–67.

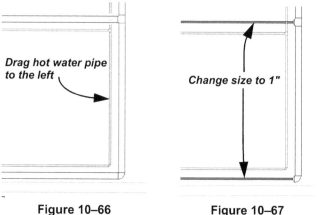

Figure 10–66   **Figure 10–67**

7. Change the *Detail Level* to **Coarse**.

8. The Piping needs to be moved out of the hall. Select one of the horizontal cold water pipes and drag it into the wall. Repeat with the other cold and hot pipes, as shown in Figure 10–68.

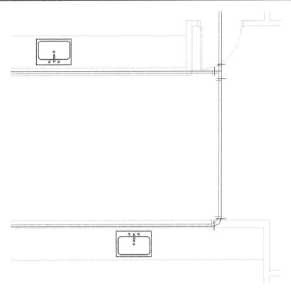

Figure 10–68

- Zoom in as needed to place the pipes inside the wall.

9. Save the project.

Task 3 - Connect the sinks into the piping.

At this point there are only four sinks in the classroom wing: two on the first floor and two directly above on the second floor. In this task, you will attach piping to the sinks. In the next task, you will copy the entire set of four sinks and related piping to the rest of the locations.

1. Return to the **1 - Plumbing** view.

2. Use the **Connect Into** command to connect the sinks to the hot and cold water pipes, as shown in Figure 10–69.

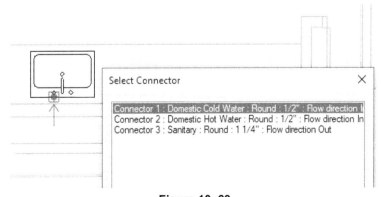

Figure 10–69

---

3. Open the Plumbing>Plumbing>Sections (Building Section)> **Classroom Section** view.

4. Select the crop region and drag the top blue grip control up until you can see the second floor.

5. Select the second floor sink and use the **Connect Into** command to connect to the vertical pipes, as shown in Figure 10–70.

   Note: You must connect the first floor before connecting the second floor. If you try to connect them in the reverse order, it will not work.

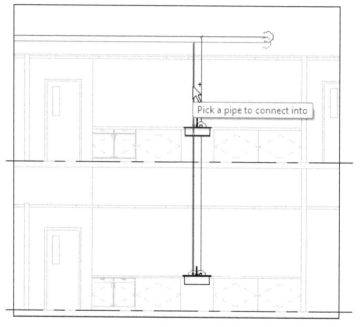

Figure 10–70

6. Save the project.

Task 4 - Copy the sinks and piping to other locations.

1. Continue working in the **Classroom Section** view.

2. Select the crop region and drag the left side control farther to the lefts so that you can see the rest of the sinks along the same side of the hall.

3. Select the sinks, vertical pipes, and associated connectors (use a window selection),

4. In the *Modify | Multi-Select* tab>Modify panel, click
    (Copy).

5. In the Options Bar, select **Constrain** and **Multiple**.

6. As the start point of the copy, select the alignment line at the middle of one of the sinks.

7. Copy the elements to the same alignment line on the next sink, as shown in Figure 10–71.

You can select other points as the start point, just ensure that they are ones that you can place directly on the sinks in the linked architectural model.

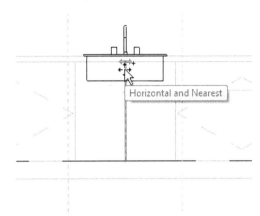

Figure 10–71

8. Continue copying the elements down the hall until all of the new sinks and piping are in place, as shown in Figure 10–72.

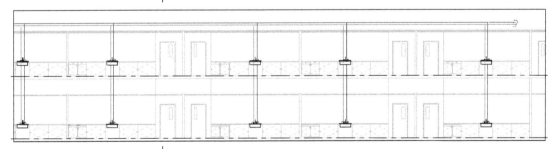

Figure 10–72

9. Click **Modify**.

10. Save the project.

Task 5 - Modify fittings.

1. Continue working in the **Classroom Section** view.

2. Hover the cursor over one of the vertical pipes coming from the original sink and press <Tab>. The full length of the connected pipe should highlight, as shown in Figure 10–73.

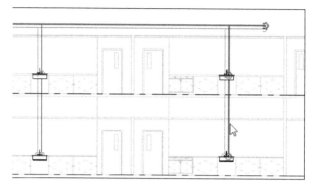

Figure 10–73

3. Hover the cursor over one of the vertical pipes from another sink and press <Tab> until the pipes highlight.

   - If the pipes connect to all of the other pipes, go to Step 8.
   - If the pipes do not connect into the other pipes, go to Step 4.

4. If you continue pressing tab you will see that the two sinks are connected in a Piping System, as shown in Figure 10–74.

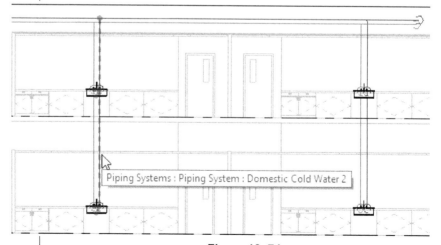

Figure 10–74

5. Zoom in on the fittings.

6. Select the Tee and Transition fittings (as shown in Figure 10–75) and delete them.

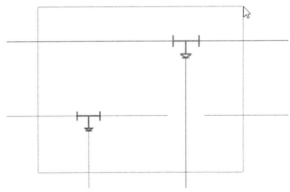

Figure 10–75

7. Select the open end of the vertical pipe and drag it up to the horizontal pipe. The pipes are connected and new fittings are applied. Continue to do this all the way down the hall, including the last set of connections.

   • Alternatively, you can use the **Trim/Extend Multiple Elements** tool. Select the cold water main as the reference and select each of the vertical cold water pipes to extend them to the main. Repeat with the hot water pipes.

8. Delete the extra pipe beyond the last tee fittings. Then, select each tee fitting and click the **Elbow** control, as shown in Figure 10–76.

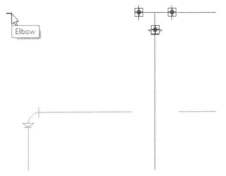

Figure 10–76

9. Zoom out and test the piping for continuity.

10. Save and close the project or continue to the optional task.

Task 6 - (Optional) Add piping to the rest of the sinks in the south wing.

1. Open the **1 - Plumbing** plan.

2. Select the Classroom Section marker and copy it to the other side.

3. Select the new section and flip it so it faces the sinks, as shown in Figure 10–77.

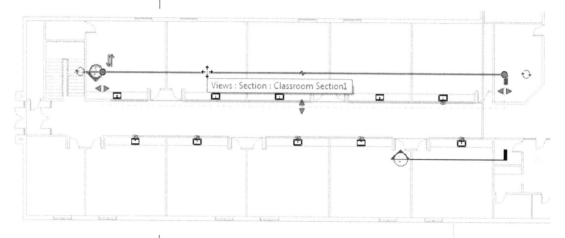

Views : Section : Classroom Section1

Figure 10–77

4. Repeat the process of connecting the sink to the mains and then copying them along the hall.

5. Save and close the project.

10.4 Adding Fire Protection Systems

Fire protection systems work in much the same way as plumbing and hydronic piping systems. You place sprinkler heads where they are required and add piping to connect them, as shown in Figure 10–78. The systems are created automatically based on the sprinkler type.

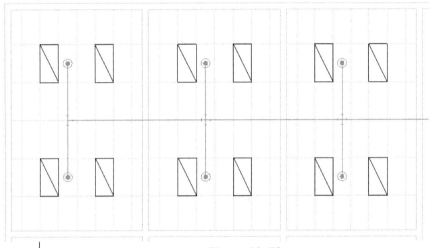

Figure 10–78

- Sprinkler types include wet and dry. All sprinklers in a system must be of the same type.

- To insert sprinklers, in the *Systems* tab>Plumbing & Piping panel, click ⬙ (Sprinkler) or type **SK**.

- You can load sprinklers from the *Fire Protection>Sprinklers* folder of the library.

- Hosted sprinklers need to be placed on ceilings. Therefore, it is best to use a reflected ceiling plan when adding them.

Practice 10d | Add Fire Protection Systems

Practice Objectives

- Add two different types of sprinklers.
- Add piping.

In this practice, you will add both wet and dry sprinklers. You will also add piping that connects the sprinklers, as shown in Figure 10–79.

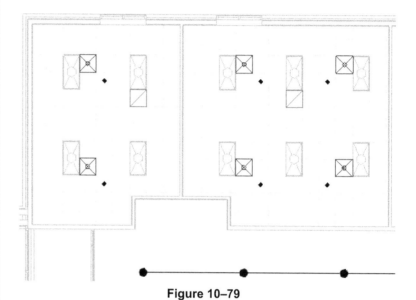

Figure 10–79

Task 1 - Add sprinklers.

1. In the practice files *Plumbing* folder, open **Fire-Protection-School-MEP.rvt**.

2. Open the Plumbing>Fire>Ceiling Plans>**1- Fire RCP** view.

3. Zoom in on the north wing.

4. In the *Systems* tab>Plumbing & Piping panel, click ☐ (Sprinkler) or type **SK**.

5. A warning displays noting that no sprinklers are loaded in the project yet. Click **Yes** to load them.

6. Navigate to the *Fire Protection>Sprinklers* folder and select both **Sprinkler - Dry - Pendent - Hosted.rfa** and **Sprinkler - Pendent.rfa**. Click **Open**.

7. In the Type Selector, select **Sprinkler - Dry - Pendent - Hosted: 1/2" Dry Pendent**.

8. In the *Modify | Place Sprinkler* tab>Placement panel, click (Place on Face).

9. Move the cursor over the hallway. A ⊘ symbol displays because there is no ceiling in this area.

10. Move the cursor into one of the classrooms where there is a ceiling. Place one of the sprinklers on a grid intersection and then move it so it is in the center of one of the ceiling tiles.

11. Copy the sprinkler to additional locations in the two classrooms, similar to that shown in Figure 10–80.

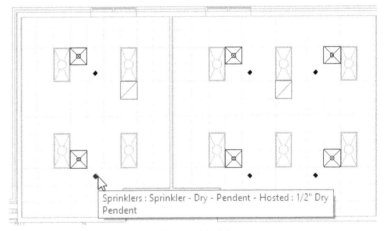

Figure 10–80

12. Start the **Sprinkler** command again. In the Type Selector, select **Sprinkler - Pendent: 1/2" Pendent**. This is a non-hosted sprinkler so you can place it in the hall where there is no ceiling.

13. In Properties, set the *Offset from Host* to **9'-0"**.

14. Place sprinklers down the hall at a spacing of **6'-0"** off the vestibule door and then **12'-0"** on center, as shown in Figure 10–81. You can place the first one and then array or copy the rest.

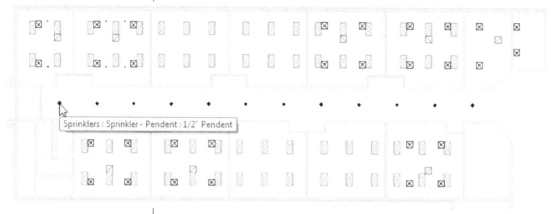

Sprinklers : Sprinkler - Pendent : 1/2" Pendent

Figure 10–81

- If you array the sprinklers, toggle off **Group and Associate** or ungroup the sprinklers after you finish.

15. Save the project.

Task 2 - Add piping for fire protection systems.

1. Select the left most sprinkler in the hallway. Right-click on the connector and select **Draw Pipe**.

2. In the *Modify | Place Pipe* tab>Sloped Piping panel, select
   (Slope: Off) to make sure this piping is not sloped.

3. In the Type Selector, select **Pipe Types: Copper.**

4. In the Options Bar, the *Diameter* and *Middle Elevation* match the location of the connector. Change the *Middle Elevation* to **10'-0"** and press <Enter>. This moves the first segment of the pipe directly up from the sprinkler.

5. Draw the pipe down the hallway and past the last sprinkler as shown in Figure 10–82.

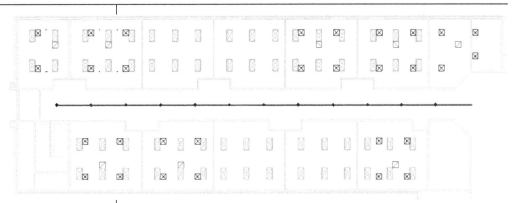

Figure 10–82

6. Open the Plumbing>Fire>Sections (Wall Section)>**Hallway Section** view.

7. Zoom in so that one of the sprinklers is displayed, as shown in Figure 10–83. Note that some of the sprinklers are not connected.

Toggle on 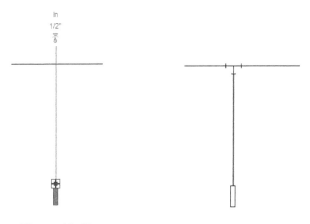 *(Thin Lines), if required, to see the pipes and fittings clearly.*

8. Select the first unconnected sprinkler. In the *Modify | Sprinklers* tab>Layout panel, click (Connect Into).

9. Select the horizontal pipe to connect into. The new connection is created with appropriate fittings, as shown in Figure 10–84.

Figure 10–83   **Figure 10–84**

10. Continue connecting the sprinklers to the horizontal pipe.

11. Save and close the project.

Chapter Review Questions

1. After tying in piping to a sloped sanitary pipe, the automatically placed fittings are facing the wrong direction, as shown in Figure 10–85. How would you fix this?

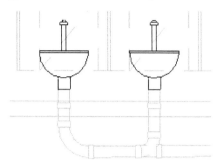

Figure 10–85

   a. Use **Rotate**.

   b. Place its opposite type.

   c. Click the **Flip** arrow.

   d. Click **AutoSlope** in the ribbon.

2. Which placement option can be used for placing a face based plumbing fixture on the wall, as shown in Figure 10–86?

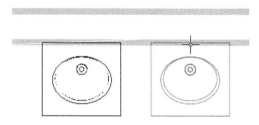

Figure 10–86

   a. **Place on Vertical Face**

   b. **Place on Face**

   c. **Place on Work Plane**

3. How do you specify the direction in which a pipe slopes as you are creating it, as shown in Figure 10–87?

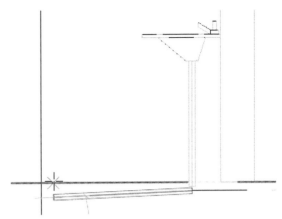

Figure 10–87

 a. Set the *Slope Value* in the Options Bar.

 b. Draw the pipe in a section view to ensure that it slopes correctly.

 c. Create it flat and slope it later.

 d. Set the *Slope Value* in the ribbon.

4. You can copy pipe, pipe fittings, and pipe accessories.

 a. True

 b. False

Command Summary

Button	Command	Location
Plumbing & Piping Tools		
	Flex Pipe	• **Ribbon:** *Systems* tab>Plumbing & Piping panel • **Shortcut:** FP
	Mechanical Equipment	• **Ribbon:** *Systems* tab>Mechanical panel • **Shortcut:** ME
	Mechanical Settings	• **Ribbon:** *Systems* tab>Mechanical panel title • **Shortcut:** MS
	Parallel Pipes	• **Ribbon:** *Systems* tab>Plumbing & Piping panel
	Pipe	• **Ribbon:** *Systems* tab>Plumbing & Piping panel • **Shortcut:** PI
	Pipe Accessory	• **Ribbon:** *Systems* tab>Plumbing & Piping panel • **Shortcut:** PA
	Pipe Fitting	• **Ribbon:** *Systems* tab>Plumbing & Piping panel • **Shortcut:** PF
	Pipe Placeholder	• **Ribbon:** *Systems* tab>Plumbing & Piping panel
	Plumbing Fixture	• **Ribbon:** *Systems* tab>Plumbing & Piping panel • **Shortcut:** PX
	Sprinkler	• **Ribbon:** *Systems* tab>Plumbing & Piping panel
Pipe Modification		
	Add Insulation	*With one or more Pipes selected:* • **Ribbon:** *Modify	Pipe* tab>Edit panel *With Pipes and Pipe Fittings selected:* • **Ribbon:** *Modify	Multi-Select* tab>Edit panel
	Automatically Connect	• **Ribbon:** *Modify	Place Pipe* tab> Placement Tools panel
	Cap Open Ends	• **Ribbon:** *(with one or more pipes selected) Modify	contextual* tab>Edit panel

	Change Type	*With one or more Pipes selected*:
		• **Ribbon:** *Modify	Pipe* tab>Edit panel
		With Pipes and Pipe Fittings selected:
		• **Ribbon:** *Modify	Multi-Select* tab>Edit panel
	Convert Placeholder	• **Ribbon:** *Modify	Pipe Placeholders* tab>Edit panel
	Edit Insulation	*With one or more Pipes selected*:
		• **Ribbon:** *Modify	Pipe* tab>Edit panel
		With Pipes and Pipe Fittings selected:
		• **Ribbon:** *Modify	Multi-Select* tab>Edit panel
	Inherit Elevation	• **Ribbon:** *Modify	Place Pipe* tab> Placement Tools panel
	Inherit Size	• **Ribbon:** *Modify	Place Pipe* tab> Placement Tools panel
	Justification (Settings)	• **Ribbon:** *Modify	Place Pipe* tab> Placement Tools panel
	Justify	• **Ribbon:** (*with one or more Pipes selected*) *Modify	Pipe* tab>Edit panel or (*with Pipes and Pipe Fittings selected*) *Modify	Multi-Select* tab>Edit panel
	Reapply Type	*With one or more Pipes selected*:
		• **Ribbon:** *Modify	Pipe* tab>Edit panel
		With Pipes and Pipe Fittings selected:
		• **Ribbon:** *Modify	Multi-Select* tab>Edit panel
	Remove Insulation	*With one or more Pipes selected*:
		• **Ribbon:** *Modify	Pipe* tab>Edit panel
		With Pipes and Pipe Fittings selected:
		• **Ribbon:** *Modify	Multi-Select* tab>Edit panel
	Slope	• **Ribbon:** (*when piping in a system is selected*) *Modify	Multi-Select* tab> Edit panel

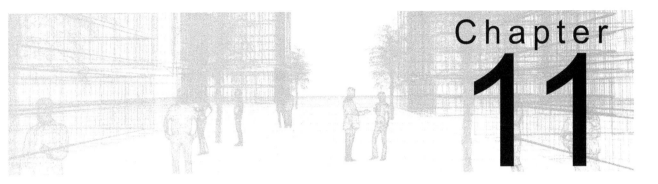

Chapter 11

Advanced Systems for HVAC and Plumbing

HVAC and plumbing networks are automatically placed in systems as you connect the elements. However, there are times when you want to create a system first, and then use automatic layouts to connect everything together with ducts or pipes. It is also important to test the systems to ensure that they are completely connected and they have the correct flow and sizes.

Learning Objectives in This Chapter

- Create duct and piping systems without first connecting the components.
- Modify duct and piping systems by adding or removing elements, renaming them, and dividing them.
- Create automatic duct and piping layouts that connect elements in systems.
- Test systems by showing disconnects, checking systems, using the System Inspector, and viewing schedules.

11.1 Creating and Modifying Systems

When you place components and connect them using ducts or pipes, systems are automatically created, as shown for several duct systems in Figure 11–1. You can also create systems before you connect components, which is especially helpful if you want to use the automatic layout tools that connect components for you.

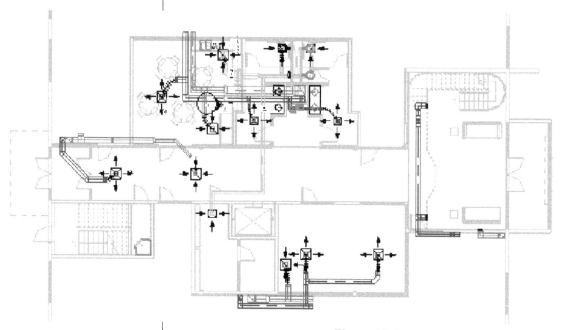

Figure 11–1

How To: Create a Duct or Piping System

1. Select at least one of the components that is to be part of the system, such as air terminals or plumbing fixtures.

   - The elements must all be the same system type.
   - Do not select the source equipment at this time.

2. In the *Modify | contextual* tab>Create Systems panel, click the related systems button, such as 🖰 (Duct) or 🖰 (Piping).

   - You can also right-click on an air terminal or plumbing fixture connector and select **Create Duct/Piping System**.

3. Proceed as follows:

If you started the command...	Then...
By right-clicking on a connector	In the Create System dialog box, the *System type* is preset.
Using a button	There are multiple options. Select the type of system you want to create from the drop-down list, as shown in Figure 11–2.

Figure 11–2

For information about creating system types and applying color information, see Section A.4 Work with System Graphics.

- If you want to continue working in the system, select **Open in the System Editor**.

4. In the *System name* field, enter a name and click **OK**.
5. If you did not open the System Editor in the previous step, in the *Modify | Duct Systems* or *Modify | Piping Systems* tab>System Tools panel, click (Edit System).
6. In the *Edit Duct System* or *Edit Piping System* tab (shown in Figure 11–3), you can:
   - Add and remove elements from the system.
   - Select the equipment connected to the system.

Figure 11–3

7. Click (Finish Editing System).

If multiple systems are applied to an element, the color returns to the neutral black.

- The elements take on the color of the system (if specified), as shown for a sanitary system in Figure 11–4.

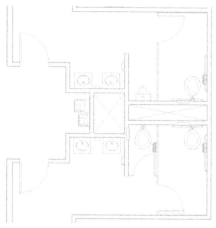

Figure 11–4

Hint: Using the System Browser While Creating Systems

It is helpful to have the System Browser open when you are creating systems because it can help you to identify which elements have been assigned to a system and which still need assignment, as shown in Figure 11–5.

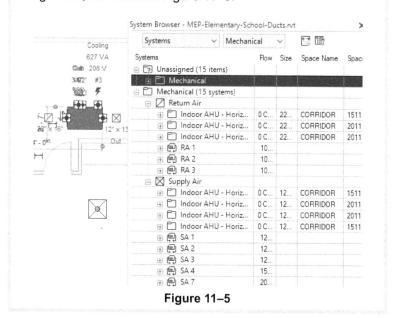

Figure 11–5

Modifying Systems

You can modify a system at any time. Hover the cursor over one of the elements and press <Tab> until you see the system border highlighted (as shown in Figure 11–6), and then select it. The tools you use to modify systems display in the related *Modify | Duct Systems* or *Modify | Piping Systems* tab.

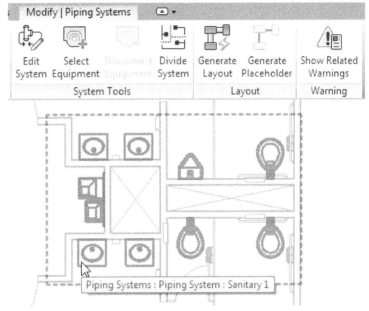

Figure 11–6

- You can change the *System Name* in Properties.

- (Edit System) takes you to the *Edit Duct System* or *Edit Piping System* tab, which enables you to add and remove elements from the system and select equipment.

- (Select Equipment) prompts you to select a mechanical equipment component in the project.

- (Generate Layout) displays various placeholder layout solutions. Specify slope and routing parameters for ductwork and piping.

Dividing Systems

Systems can be divided if they have more than one network of ducts or pipes. In the example shown in Figure 11–7, there are three networks of ducts, each of which are connected to a different air handling unit.

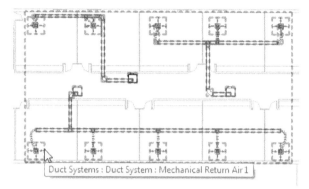

Figure 11–7

- If you need to divide a system even further, add another piece of equipment and connect some of the existing components to it.

How To: Divide Systems

1. Select the system you want to divide.
2. In the *Modify | Duct Systems* or *Modify | Piping Systems* tab>System Tools panel, click (Divide System).
3. An alert box displays indicating the number of networks that are to be converted into individual systems.
4. Click **OK**. The systems are separated as shown in Figure 11–8.

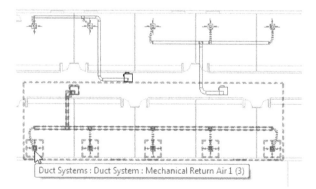

Figure 11–8

Practice 11a | Create and Modify HVAC Systems

Practice Objectives

- Review elements in the System Browser.
- Create duct systems.

In this practice, you will view unassigned elements in the System Browser and then add them to a new a supply air duct system, as shown in Figure 11–9. You will repeat the process with the return air duct system.

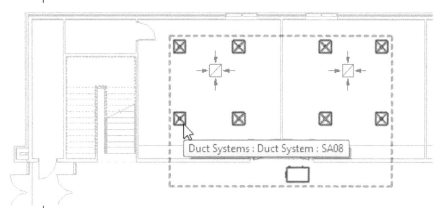

Figure 11–9

1. In the practice files *Systems* folder, open **HVAC-Systems-School-MEP.rvt**.

2. Open the System Browser by pressing <F9>.

3. In the System Browser, set the *View* to **Systems** and the discipline to **Mechanical**, as shown in Figure 11–10.

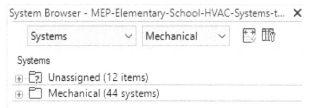

Figure 11–10

4. In the System Browser, expand **Unassigned>Mechanical> Supply Air**. Note that there are several air terminals and an AHU listed, as shown in Figure 11–11.

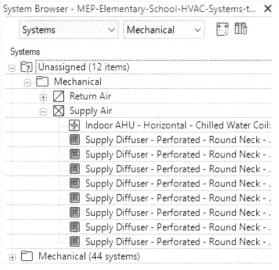

Figure 11–11

5. Select one of the unassigned Supply Diffusers. Right-click and select **Show** to automatically zoom in on the selected diffuser. Click **Close**.

6. Zoom out enough so that you can see the classroom the diffuser is in.

7. In the *Modify | Air Terminals* tab>Create Systems panel, click

    (Duct).

8. In the Create Duct System dialog box, type **01 - SA08**. Select **Open in System Editor** and then click **OK**.

9. In the *Edit Duct Systems* tab>Edit Duct System panel, click

    (Select Equipment) and select the nearby AHU unit.

10. Click 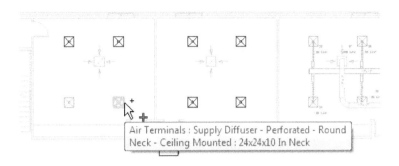 (Add to System) and select the air terminals in the other two classrooms, as shown in Figure 11–12.

Air Terminals : Supply Diffuser - Perforated - Round Neck - Ceiling Mounted : 24x24x10 In Neck

Figure 11–12

11. Click ✔ (Finish Editing System).

12. Select one of the air terminals in the new system and in the System Browser, expand the highlighted levels until the new system displays, as shown in Figure 11–13.

This would have been very hard to identify without the selection because the system listing is under the AHU unit.

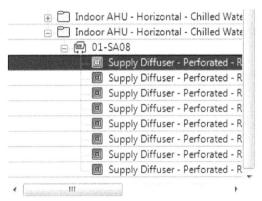

Figure 11–13

13. In the same classrooms, select the two return air terminals.

14. In the *Modify | Air Terminals* tab>Create Systems panel, click (Duct).

15. In the Create Duct System dialog box, type the *System Name* **01 - RA08**. Do not select **Open in System Editor**. Click **OK**.

16. In the *Modify| Duct Systems* tab>System Tools panel, click

    (Select Equipment) and select the same AHU unit.

17. The new system displays, as shown in Figure 11–14.

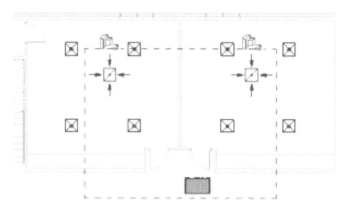

Figure 11–14

18. Save and close the project.

Practice 11b | Create and Modify Plumbing Systems

Practice Objective

- Create plumbing and fire protection systems.

In this practice, you will create sanitary and domestic cold water systems for a series of water closets. You will then investigate an existing fire protection system and create an additional one, as shown in Figure 11–15.

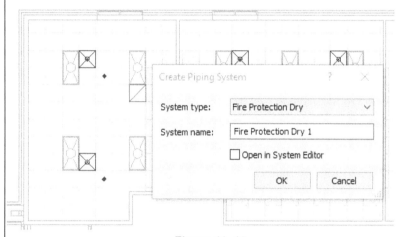

Figure 11–15

Task 1 - Create systems for the water closets.

1. In the practice files *Systems* folder, open the project **Plumbing-Systems-School-MEP.rvt**.

2. Open the Plumbing>Plumbing>Floor Plans>**1 - Plumbing Plan** view.

3. Zoom in on the Women's restroom closest to the main entrance and select one of the water closets.

4. In the *Modify | Plumbing Fixtures* tab>Create Systems panel, click (Piping).

5. In the Create Piping System dialog box, ensure that the *System Type* is set to **Sanitary**. Accept the default name and select **Open in System Editor**, as shown in Figure 11–16. Click **OK**.

Figure 11–16

6. The *Edit Piping System* tab displays with (Add to System) selected.

7. Select the other water closets in the room.

8. Click (Finish Editing Systems). The new system is created, and all of the water closets display in green to indicate that they are part of the sanitary system, as shown in Figure 11–17.

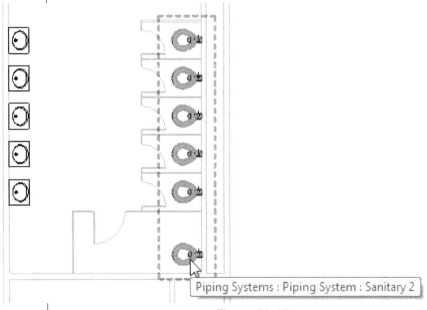

Figure 11–17

9. Select all of the water closets in the room.

10. In the *Modify | Plumbing Fixtures* tab>Create Systems panel, click 📋 (Piping). This option is available because there is another system that the water closets can be assigned to.

11. In the Create Piping System dialog box, set the *System Type* to **Domestic Cold Water**. Accept the default name, ensure that the **Open in System Editor** option is not selected, and then click **OK**.

   • You do not need to open the System Editor because you have already selected all of the elements you want in the system.
   • All of the water closets are now part of the Domestic Cold Water and Sanitary systems and display black because they are connected to more than one system.

12. Save the project.

Task 2 - Create a fire protection system.

1. Open the Plumbing>Fire>Ceiling Plans>**1 - Fire RCP** view.

2. In the north wing, select one of the sprinklers in the hall. Note that the option to create a system is not available because the system was automatically created when the piping was added.

3. Select the *Piping Systems* tab. The System Tools panel displays, as shown in Figure 11–18.

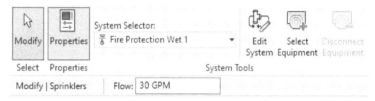

Figure 11–18

4. Click 📋 (Edit System).

5. With 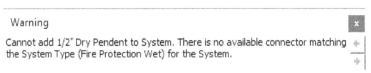 (Add to System) selected, select one of the classroom sprinklers. A warning displays (as shown in Figure 11–19) noting that you cannot add this sprinkler to the wet system because it belongs in a dry system. Close the Warning dialog box.

Warning   ❎

Cannot add 1/2" Dry Pendent to System. There is no available connector matching ← the System Type (Fire Protection Wet) for the System.   ⤵

Figure 11–19

6. Click ✖ (Cancel Editing System).

7. Select all of the classroom sprinklers in the two rooms at the end of the hall.

8. In the *Modify | Sprinklers* tab>Create Systems panel, click (Piping).

9. In the Create Piping System dialog box, leave the default system type and system name and ensure that **Open in System Editor** is not selected, then click **OK**. The software knows that this sprinkler needs to be part of a dry system, as shown in Figure 11–20.

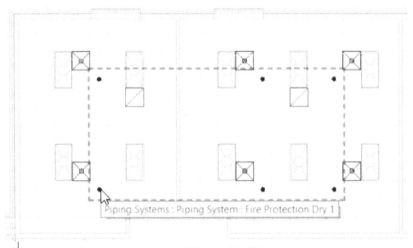

Piping Systems : Piping System : Fire Protection Dry 1

Figure 11–20

10. Save the project.

11.2 Creating Automatic Layouts

Once you have created a duct or piping system, you can automatically create a layout of ducts or pipes. These tools create various routes for the layout as shown for ducts in Figure 11–21.

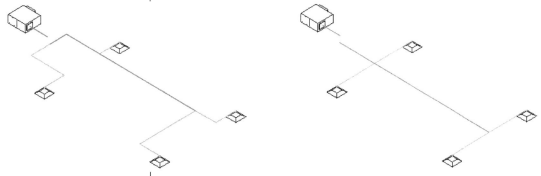

Figure 11–21

How To: Generate an Automatic Layout

1. Hover the cursor over one of the elements and press <Tab> until you see the outline of the system, as shown with a duct system in Figure 11–22. Click to select the system.

You can view the solutions in the plan or a 3D view.

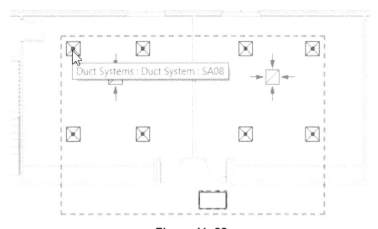

Figure 11–22

2. In the *Modify | Duct Systems* or *Modify | Pipe Systems* tab>Layout panel, click (Generate Layout).

3. In the *Generate Layout* tab>Modify Layout panel, click

   🔘 (Place Base). This is used if a system is not connected to equipment (such as the sanitary system shown in Figure 11–23) or in the early stages of setting up the layouts.

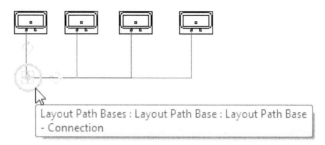

Figure 11–23

- When you place the base, 🔘 (Modify Base) automatically starts. Make changes to the base including the offset from the level and size.
- Use the rotate controls on the base to ensure that it is pointing in the correct direction
- If you no longer want the base, click 🔘 (Remove Base).

4. If you need the pipe to slope, before selecting a layout, use the Slope panel to specify the slope for piping systems.
5. In the Options Bar, click **Settings** and set the types and offsets that apply to this layout.
6. In the Options Bar, select a *Solution Type,* as shown in Figure 11–24, and click ▷ (Next Solution) or ◁ (Previous Solution) to cycle through the possible options.

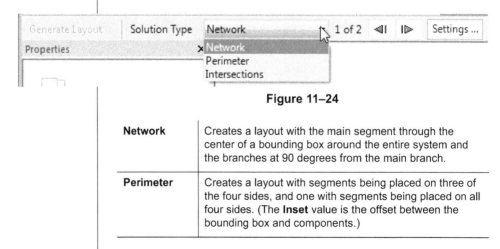

Figure 11–24

Network	Creates a layout with the main segment through the center of a bounding box around the entire system and the branches at 90 degrees from the main branch.
Perimeter	Creates a layout with segments being placed on three of the four sides, and one with segments being placed on all four sides. (The **Inset** value is the offset between the bounding box and components.)

Intersections	Creates a layout with segments extending from each connector of the components. Where they intersect perpendicularly, proposed intersection junctions are created.

- Blue-colored lines identify the main trunk, while green-colored lines identify branches off of the trunk.

- Gold-colored lines indicate a potential open connection that might cause problems when the ducts or pipes are added (as shown in Figure 11–25), or other issues related to adequate space to place the required fittings.

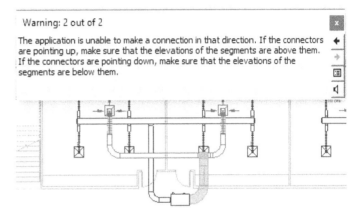

Figure 11–25

7. In the *Generate Layout* tab>Generate Layout panel, click

   ✔ (Finish Layout) when you have a solution that looks best.

- From the Options Bar, click on **Settings...**. The Conversion Settings dialog box (shown for ducts in Figure 11–26) displays and enables you to set the type of duct or pipe and the offset from the level where you are working.

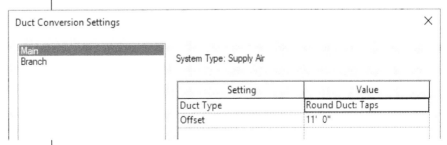

Figure 11–26

- These settings are specific to this system only. Global settings are defined in Mechanical Settings.

- For duct branches, you can also specify a *Flex Duct Type* and *Maximum Flex Duct Length* if you want air terminals automatically connected that way.

How To: Customize the Layout

1. Using 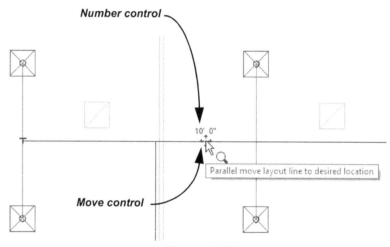 (Solutions), select a layout design similar to what you want to use.
2. In the *Generate Layout* tab>Modify Layout panel, click (Edit Layout).
3. Select one of the layout lines. You can use the move control to change the location of the line, as shown in Figure 11–27. You can also change the height of the offset by clicking on the number control.

Number control

10' 0"

Parallel move layout line to desired location

Move control

Figure 11–27

4. Click (Solutions) to finish customizing the layout. In the Options Bar, the *Solution Type* list now has **Custom** as an additional option to the standard three solution types.
   - The software only permits one custom option at a time.
5. In the *Generate Layout* tab>Generate Layout panel, click (Finish Layout).

- When the automatic/custom layout is completed, it is important to check the entire system to ensure that the layout is correct. Ensure that you check slopes and fitting directions.

Practice 11c | Create Automatic HVAC Layouts

Practice Objectives

- Create ducts using the Generate Layout tool with both standard and custom layouts.
- Modify ductwork after it has been placed.

In this practice, you will create supply ducts using the **Generate Layout** tool and modify the ductwork in the layout after it has been placed. You will also create a custom layout for the return ducts and modify the ductwork. The final systems are shown in Figure 11–28.

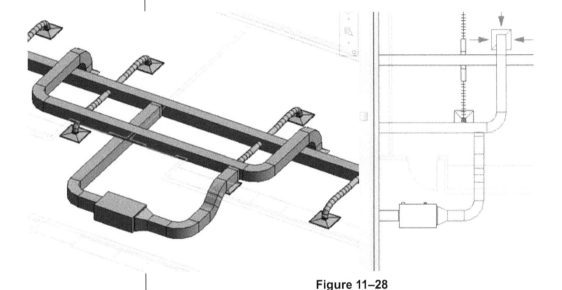

Figure 11–28

Task 1 - Create an automatic ductwork layout.

1. In the practice files *Systems* folder, open the project **HVAC-Layouts-School-MEP.rvt.**

2. Close any other open projects.

3. Open Mechanical>HVAC>Floor Plans> 01 Mechanical Plan> **01 Mechanical - Area B**. Close any other open views.

4. Open the Mechanical>HVAC>3D Views>**01 Mechanical - Area B 3D** view.

5. Type **WT** (Window Tile).

6. In the plan, hover the cursor over one of the supply air terminals and press <Tab> until the system displays. Click to select it, as shown in Figure 11–29.

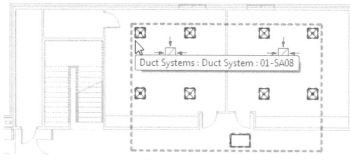

Figure 11–29

7. In the *Modify | Duct Systems* tab>Layout panel, click 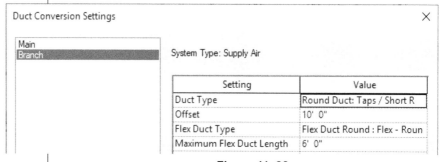 (Generate Layout).

8. In the *Generate Layout* tab>Modify Layout panel, click (Solutions).

9. In the Options Bar, click **Settings...**.

10. In the Duct Conversion Settings dialog box, select **Main** and set the following parameters:

   • *Duct Type:* **Rectangular Duct: Radius Elbows/Taps**

   • *Offset*: **10'-0"**

11. Select **Branch** and set the following parameters, as shown in Figure 11–30:

   • *Duct Type*: **Round Duct: Taps / Short Radius**

   • *Offset*: **10'-0"**

   • *Flex Duct*: **Flex Duct Round: Flex - Round**

   • *Maximum Flex Duct Length*: **6'-0"**

Duct Conversion Settings   ✕

| Main |
| Branch |

System Type: Supply Air

Setting	Value
Duct Type	Round Duct: Taps / Short R
Offset	10' 0"
Flex Duct Type	Flex Duct Round : Flex - Roun
Maximum Flex Duct Length	6' 0"

Figure 11–30

12. Click **OK**.

13. In the Options Bar, use the arrow buttons and Solution Types to try out several different solutions. End with the solution

    Network 1 of 6, shown in Figure 11–31 and click ✓ (Finish Layout).

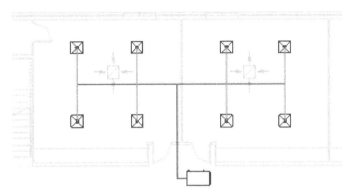

Figure 11–31

14. A warning displays prompting you that there is an open connection, and the horizontal duct is highlighted, as shown in Figure 11–32. You can see in the 3D view that it is missing an endcap.

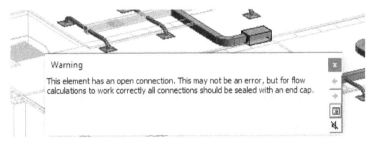

Figure 11–32

15. Click in the 3D view to activate it and select the main horizontal duct.

16. In the *Modify | Ducts* tab>Edit panel, click 𝍌 (Cap Open Ends).

17. Save the project.

Task 2 - Create a custom ductwork layout.

1. Continue working with the same two views open.

2. In the plan view, select the Return Air System.

3. In the *Duct Systems* tab>Layout panel, click ⬚ (Generate Layout).

4. In the *Generate Layout* tab>Modify Layout panel, click ⬚ (Solutions).

5. View the various solutions. Most of them have some problem with the layout. When the gold lines display it is a warning that the layout could fail in those areas.

6. In the Options Bar, click **Settings...**.

7. In the Duct Conversion Settings dialog box, select **Main** and change the options as follows:

   - *Duct Type*: **Rectangular Duct: Radius Elbow and Taps**
   - *Offset*: **11'-6"**

8. Select **Branch** and change the options as follows:

   - *Duct Type*: **Rectangular Duct: Radius Elbow and Taps**
   - *Offset*: **11'-6"**
   - *Flex Duct Type*: **None**

9. Click **OK**. This still did not correct all of the problems, but it solved some by changing the heights of the ducts.

10. Cycle through the solutions to review the options.

11. Stay on Network 3 of 5. In the *Generate Layout* tab>Modify Layout panel, click ⬚ (Edit Layout).

12. In the plan view, select the vertical line shown in Figure 11–33 and move it slightly to the left.

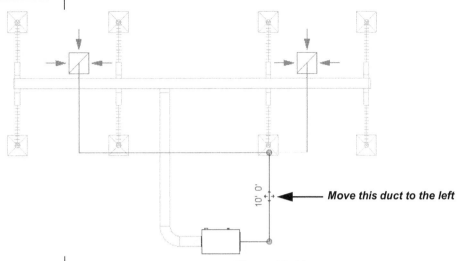

Figure 11–33

13. Click ✎ (Finish Layout). There are still some problems that need to be corrected, as shown in Figure 11–34.

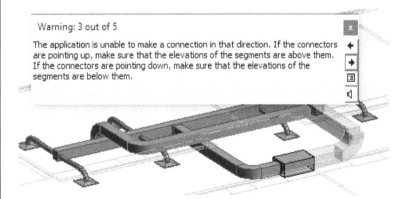

Figure 11–34

14. In the Warning dialog box, click through the various warnings to see the other issues. The corresponding duct is also highlighted. You can see that they are all related to the ducts coming from the air handling unit.

- If you selected a different layout there will be different issues but the principles of fixing them are still the same.

15. Close the Warning dialog box.

16. Save the project.

Task 3 - Correct issues with the layout.

1. Select the ducts and related duct fittings coming out of the air handling unit and delete them up to the main horizontal duct, as shown in Figure 11–35.

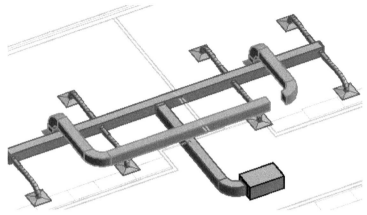

Figure 11–35

2. Drag the horizontal duct over to the duct going to the upper air terminal so that it connects as shown in Figure 11–36.

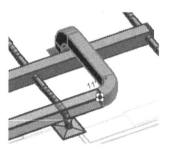

Figure 11–36

3. Select the Mechanical Equipment unit, right-click on the Return Air control and select **Draw Duct**.

4. In the Type Selector, verify that the type is set to **Rectangular Duct: Radius Elbows/Taps**.

5. In the Options Bar, set the *Width* and *Height* to **12"** and the *Middle Elevation* to **10'-0"**, as shown in Figure 11–37.

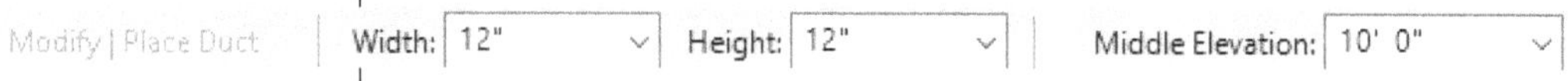

Modify | Place Duct   Width: 12"   Height: 12"   Middle Elevation: 10' 0"

Figure 11–37

6. Draw the duct out **3'-6"**.

7. In the Options Bar, set *Middle Elevation* to **11'-6"** and continue drawing the duct until it connects with the main horizontal duct. The appropriate fittings are added to resize the duct coming from the AHU and changing the height going to the other duct, as shown in Figure 11–38.

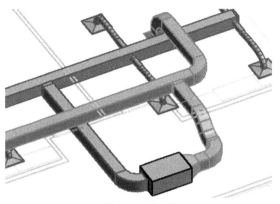

Figure 11–38

8. Save and close the project.

Practice 11d | Create Automatic Plumbing Layouts

Practice Objectives

- Create pipes using the Generate Layout tool with both standard and custom layouts.
- Modify pipes after they have been placed.

In this practice, you will create a piping layout for a sprinkler system. You will then create a sanitary system and use the layout tools, including **Place Base**, to add sloped piping, as shown in Figure 11–39.

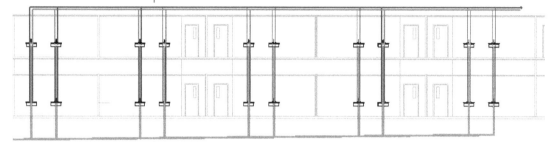

Figure 11–39

Task 1 - Create a piping layout for a sprinkler system.

1. In the practice files *Systems* folder, open the project **Plumbing-Layouts-School-MEP.rvt**.

2. Open the Plumbing>Fire>Ceiling Plans>**1 - Fire RCP** view and close any other open views.

3. Open the Plumbing>Fire>3D Views>**1- Fire 3D** view.

4. Type **WT** to tile the two windows so that both the 3D view and the north wing of the RCP display.

5. Hover the cursor over one of the sprinklers in the classroom and press <Tab> until the piping systems displays, as shown in Figure 11–40. Click to select the system.

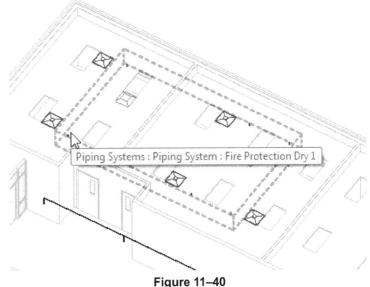

Piping Systems : Piping System : Fire Protection Dry 1

Figure 11–40

6. In the *Modify | Piping Systems* tab>Layout panel, click (Generate Layout).

7. In the *Generate Layout* tab>Modify Layout panel, click (Solutions).

8. In the Slope panel, set the *Slope Value* to **0" / 12"**.

9. In the Options Bar, click **Settings...**.

10. In the Pipe Conversion Settings dialog box, set the following parameters and then click **OK**.

Main:

- *Pipe Type:* **Pipe Types: Copper**
- *Offset:* **9'-6"**

Branch:

- *Pipe Type:* **Pipe Types: Copper**
- *Offset:* **9'-0"**

11. In the Options Bar, work through the *Solution Types* and try out several different solutions. Many of them have issues, as shown by the gold lines in Figure 11–41.

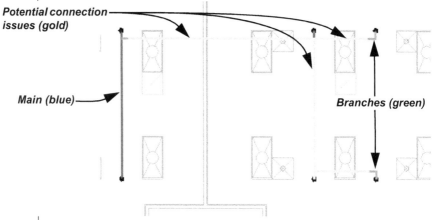

Figure 11–41

12. In this case, the *Offset* specified in the settings does not work. In the Options Bar, click **Settings...**.

13. Change the branch so that it is *Offset* to **9'-6"** and click **OK**.

14. This time the options work. Select one that you like and click

 (Finish Layout).

15. Save the project.

Task 2 - Create a piping layout for a sanitary system.

1. Open the Plumbing>Plumbing>3D views>**3D Plumbing** view and maximize it.

2. Close any other open views.

3. Hover the cursor over one of the sinks in the classroom wing and press <Tab> to highlight the various elements. Note that there are piping networks and domestic hot and cold water systems, but there is no sanitary system.

4. Create a sanitary system linking all of the sinks, as shown in Figure 11–42. (**Hint:** Select one, right-click, and select **Select All Instances>Visible in View**.)

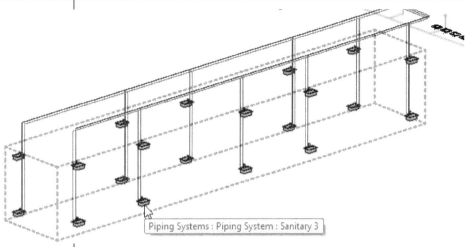

Piping Systems : Piping System : Sanitary 3

Figure 11–42

5. Open the Plumbing>Plumbing>Sections (Building Section)> **Classroom Section Sanitary** view.

6. Type **WT** to tile the two views and arrange them so that the sinks display in each view.

7. Select the sanitary system.

8. In the *Modify | Piping Systems* tab>Layout panel, click (Generate Layout).

9. In the *Generate Layout* tab>Modify Layout panel, click (Solutions).

10. In the Options Bar, click **Settings...**.

11. In the Pipe Conversion Settings dialog box, set the following parameters and click **OK**.

Main:

• *Pipe Type:* **Pipe Types: PVC - DWV**
• *Offset:* (negative) **-4'-0"**

Branch:

• *Pipe Type:* **Pipe Types: PVC - DWV**
• *Offset:* (negative) **-4'-0"**

12. In the Generate Layout tab, set the *Slope Value* to **1/8" / 12"**.

13. Verify that the 3D Plumbing view is active, then in the Modify Layout panel, click 📷 (Place Base).

14. Select a point outside and to the left of the building, as shown in Figure 11–43.

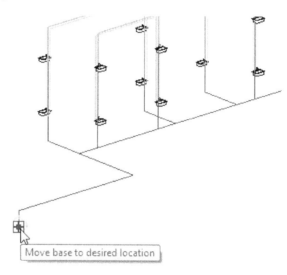

Figure 11–43

15. The **Modify Base** command is automatically selected. In the Options Bar, change the *Offset* to (negative) **-8'-0"** and the *Diameter* to **1"**.

   • If the Base pipe is too large it causes problems with the connections to the sinks. You can change the main trunk pipe sizes after the layout is finished.

16. In the Modify Layout panel, click 🔧 (Solutions).

17. In the Options Bar, work through the *Solution Types* and try out several different solutions. Select the one you want.

18. Click ✔ (Finish Layout).

19. If warnings display, read them and zoom in to see what is wrong. Then, undo until you are back in the layout and try the process again.

20. Save and close the project.

11.3 Testing Systems

As you start working with connectors and systems, it is important to check how the system is working. For a quick way to test the continuity of a system, hover the cursor over one of the linear connections and press <Tab> until the system highlights. For the example shown in Figure 11–44, one of the ducts is not attached to the fitting and therefore is not highlighted.

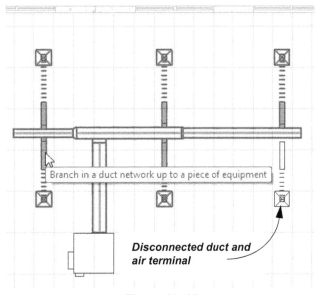

Figure 11–44

If there are issues with a selected system, the Warning panel displays in the related *Modify* toolbar, as shown in Figure 11–45.

Click 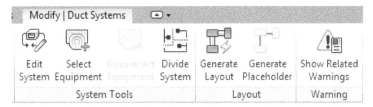 (Show Related Warnings) to open the dialog box and review the issues.

Figure 11–45

Often, these warnings are corrected as you continue working in a system and complete the full connection. However, some errors need to be corrected before the system works as required.

Hint: Displaying Only the MEP Analysis Panels

If you are using a copy of Autodesk Revit that has not been optimized for MEP, it is helpful to toggle off the Structural Analysis tools so that you can see the full MEP analysis panels. In the *File* tab, click **Options**. In the Options dialog box, in the User Interface panel, clear the **Structure** check mark and any other tabs options that you may not be using such as Massing and Site, as shown in Figure 11–46.

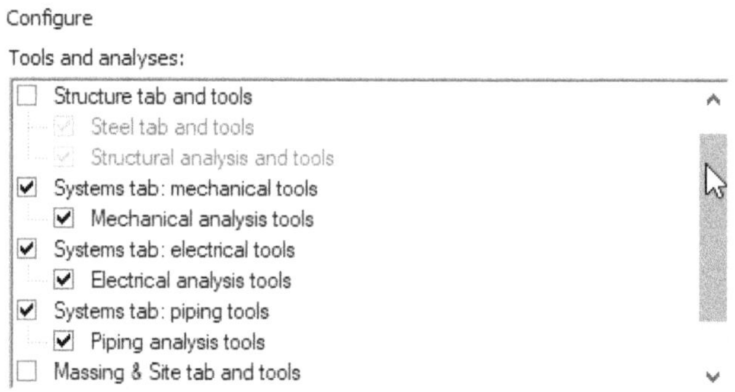

Configure

Tools and analyses:

☐ Structure tab and tools
   ☑ Steel tab and tools
   ☑ Structural analysis and tools
☑ Systems tab: mechanical tools
   ☑ Mechanical analysis tools
☑ Systems tab: electrical tools
   ☑ Electrical analysis tools
☑ Systems tab: piping tools
   ☑ Piping analysis tools
☐ Massing & Site tab and tools

Figure 11–46

Showing Disconnects

Duct and piping systems can be analyzed and reviewed for issues. This includes searching for disconnects and checking the various systems. For the example shown in Figure 11–47, there are open connectors at three different places. Once the tee fitting is changed to an elbow fitting, and the flex duct connects the end of the existing duct to the air terminal, the warnings are removed.

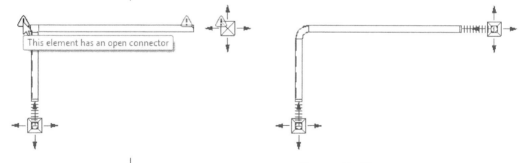

This element has an open connector

Figure 11–47

How To: Show Disconnects

1. In the *Analyze* tab>Check Systems panel, click 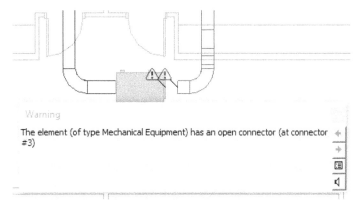 (Show Disconnects).
2. In the Show Disconnects Options dialog box, select the types of systems you want to display and click **OK**.

3. The disconnects displays ⚠ (Warning).
    *   The disconnects continue to display until you either correct the situation or run **Show Disconnects** again and clear all of the selections.

4. Hover the cursor over the warning icon to display a tooltip with the warning, or click on the icon to open the Warning dialog box, as shown in Figure 11–48.

Figure 11–48

How To: Use the Check Systems Tools

1. In the *Analyze* tab>Check Systems panel, click 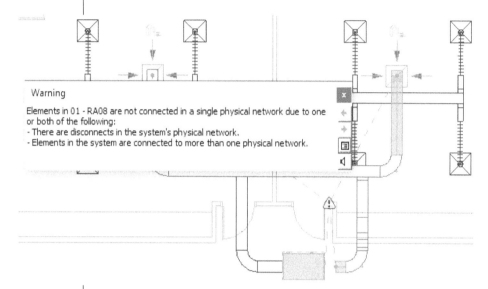 (Check Duct Systems) or (Check Pipe Systems) to toggle them on.

2. The (Warning) icon displays where there are problems. Click one of the icons to open the Warning alert box, as shown in Figure 11–49.

Warning

Elements in 01 - RA08 are not connected in a single physical network due to one or both of the following:
- There are disconnects in the system's physical network.
- Elements in the system are connected to more than one physical network.

Figure 11–49

- For icons that have more than one warning, in the Warning alert box, click (Next Warning) and (Previous Warning) to search through the list.

3. Click (Expand Warning Dialog) to open the dialog box, as shown in Figure 11–50. You can expand each node in the box and select elements to display or delete.

*If there are a lot of warnings to review, click **Export...** and save the HTML report to review separately.*

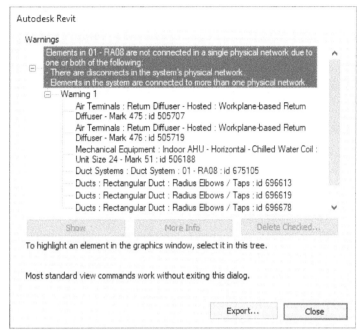

Figure 11–50

System Inspector

The System Inspector provides information such as flow rate, static pressure, and pressure loss at every point in a system, as shown in Figure 11–51 for a domestic cold water system. The System Inspector also enables you to make changes to components of a system as you complete an inspection.

The System Inspector works with all duct and piping systems except fire suppression systems.

For information about pressure loss reporting, see Section A.5 Pressure Loss Reports.

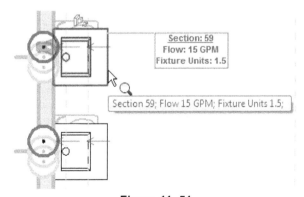

Figure 11–51

- The System Inspector does not display in the ribbon if an open system is selected.

- The pressure loss method settings for duct and pipe fittings and accessories can be set up in Properties.

How To: Use the System Inspector

1. Select any part of a system (e.g., air terminals, ductwork, piping, mechanical equipment, or plumbing fixtures, etc.).
2. In the contextual *Modify* tab>Analysis panel, click

   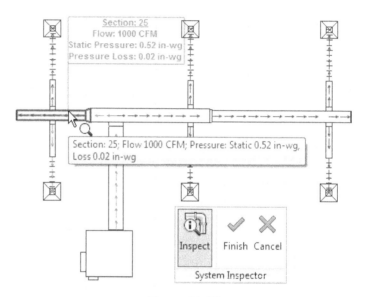 (System Inspector). The floating System Inspector panel displays as shown in Figure 11–52.

3. Click (Inspect). The air flow displays in the system, as shown in Figure 11–52. Move the cursor over a section of system to display information, such as the Flow, Static Pressure, and Pressure Loss for duct systems.

*In the System Browser, right-click on the top level of a system and select **System Inspector**.*

The red path displays the greatest static pressure.

Section: 25
Flow: 1000 CFM
Static Pressure: 0.52 in-wg
Pressure Loss: 0.02 in-wg

Section: 25; Flow 1000 CFM; Pressure: Static 0.52 in-wg, Loss 0.02 in-wg

Inspect Finish Cancel

System Inspector

Figure 11–52

4. If you need to change a component of the system, remain in the System Inspector:
   1. In the Select panel, click (Modify).
   2. Select the component.
   3. Make changes to the component on the screen using the controls or in the Properties.

5. Click (Inspect) to return to the flow pattern.

6. Click (Finish).

- If you select a piece of mechanical equipment that is attached to more than one duct-based or pipe-based system, the Select a System dialog box displays, as shown in Figure 11–53. Select the system you want to inspect and click **OK**.

Figure 11–53

- The System Inspector displays in a floating panel by default. You can move it or make it a part of the ribbon by clicking **Return Panels to Ribbon**, as shown in Figure 11–54.

Figure 11–54

Duct and Pipe Color Fill Legends

An additional way to view information about ducts and pipes is to create a color fill legend, as shown in Figure 11–55 for friction in ducts.

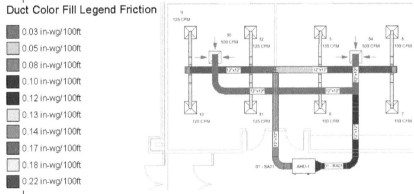

Figure 11–55

- These color fill schemes and legends are similar to those created for spaces and zones.

How To: Create a Color Fill Legend

1. In the *Annotate* tab>Color Fill Panel, click 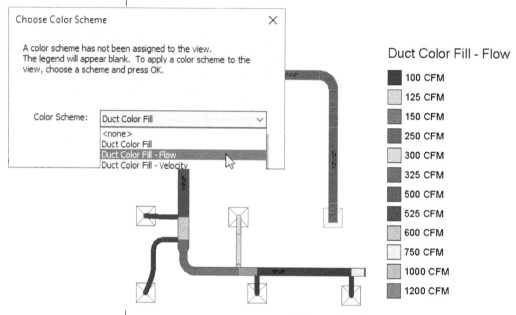 (Duct Legend) or (Pipe Legend) and place the legend.
2. If a color scheme is not assigned to the view, the Choose Color Scheme dialog box displays. Choose a scheme from the list. When you click **OK**, the view is filled to match the legend, as shown in Figure 11–56.

Choose Color Scheme   ✕

A color scheme has not been assigned to the view. The legend will appear blank. To apply a color scheme to the view, choose a scheme and press OK.

Color Scheme: Duct Color Fill ⌄

    <none>
    Duct Color Fill
    Duct Color Fill - Flow
    Duct Color Fill - Velocity

Duct Color Fill - Flow

- 100 CFM
- 125 CFM
- 150 CFM
- 250 CFM
- 300 CFM
- 325 CFM
- 500 CFM
- 525 CFM
- 600 CFM
- 750 CFM
- 1000 CFM
- 1200 CFM

Figure 11–56

3. To make changes to the color fill scheme, select the legend and in the *Modify | Duct/Pipe Color Fill Legends* tab>Scheme panel, click (Edit Scheme).
4. The Edit Color Scheme dialog box opens where you select the color scheme you want to use, as shown in Figure 11–57.

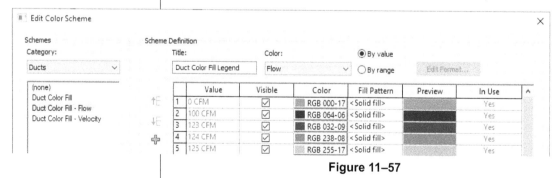

Figure 11–57

- You can also reach the Edit Color Scheme dialog box through the view properties. With nothing selected, in Properties beside *System Color Schemes*, click **Edit...**. In the Color Schemes dialog box, click the color scheme button for either **Pipes** or **Ducts**. The Edit Color Scheme dialog box displays.

- To create new color schemes or modify existing ones, see *Section A.2 Defining Color Schemes*.

Analyzing Systems with Schedule

No schedules are included with the default MEP templates (**Electrical-Default.rte**, **Mechanical-Default.rte**, **Plumbing-Default.rte**, and **Systems-Default.rte**) provided by the Autodesk® Revit® software, but many firms create typical ones that can be used in most projects. These schedules are helpful for analyzing the systems (such as displaying the flow rate, keeping track of the systems, etc.), as shown in Figure 11–58.

- The **Construction-Default.rte** template file includes some useful MEP quantities schedules.

PLUMBING SYSTEM SCHEDULE			
System Type	System Name	Comments	Flow
Domestic Cold Water	01 - DCW1	North Wing Classroom sinks	42 GPM
Domestic Cold Water	01 - DCW2	South Wing Classroom sinks	42 GPM
Domestic Cold Water	01 - DCW3	Men's Restroom	51 GPM
Domestic Cold Water	02 - DCW1	North Wing Classroom sinks	42 GPM
Domestic Cold Water	02 - DCW2	South Wing Classroom sinks	42 GPM
Domestic Cold Water	02 - DCW3	Men's Restroom	51 GPM
Domestic Cold Water	02 - DCW4	Women's Restroom	57 GPM
Domestic Hot Water	01 - DHW1	North Wing Classroom sinks	23 GPM
Domestic Hot Water	01 - DHW2	South Wing Classroom sinks	23 GPM
Domestic Hot Water	01 - DHW3	Men's Restroom	12 GPM
Domestic Hot Water	02 - DHW1	North Wing Classroom sinks	23 GPM
Domestic Hot Water	02 - DHW2	South Wing Classroom sinks	23 GPM
Domestic Hot Water	02 - DHW3	Men's Restroom	12 GPM
Domestic Hot Water	02 - DHW4	Women's Restroom	12 GPM
Sanitary	01 - SAN1	North Wing Classroom sinks	Not Computed
Sanitary	01 - SAN2	South Wing Classroom sinks	Not Computed
Sanitary	01 - SAN3	Men's Restroom	Not Computed
Sanitary	02 - SAN1	North Wing Classroom sinks	Not Computed
Sanitary	02 - SAN2	South Wing Classroom sinks	Not Computed
Sanitary	02 - SAN3	Men's Restroom	Not Computed
Sanitary	02 - SAN4	Women's Restroom	Not Computed

Figure 11–58

Some schedules even have highlighting to indicate where something needs to be changed.

Practice 11e | Test HVAC Systems

Practice Objectives

- Investigate warnings and use Check Duct Systems.
- Review disconnects.
- Add a duct color fill legend.
- Review a schedule setup to show the airflow in spaces.
- Correct issues discovered by the testing tools

In this practice, you will review warnings, run **Check Duct Systems**, and **Show Disconnects**. You will then correct any problems and run the **System Inspector**. You will add a color fill legend to test the velocity and make corrections as shown in Figure 11–59. You will also review a schedule that displays the airflow of rooms and add air terminals to spaces where the airflow is negative.

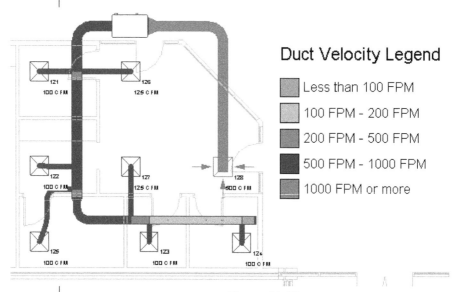

Figure 11–59

Task 1 - Review warnings and check duct systems.

1. In the practice files *Systems* folder, open **HVAC-Analyze-School-MEP.rvt**.

2. Open the Mechanical>HVAC>Floor Plans>**01 Mechanical Plan- Area C (SOUTH)** view. This displays the office area near the front entrance of the building.

3. Hover over a supply duct and press <Tab> until you see the duct system highlight, as shown in Figure 11–60. Click to select it.

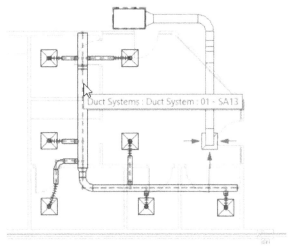

Figure 11–60

4. In the *Modify | Duct Systems* tab>Warning panel, click (Show Related Warnings).

5. Review the contents of the dialog box, as shown in Figure 11–61.

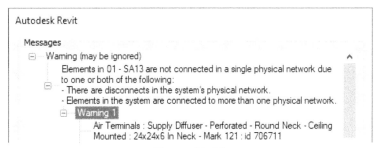

Figure 11–61

6. Close the dialog box.

7. In the *Analyze* tab>Check Systems panel, click 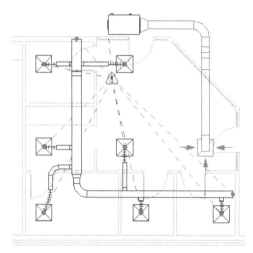 (Check Duct Systems). The duct system is not working, as shown in Figure 11–62.

Figure 11–62

8. Note that there is a duct missing, which should be coming out of the air handling unit. Use the **Draw Duct** tool and set the type to **Rectangular Duct: Radius Elbows / Taps**. Then, draw a horizontal duct coming from the AHU (as shown in Figure 11–63).

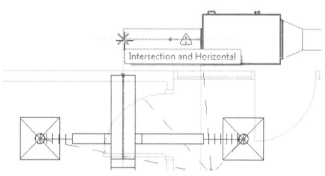

Intersection and Horizontal

Figure 11–63

9. Use (Trim/Extend to Corner) to clean up the intersection and automatically apply the required elbow fitting.

10. Now that the duct system is working as expected, toggle off **Check Duct Systems**.

11. Save the project.

Task 2 - Check and correct duct disconnects.

1. In the *Analyze* tab>Check Systems panel, click 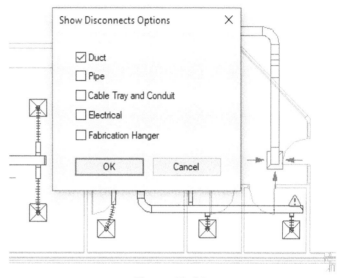 (Show Disconnects).

2. In the Show Disconnects Options dialog box, select **Duct** (as shown in Figure 11–64) and click **OK**. While the system is now connected correctly, there is still a disconnect at the end of the system, as shown in Figure 11–64.

Figure 11–64

3. Select the duct, right-click on the open connector, and select **Cap Open End**, as shown in Figure 11–65. This solves the problem on this end of the system.

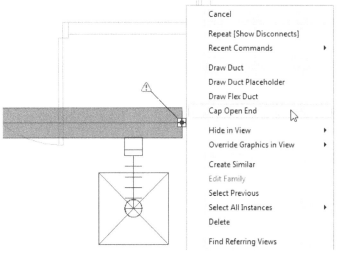

Figure 11–65

4. Hover over a duct and press <Tab> until you see the duct system highlight and then click to select it.

5. The *Modify | Duct Systems* tab>Analysis panel, click (System Inspector).

6. In the System Inspector panel, click (Inspect).

7. Hover the cursor over parts of the system to view the information, as shown in Figure 11–66.

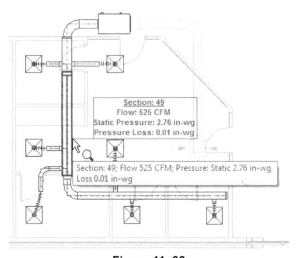

Figure 11–66

8. When you are finished inspecting the system, click

   ✓ (Finish).

9. Toggle off the **Show Disconnects** options for ducts.

10. Save the project.

Task 3 - Add a duct color fill scheme and legend.

---

1. In the *Analyze* tab>Color Fill panel, click 🖼 (Duct Legend).

2. Place the legend near the office area.

3. In the Choose Color Scheme dialog box, select **Duct Color Fill - Velocity** and click **OK**. The legend and color scheme display as shown in Figure 11–67.

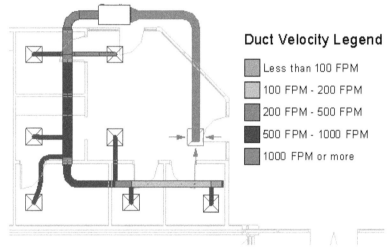

Figure 11–67

4. You can see from the colors that some of the velocity is set too high.

5. Open the Visibility Graphics dialog box and in the *Annotation Categories* tab, toggle on **Air Terminal Tags**. Click **OK**.

6. The tags display the Flow associated with the diffusers. Select the tag of the diffuser with too large of a flow, as shown in Figure 11–68, and change it to **125 CFM**.

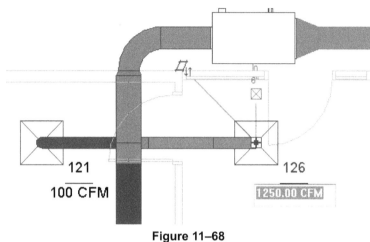

Figure 11–68

7. The colors change to the expected amounts, as shown in Figure 11–69.

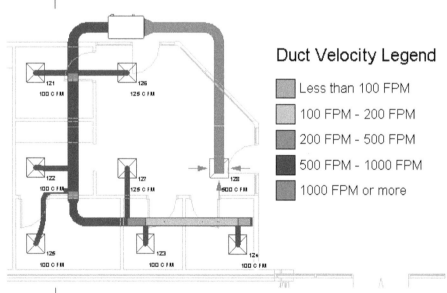

Figure 11–69

8. Save the project.

Task 4 - Work with schedules.

Note that the changes you made to the Area C (SOUTH) plan are also reflected in the main plan as it is a dependent view.

1. Open the **01 Mechanical Plan** view and zoom out to see the entire building.

2. In the Project Browser, scroll down to the *Schedules* area and open **Space Airflow Check**.

3. Drag the tab of the schedule view so it is undocked from the main part of the user interface. Then, drag the window until it is just under the **01 Mechanical Plan** tab. It should automatically dock as shown in Figure 11–70.

4. In the plan view, zoom in so you see the south wing. In the schedule view, scroll down to *Space Number* **2008** and **2010**. Neither of these spaces have any air terminals and therefore have a negative *Airflow Check* number, as shown in Figure 11–70.

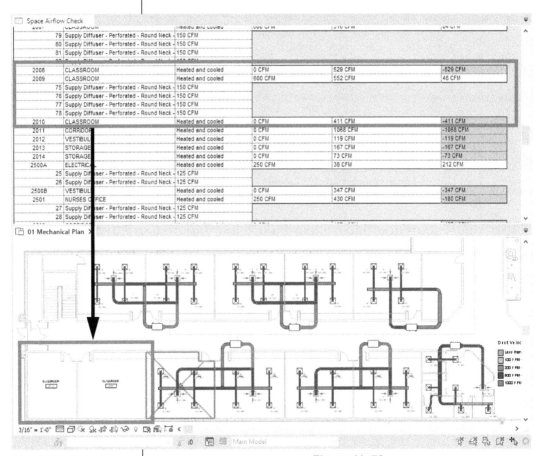

Figure 11–70

5. In the **01 Mechanical Plan** view, select one of the existing supply air terminals. Right-click and select **Create Similar**. This starts the **Air Terminal** command and sets the type and Properties to match the original.

6. In the *Modify | Place Component* tab>Placement panel, click 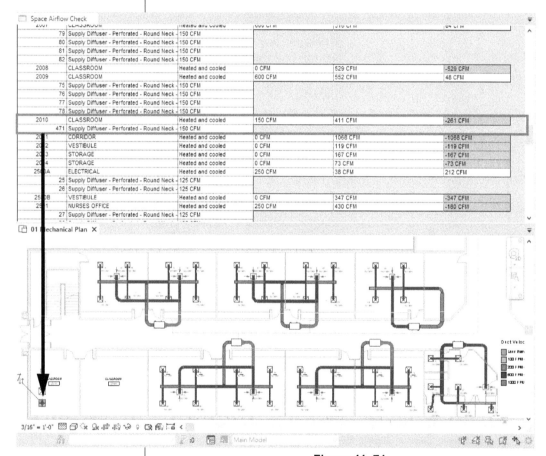 (Place on Face).

7. Add an air terminal in Classroom 2010. The schedule automatically updates and includes the flow rate of the air terminal in the *Airflow Check*, as shown in Figure 11–71.

Figure 11–71

8. Add as many air terminals as required to have a positive airflow.

9. Close the schedule view and zoom to fit the plan view.

10. Save the project.

Practice 11f | Test Plumbing Systems

Practice Objectives

- Investigate warnings and use Check Pipe Systems.
- Review disconnects.
- Correct issues discovered by the testing tools.
- Add a piping color fill legend.

In this practice, you will review warnings, run **Check Pipe Systems**, and **Show Disconnects**. You will then correct some of the problems in the south wing, as shown in Figure 11–72. You will also add a piping color fill legend that shows the sizes of pipes in the view.

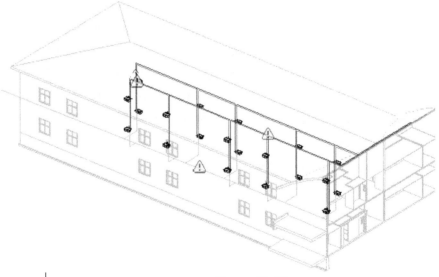

Figure 11–72

Task 1 - Review warnings and check pipe systems.

1. In the practice files *Systems* folder, open **Plumbing-Analyze-School-MEP.rvt**.

2. Open the Plumbing>Plumbing>3D Views>**3D Plumbing Area B** view.

3. Hover over a one of the domestic cold water system pipes in the south wing of the building and press <Tab> until you see the system highlight, as shown in Figure 11–73. Click to select it.

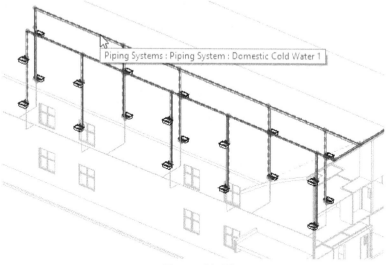

Figure 11–73

4. In the *Modify | Pipe Systems* tab>Warning panel, click

   (Show Related Warnings).

5. Review the contents of the dialog box, as shown in Figure 11–74.

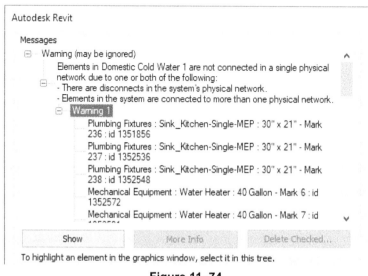

Figure 11–74

6. Close the dialog box.

7. In the *Analyze* tab>Check Systems panel, click 🔍 (Check Pipe Systems). The pipe system is not working, as shown in Figure 11–75.

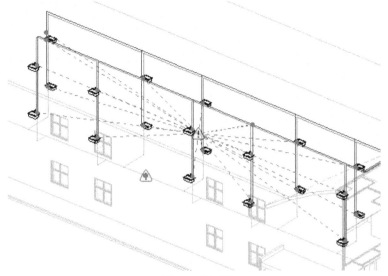

Figure 11–75

8. Toggle off **Check Pipe Systems**.

9. Save the project.

Task 2 - Check and correct pipe disconnects.

---

1. Continue working in the 3D view.

2. In the *Analyze* tab>Check Systems panel, click ⚲ (Show Disconnects).

3. In the Show Disconnects Options dialog box, select **Pipe** and click **OK**.

4. Zoom in on parts of the south wing and discover the issues. Correct the places where there are extra fittings or the pipes are not connected correctly. For example, the cold water pipes in Figure 11–76 need a connector. Delete the extra fitting, connect the horizontal pipes, and then connect the vertical pipe into the horizontal pipe. The correct fitting is applied as shown in Figure 11–77.

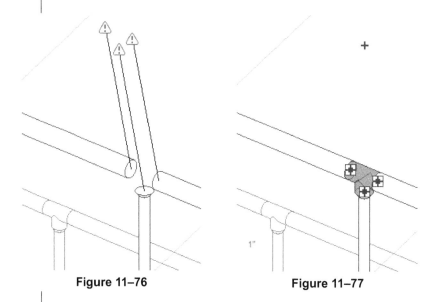

Figure 11–76   Figure 11–77

5. In the *Analyze* tab>Check Systems panel, click (Show Disconnects). Clear the check from **Pipe** and click **OK**.

6. Save the project.

Task 3 - Add a pipe color fill scheme and legend.

1. Open the Plumbing>Plumbing>Floor Plans>**1- Sanitary** view.

2. In the *Analyze* tab>Color Fill panel, click (Pipe Legend).

3. Place the legend where the sanitary line exits the building.

4. In the Choose Color Scheme dialog box, select **Pipe Color Fill Size** and click **OK**. The legend and color scheme displays, as shown in Figure 11–78.

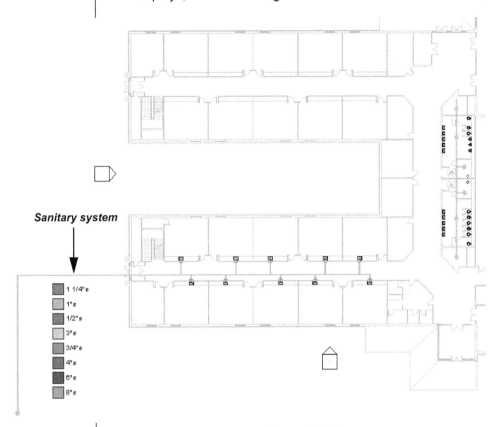

Figure 11–78

5. You can see that all the sanitary pipes in the south wing of the building are too small. Starting from the far end of the system, select several of the pipes and fittings. Change the size to **3"**.

6. Continue selecting pipes and fittings and adding to the size incrementally down the line. The colors change to match the legend as shown in Figure 11–79.

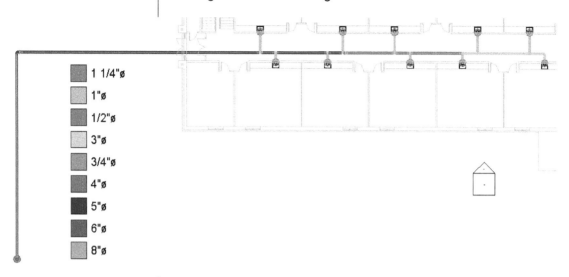

Figure 11–79

7. Zoom out to see the entire building.

8. Save and close the project

Chapter Review Questions

1. How many elements must be selected before you can create a duct or piping system?

   a. One

   b. Two

   c. Three

   d. None need to be selected first.

2. How do you specify which type of system you want to create when the element has multiple options, such as the lavatory shown in Figure 11–80?

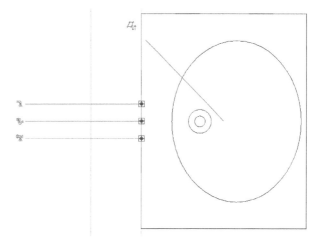

Figure 11–80

   a. Select the appropriate connector to start the system.

   b. In the contextual tab, select the appropriate system button.

   c. In the Options Bar, select the system type from the drop-down list.

   d. Select the system type from the drop-down list in the dialog box that opens when you click **Create System**.

3. The purpose of a Base is to serve as a placeholder equipment connection point when generating an automatic layout.

   a. True

   b. False

4. Match the color of a line when generating a layout with what the color indicates.

Color	Indicates
a. Gold	_____ Branch
b. Blue	_____ Modeling Error
c. Green	_____ Main

5. Flex duct can be placed automatically on which of the following components of a layout?

a. Main lines

b. Branch lines

c. Both

6. What is a common problem when generating layouts?

a. Unable to edit standard solutions into custom layouts.

b. The direction of the connector does not match how the automatic layout wants to connect to it.

c. Cannot specify which family/type for the main and branch lines to use separately.

7. What is required before you can create an automatic ductwork layout?

a. Duct System

b. Air Terminals only

c. Duct placeholders

d. All air terminals and equipment placed for the entire project.

Command Summary

Button	Command	Location
System Tools		
	Add to System	• **Ribbon:** *Edit Duct or Piping Systems* tab>Edit Duct or Piping System panel
	Disconnect Equipment	• **Ribbon:** *Edit Duct or Piping Systems* tab> System Tools panel
	Divide Systems	• **Ribbon:** *Modify	Duct or Piping Systems* tab>Systems Tools panel
	Duct (System)	• **Ribbon:** *Modify	contextual* tab>Create Systems panel • Right-click: Create Duct System
	Edit System	• **Ribbon:** *Duct or Piping Systems* tab>System Tools panel
	Remove from System	• **Ribbon:** *Edit Duct or Piping Systems* tab>Edit Duct *or Piping* System panel and *Generate Layout* tab>Modify Layout panel
	Select Equipment	• **Ribbon:** *Duct or Piping Systems* tab>System Tools and *Edit Duct or Piping Systems* tab>Edit Duct *or Piping* System panel
	System Browser	• **Ribbon:** *View* tab>Windows panel, expand User Interface • **Shortcut:** <F9>
Automatic Duct or Piping Layout		
	Edit Layout	• **Ribbon:** *Generate Layout* tab>Modify Layout panel
	Generate Layout	• **Ribbon:** *Duct or Piping Systems* tab>Layout panel
	Modify Base	• **Ribbon:** *Generate Layout* tab>Modify Layout panel
	Place Base	• **Ribbon:** *Generate Layout* tab>Modify Layout panel
	Remove Base	• **Ribbon:** *Generate Layout* tab>Modify Layout panel
	Solutions	• **Ribbon:** *Generate Layout* tab>Modify Layout panel

Testing Systems

	Check Duct Systems	• **Ribbon**: *Analyze* tab>Check Systems panel
	Check Pipe Systems	• **Ribbon**: *Analyze* tab>Check Systems panel
	Show Disconnects	• **Ribbon**: *Analyze* tab>Check Systems panel
	Show Related Warnings	• **Ribbon**: *Modify* contextual tab>Warning panel
	System Inspector	• **Ribbon**: (When an element in a system is selected) *Modify* contextual tab>Analysis panel

Electrical Systems

Electrical systems consist of components such as lighting fixtures, electrical fixtures, fire alarms, security systems, telephone devices, and power equipment. Frequently, the various elements are connected via a power circuit or related systems. Cable trays or conduits can be added to a project, but these do not create system connections between elements.

Learning Objectives in This Chapter

- Establish electrical settings.
- Place electrical equipment, devices, and lighting fixtures.
- Create power circuits, switch systems, and other circuit systems.
- Create and modify electrical panel schedules.
- Add cable trays and conduits, including parallel conduit runs and fittings.

12.1 About Electrical Systems

Electrical systems in the Autodesk® Revit® software are circuits consisting of devices, lighting fixtures, and other electrical equipment. They are elements in a project and are added to the model using the tools in the Ribbon. There can be different types of electrical plan views based on the type of information required. A typical electrical view plan might display power, systems, or lighting layouts as shown in Figure 12–1.

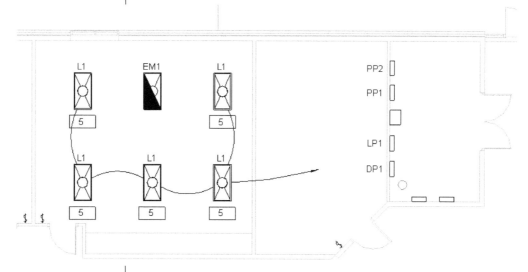

Figure 12–1

There are several steps in the process of creating an Electrical system:

1. Place electrical equipment such as distribution panels.
2. Define the Distribution System in the Properties of the electrical equipment.
3. Place electrical devices, such as receptacles and lighting fixtures. Each device represents an electrical load in the system.
4. Select an electrical device or lighting fixture, and create a power circuit for it and similar devices in the same room or area of the building.
5. Assign circuits to electrical equipment (e.g. Panel).

The tools for creating and placing Electrical components and circuits are located in the *Systems* tab>Electrical panel, as shown in Figure 12–2.

*To make room for the Electrical tools, in the File tab, click **Options**. In the Options dialog box, on the User Interface pane, clear the checks from **Systems tab: mechanical tools** and **Systems tab: piping tools**.*

Figure 12–2

Electrical Settings

Electrical settings contain many parameters used for various electrical component placement and system/circuit creation. They include wiring parameters, voltage definitions, distribution systems, cable tray and conduit settings, load calculation settings, and circuit naming settings.

In *Manage* tab>Settings panel, expand (MEP Settings) and click (Electrical Settings), or in the *Systems* tab>Electrical panel, click (Electrical Settings), to open the Electrical Settings dialog box, as shown in Figure 12–3.

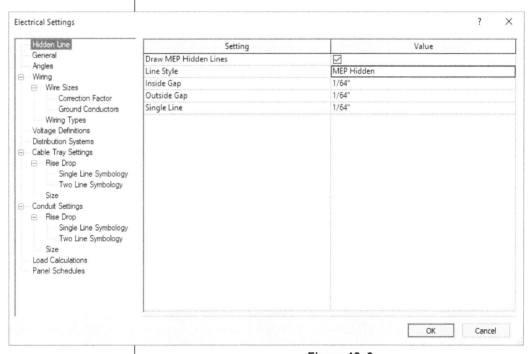

Figure 12–3

The different categories in the left pane have their own specific settings that are available when the category is selected.

Hidden Line	Settings for cable tray and conduit hidden line styles and gaps.
General	Parameters and formats for symbols and styles for various electrical component values, including phase naming. Enables you to specify the sequence in which power circuits are generated (i.e., **Numerical**, **Group by Phase**, or **Odd then Even**). You can also set the default Circuit Rating to match the country for which you are designing. Some engineers like to set this to **0** so they know which circuits they have not yet reviewed.
Angles	Enables to set angle increments or specify the use of specific angles for drawing cable trays and conduit. This is typically used to match industry standards for factory fittings.
Wiring	Determines how wires and wire sizes are displayed and calculated. Includes type of wires available based on material, temperature, and insulation ratings. Specifies which wire types can be used in a project.
Voltage Definitions	Lists the ranges of voltages that can be assigned to the Distribution Systems.
Distributions Systems	Defines available distribution systems. You can add and delete systems, as required. The System includes the Phase, Configuration (Wye or Delta), number of wires, and the **L-L Voltage** and **L-G Voltage** options.
Cable Tray Settings	Specifies annotative scaling for cable tray fittings and rise/drop symbology. Specifies cable tray sizes available in a project.
Conduit Settings	Specifies annotative scaling for conduit fittings, size prefix and suffix, and rise/drop symbology. Specifies conduit sizes available in a project.
Load Calculations	Specifies whether to enable load calculations for loads in spaces, and defines Load Classifications and Demand Factors. Available methods include Sum true load and reactive load, as well as Sum apparent load.
Panel Schedules	Specifies settings for spares and spaces, and for merging multi-poled circuits

- Load Classifications are assigned to Device Connectors, and Demand Factors are assigned to Load Classifications.

12.2 Placing Electrical Components

There are many different types of electrical components that can be added to a model, as shown in Figure 12–4. Components consist of panels, transformers, switches, receptacles, various communication and safety devices, and lighting fixtures. There are different commands for different types of electrical components and devices.

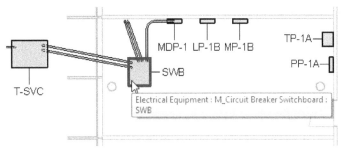

Figure 12–4

- Electrical components can be placed in any view, including plan, elevation, and 3D.

- There are three primary types of electrical components: Electrical Equipment, Electrical Devices, and Lighting Fixtures. The process of adding the components to the project is essentially the same.

Electrical Equipment

Electrical equipment includes panels and transformers, which can be placed either as hosted or unhosted components. Panels are typically hosted onto a wall, surface or flush mount, as shown in Figure 12–5, and a transformer could be placed anywhere including ceiling hung. Other electrical equipment includes motor control centers, switchboards, and generators.

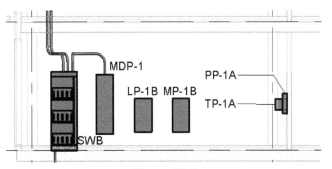

Figure 12–5

Electrical Devices

Electrical devices include a variety of devices, including receptacles, switches, telephone/communication/data terminal devices, junction boxes, nurse call devices, wall speakers, starters, smoke detectors, and fire alarm manual pull stations, shown in Figure 12–6. These devices are typically face-based components, and are often placed on a wall.

Figure 12–6

Lighting Fixtures

Most lighting fixtures are face-based components, and are therefore placed on a ceiling or on a wall. Examples of lighting fixtures are shown in Figure 12–7.

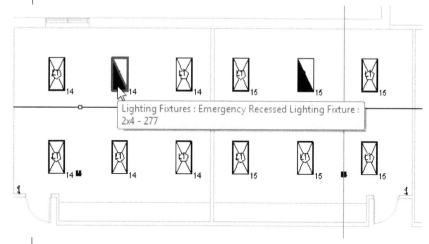

Figure 12–7

- Lighting fixtures can also be copied and monitored from a linked architectural file.

How To: Place Electrical Components

1. In the *Systems* tab>Electrical panel, click on one of the following, or type the associated shortcut:

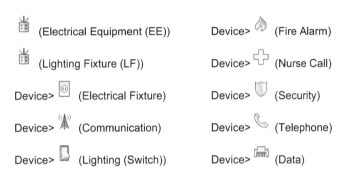

    (Electrical Equipment (EE))   Device> (Fire Alarm)

    (Lighting Fixture (LF))   Device> (Nurse Call)

    Device> (Electrical Fixture)   Device> (Security)

    Device> (Communication)   Device> (Telephone)

    Device> (Lighting (Switch))   Device> (Data)

2. In Type Selector, select the type you want to use.
3. In Properties, set any applicable parameters.

4. In the *Modify | contextual* tab>Tag panel, click (Tag on Placement) to select or clear, as required. If you have selected **Tag on Placement**, set the parameters for the tags in the Options Bar.

Automatically placing the tags is typically recommended for electrical equipment.

5. In the Placement panel, click (Place on Vertical Face), (Place on Face), or (Place on Work Plane).

   - The placement panel does not display for some components. These are placed on the current level with an offset as needed.

6. Place the component. Use alignment lines, temporary dimensions, and snaps to aid placement.
7. Continue to place additional components, or click (Modify) to exit the command.

- After placing components, you can move them to a different location by clicking and dragging it to the new location, as needed.

Hint: Placing Devices Directly Beside or Above Each Other

Electrical device families are model families with an embedded annotation family. This is so that the actual device box displays in sections and 3D views and a symbol displays in plan view, as shown in Figure 12–8.

Section view   *Plan view*

Figure 12–8

Some families do not work well if two devices need to be placed directly next to or above each other. For example, in Figure 12–9, devices that are placed correctly in a section view result in overlapping, illegible symbols in plan. Moving the symbol in the plan view also moves the device in the model.

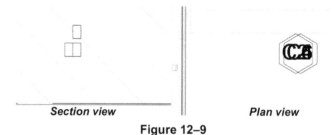

Section view   *Plan view*

Figure 12–9

Many offices create custom device families, which include offset parameters so that the annotation family can move separately from the model family as shown in Figure 12–10.

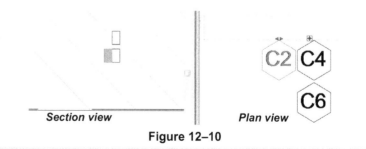

Section view   *Plan view*

Figure 12–10

Working with Lighting Fixtures

- Hosted fixtures have an **Elevation from Level** parameter. For example, if the fixture is being placed on a vertical face (e.g., a sconce on a wall), this value can be set to control the height above the level.

- If the fixture is being placed on a face, such as a ceiling, the **Elevation from Level** parameter is automatically determined by the height of the light fixture, which in Figure 12–11 is the same as the ceiling height.

- Some fixtures have an additional **Offset from Host** parameter. This enables you to specify that the fixture be offset from the host, such as a fluorescent fixture, which hangs below the ceiling. In this case, adjust the elevation value to reflect the new elevation of the fixture, as shown in Figure 12–11.

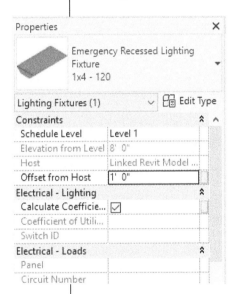 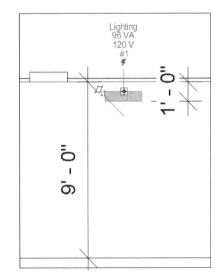

Figure 12–11

- Light fixtures that are hosted by a ceiling in a linked model move automatically with any changes that the architects make to the ceiling height. This can be an advantage of using face-based fixtures.

- If the architect deletes the ceiling and puts a new one in the linked model, the hosted lighting fixtures are orphaned and do not move with changes in the ceiling height. A Warning dialog box opens when you reload the linked model or reopen the MEP project, as shown in Figure 12–12. Use the **Coordination Monitoring** tools to address the issue.

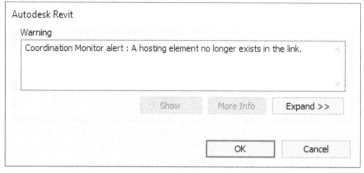

Figure 12–12

- Some firms add reference planes and place the hosted families on them instead of in the ceiling. This gives them control over the height of the families. If the architect moves the ceilings up or down, the engineer adjusts the height of the reference plane to match.

How To: Place a Light Fixture Using Reference Planes

1. Cut a section through the area where you are placing the light fixtures.
2. In the *Systems* tab>Work Plane panel, click ✐ (Ref Plane).
3. Draw a reference plane at the ceiling height.
4. Select the reference plane and, in Properties, type in a name. When you select the reference plane the name displays as shown in Figure 12–13.

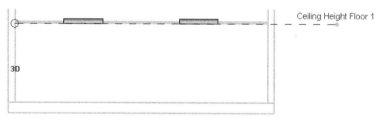

Figure 12–13

5. Switch to a ceiling plan view.
6. Start the **Lighting Fixture** command.
7. In the Type Selector, select a lighting fixture.

8. In the *Modify | Place Fixture* tab>Placement panel, click

 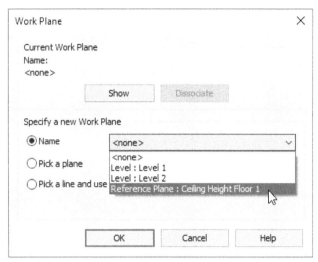 (Place on Workplane).
9. In the Work Plane dialog box, select the named reference plane you created (shown in Figure 12–14), and click **OK**.

Figure 12–14

10. Add the lighting fixtures. They align to ceiling grids even though they are not hosted by the ceiling.

• Architectural light fixtures cut holes in the architectural ceiling. If the electrical engineer needs to put fixtures in a different place, they usually toggle off the visibility of the linked architectural light fixtures first. This results in holes in the ceiling, as shown in Figure 12–15. To correct this issue, the engineer needs to request that the architect move the architectural lighting fixtures to the final, agreed on location.

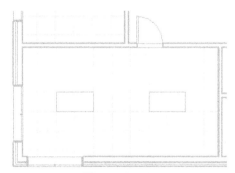

Figure 12–15

Practice 12a

Place Electrical Components

Practice Objectives

- Add lighting fixtures.
- Add electrical equipment.

In this practice, you will insert lighting fixtures and add two electrical panels, one for standard lights and the other for emergency lights, as shown in Figure 12–16.

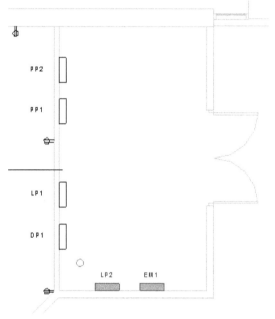

Figure 12–16

Task 1 - Add lighting fixtures.

1. In the practice files *Electrical* folder, open **Electrical-School-MEP.rvt**.

2. In the *Systems* tab>Electrical panel title bar, click ⌐ (Electrical Settings).

3. In the Electrical Settings dialog box, click **Distribution Systems**. Review the list of systems available (as shown in Figure 12–17) and then click **OK**.

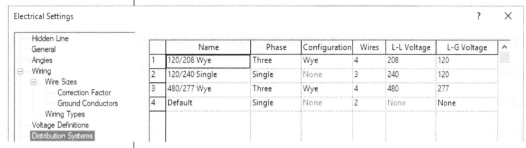

Figure 12–17

4. Open the Coordination>MEP>Ceiling Plans>**01 Electrical RCP** view and zoom to the north wing, upper left room.

5. In *Systems* tab>Electrical panel, click (Lighting Fixture).

6. In Type Selector, select **Troffer Light - 2x4 Parabolic: 2'x4'(2 Lamp) - 277V**.

7. In the *Modify | Place Fixture* tab>Placement panel, click (Place on Face).

8. Place three lighting fixtures in the upper left room. (Hint: Press <Spacebar> to rotate the fixtures before placing them.)

9. In the Type Selector, change the type to **Emergency Recessed Lighting Fixture: 2x4 - 277** and place one of these lighting fixtures, as shown in Figure 12–18.

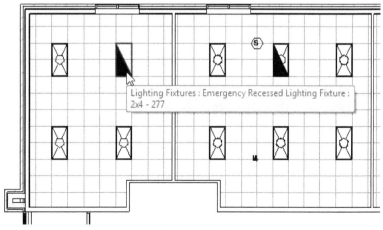

Figure 12–18

10. Click (Modify) to exit the command.

Task 2 - Add electrical equipment.

1. In the Project Browser, open the Electrical>Power>Floor Plans>**01 Electrical Room** view.

2. In *Systems* tab>Electrical panel, click ⛯ (Electrical Equipment).

3. In the *Modify | Place Equipment*>Tag panel, click ⌐① (Tag on Placement).

4. In Type Selector, select **Lighting and Appliance Panelboard - 480V MCB - Surface: 125 A**.

5. Place one panelboard on the bottom wall of the room, as shown in Figure 12–19. Note that the tag displays with a question mark because the name has not been added.

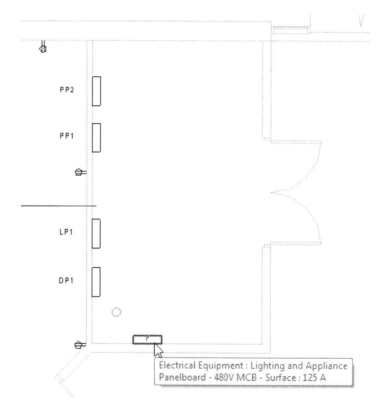

Figure 12–19

6. Click **Modify** and select the newly added panel.

7. In Properties, scroll down to the *General* area, set *Panel Name* to **LP2**, as shown in Figure 12–20.

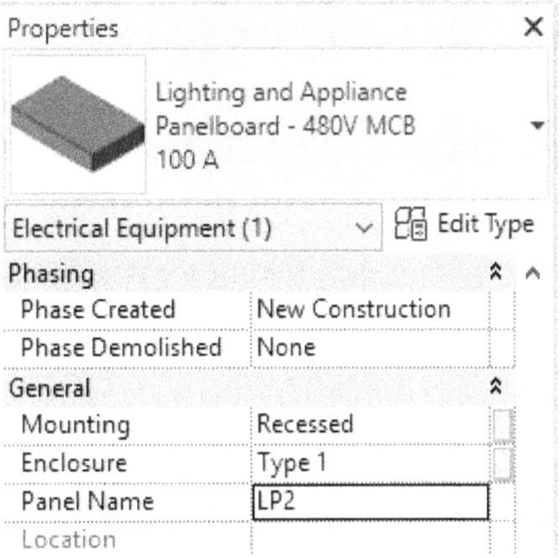

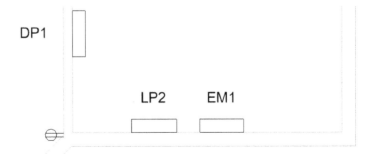

Properties   ✕

Lighting and Appliance
Panelboard - 480V MCB
100 A

Electrical Equipment (1)	∨	Edit Type

Phasing		≫ ∧
Phase Created	New Construction	
Phase Demolished	None	
General		≫
Mounting	Recessed	
Enclosure	Type 1	
Panel Name	LP2	
Location		

Figure 12–20

8. While still in Properties, scroll further down to the *Electrical - Circuiting* area and expand the Distribution System list. The only choice is **480/277 Wye** as this is the only distribution system that fits this panel.

9. Click **Modify**.

10. Start the **Electrical Equipment** command again. In the Type Selector, select **Lighting and Appliance Panelboard - 480V MCB - Surface: 400 A**. Place the panel beside the other one you just added.

11. Click **Modify** and double-click on the tag. Change the name of the tag to **EM1**. (Do not double-click on the tag too quickly or it will open the tag in the family editor, instead of allowing you to change the name.)

12. Select the tags for the LP2 and EM1 panels and move them above the panels, as shown in Figure 12–21.

DP1

LP2   EM1

Figure 12–21

13. Save and close the project.

12.3 Creating Electrical Circuits

Once you have placed the electrical equipment, devices, and lighting fixtures into the model, you need to create the electrical system (circuit) from these components. Circuits connect the similar electrical components to form the electrical system, as shown in Figure 12–22. Once the electrical system is created, you can then add, remove, or modify any of the components. You can also edit the circuit path to establish the accurate length used in voltage drop calculations and wire sizing.

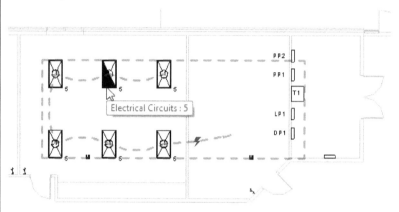

Figure 12–22

Components that are to be connected in a circuit must be of compatible voltage and distribution system.

- Circuits can be created for power, lighting, switches, data, telephones, fire alarms, nurse call or security systems, and controls. The process is similar no matter which type of circuit you are creating.

- Power systems connect compatible electrical devices and lighting fixtures in a circuit to an electrical equipment panel, as shown in Figure 12–23.

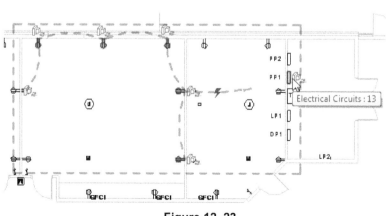

Figure 12–23

- Switch systems enable you to indicate which lights and switches are linked, as shown in Figure 12–24. This is especially useful for those cases where there are multiple lights on the same circuit that are controlled by different switches.

Linking lines are for reference only and do not plot.

You can only place one switch at a time on a switch system.

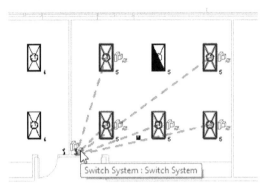

Figure 12–24

How To: Create a Circuit

1. Select at least one of the components that is to be part of the circuit.
2. In the *Modify | contextual* tab>Create Systems panel, click the related system button (i.e., ⊞ (Power), ⎁ (Switch), or ⌨ (Data)).
3. In the *Electrical Circuits* tab>System Tools panel, either:
   - Accept the existing panel,
   - Either select a panel from the drop-down list (as shown in Figure 12–25, or select a panel in the project and click ⧉ (Select Panel).

When you create a circuit, the program automatically connects to the most recently used panel in the current session of the Autodesk Revit software.

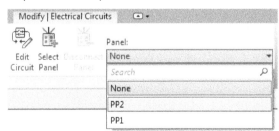

Figure 12–25

- Switch systems are not connected to a panel.
4. In the *Modify | Electrical Circuits* tab>System Tools panel, click ⧉ (Edit Circuit).

5. In the *Edit Circuit* tab>Edit Circuit panel, click ⬚ (Add to Circuit) and select the other components for that circuit.

    •   To remove components from a circuit, click ⬚ (Remove from Circuit) and select the component.

6. Click ✓ (Finish Editing Circuit).

•   If a component has more than one electrical connector, a Select Connector dialog box opens, as shown in Figure 12–26. Select the connector for which you want to make a circuit and click **OK**.

Figure 12–26

Editing Circuit Paths

You can edit circuit paths in plan or 3D views.

When you add a circuit, an automatic route is processed and the length information (used to calculate the voltage drop and wire sizing) is automatically available. Note that the results might not be what you are expecting (as shown in Figure 12–27) and you can edit the path of the circuit to ensure that it runs in the direction and height you expect, as shown in Figure 12–28. Then the length automatically updates to provide you with the correct information.

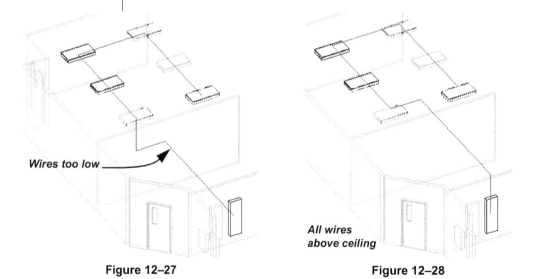

Figure 12–27   **Figure 12–28**

How To: Edit the Path of a Circuit

1. Hover the cursor over a circuit component and press <Tab> until you can select the circuit.
2. Select the *Electrical Circuits* tab in the ribbon.
3. In the System Tools panel, click 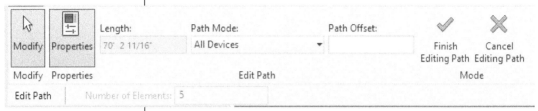 (Edit Path). The Edit Path tab displays, as shown in Figure 12–29.

   - The *Length* automatically updates as you make changes.
   - The *Number of Elements* in the circuit displays in the Options Bar.

Figure 12–29

4. In the Edit Path panel, set the *Path Mode* to **All Devices**, **Farthest Device** (as shown in Figure 12–30) or **Custom** (if you have already edited the path).

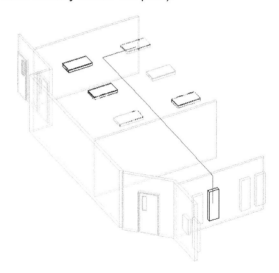

Figure 12–30

5. Change the *Path Offset* in the ribbon to modify the entire circuit path. This is especially useful to get the entire path above the ceiling.

6. Select individual circuit paths to modify the route. You can drag the path line or control points or change the path offset, as shown in Figure 12–31.

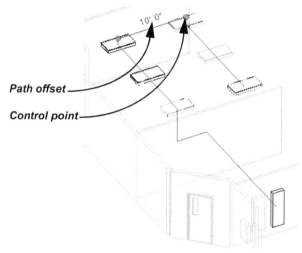

Figure 12–31

7. To add or remove control points, right-click on a control point and select **Delete Control Point** or right-click on a path line and select **Insert Control Point.**
8. When you have finished adjusting the path, in the *Edit Path* tab>Mode panel, click ✓ (Finish Editing Path)

Adding Wires

When wiring a switch system you have to connect the elements manually. Then, the switch can be placed on a power circuit and acts as sort of an outlet going back to the panel.

Wiring is typically schematic, frequently used in wiring plans such as that shown in Figure 12–32. You can create wires once you have added circuits.

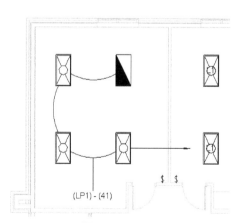

Figure 12–32

- Wires stay connected if you move a fixture, adjusting to the new location.
- Wires are view specific.
- Add conduits or cable trays to show the exact location where the wires will run.

How To: Add Wires to a View

1. Create the circuits that connect the fixtures and panel.
2. Create a duplicated view in which you want to display the wires.
3. Hover the cursor over one of the elements in the circuit. Press < Tab> to highlight the circuit and then click to select it.
4. In the *Modify | Electrical Circuits* tab>Convert to Wire panel,

   click (Arc Wire) or (Chamfered Wire). Alternatively, you can click on the **Generate arc** (or **chamfered**) **type wiring** control in the drawing area, as shown in Figure 12–33.

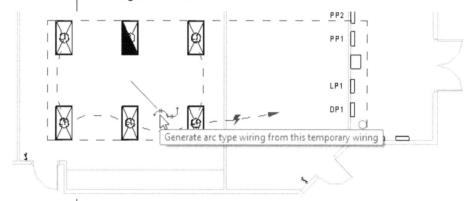

Figure 12–33

5. Click **Modify** and select the wiring. Use the controls to add, remove, and move vertices as required, as shown in Figure 12–34.

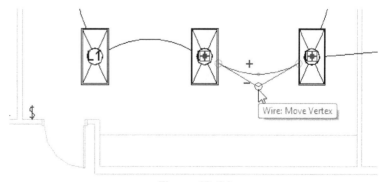

Figure 12–34

Wiring Settings

You can set up how the wires display in the Electrical Settings dialog box under the Wiring node. This includes the styles of tick marks for various wires, as shown in Figure 12–35.

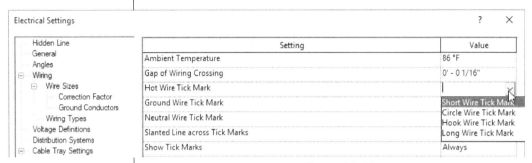

Figure 12–35

- Tick marks can be loaded from the Revit library *Annotations>Electrical>TickMarks* folder, as shown in Figure 12–36.

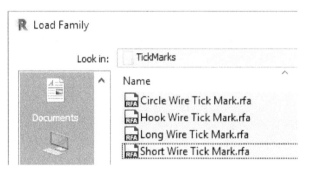

Figure 12–36

Practice 12b | Create Electrical Circuits

Practice Objectives

- Create electrical circuits for standard and emergency lighting.
- Edit the circuit path.
- Display wire connections for a wiring plan.

In this practice, you will connect light fixtures together in a power circuit. You will also create an emergency power circuit and add light fixtures to the circuit, as shown in Figure 12–37. You will edit the path of the circuit and view the changes to the length. You will also add a transformer and connect panels to it. Finally, you will display wire connections to create a wiring plan.

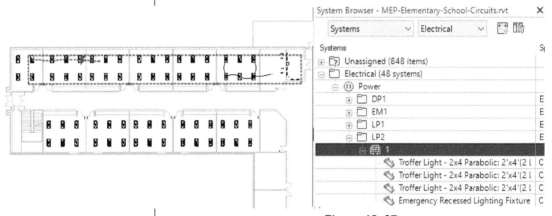

Figure 12–37

Task 1 - Create an electrical circuit system.

1. In the practice files *Electrical* folder, open **Circuits-School-MEP.rvt**.

2. Open the Electrical>Lighting>Floor Plans>**01 Lighting Plan** view and zoom to the upper left room.

3. From the north wing, select the upper left light and in the *Modify | Lighting Fixtures* tab>Create Systems panel, click ⏸ (Power).

4. In the *Modify | Electrical Circuits* tab>System Tools panel, expand the Panel list, and select **LP2**.

5. In the System Tools panel, click 🖅 (Edit Circuit).

6. In the *Edit Circuit* tab>Edit Circuit panel, ensure that 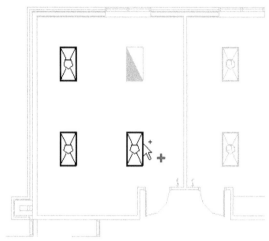 (Add to Circuit) is selected. Select the other two standard lights in the room but not the emergency light, as shown in Figure 12–38.

Do not select the emergency light fixture until the next step.

Figure 12–38

7. While still in the same circuit, select the emergency light. In the Select Connector dialog box, select **Connector 2: Power** and click **OK**.

8. Click ✔ (Finish Editing Circuit).

9. Open the System Browser.(**Hint:** Press <F9>.)

10. In the System Browser, in the *View* area, filter the list by **Systems** and **Electrical**, as shown in Figure 12–39.

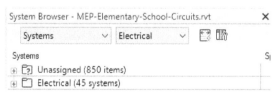

Figure 12–39

11. In the view, select one of the Troffer light fixtures which you just circuited.

12. In the System Browser, expand the highlighted nodes to display the selected light fixtures, as shown in Figure 12–40. Only one light is highlighted in the project.

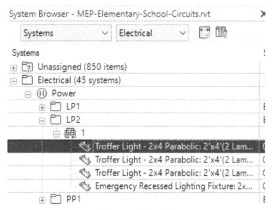

Figure 12–40

13. In the System Browser, select the related circuit **1**. The selection in the view changes to display the circuit outline, as shown in Figure 12–41.

The extents box surrounds the system and the panel with connecting arcs to each fixture in this circuit.

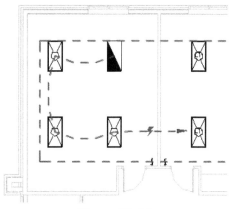

Figure 12–41

14. In Properties, review the circuit properties. In the *Electrical - Loads* area, the *Circuit Number* should be set to **1** as it is the first circuit added to this panel. This field is editable in the related panel schedule.

15. Scroll down to note the *Length* of the circuit. This is read only, but updates when you edit the circuit path.

16. Clear the selection.

17. Select the **Emergency Recessed Lighting Fixture**. In the System Browser, note that the Unassigned node highlights as well. This is because the fixture has two connectors, and you have only circuited one of them. This will be resolved in the next task.

18. Save the project.

Task 2 - Add and move emergency lighting fixtures to an emergency circuit and panel.

---

1. Continue working in the **01 Lighting Plan** view.

2. Select the emergency lighting fixture added earlier.

3. In the *Modify | Lighting Fixtures* tab>Create Systems panel, click 🔘 (Power).

Because there is now only one uncircuited connector on this fixture, the Select Connector dialog box does not open.

4. In the *Modify | Electrical Circuits* tab>Systems Tools panel, expand the Panel list and select **EM1**.

5. With the same light selected, in the Systems Tool panel, click 🔲 (Edit Circuit).

6. In the *Edit Circuit* tab>Edit Circuit panel, verify that 🔲 (Add to Circuit) is selected.

7. Select the emergency fixture in the room directly to the right of the room that you are working in.

8. In the Select Connector dialog box, select **Connection 1: Power : Emergency**.

   • Many emergency lighting fixtures have a battery backup. This is the method used when the fixtures are connected to an emergency circuit.

9. Click ✔ (Finish Editing Circuit).

10. Save the project.

Task 3 - Edit the circuit path.

1. Hover the cursor over one of the standard light fixtures in the same room and press <Tab> to select the circuit.

2. In the *Modify | Electrical Circuits* tab>System Tools panel, click  (Edit Path).

3. In the Edit Path panel, note the *Length*, *Path Mode*, and *Path Offset*, as shown in Figure 12–42.

Figure 12–42

4. Change the *Path Mode* to **All Devices** and the *Path Offset* to **10'-0"**. The *Length* also changes, as shown in Figure 12–43.

Figure 12–43

5. Modify the individual circuit path lines as desired.

6. Click (Finish Editing Path).

7. Save the project.

Task 4 - Add a step down transformer.

1. Open the Electrical>Power>Floor Plans>**01 Electrical Room** view.

2. In the *Systems* tab>Electrical panel, click (Electrical Equipment).

3. In the Type Selector, select **Dry Type Transformer - 480-208Y120 - NEMA Type 3R: 15 kVA**.

4. Place the transformer between PP1 and LP1, as shown in Figure 12–44.

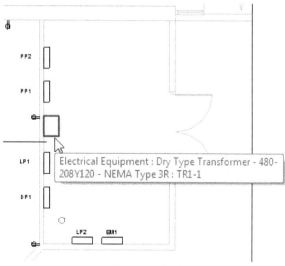

Electrical Equipment : Dry Type Transformer - 480-208Y120 - NEMA Type 3R : TR1-1

Figure 12–44

5. Click **Modify** and select the new transformer.

6. In Properties, in the *General* area, set the *Panel Name* to **TR1-1**.

7. In the *Electrical - Loads* area, set the *Secondary Distribution System* to **120/208 Wye**.

8. In the *Electrical - Circuiting* area, verify that the *Distribution System* is set to **480/277 Wye** and click **Apply**.

The transformer has a primary and secondary distribution system; both are set as properties of the transformer.

9. Click **Modify** and select the panel **PP1**.

10. In the *Modify | Electrical Equipment* tab>Create Systems panel, click (Power).

11. In the *Modify | Electrical Circuits* tab>System Tools panel, click (Select Panel).

12. Select the new TR1-1 panel. The load from panel PP1 is now assigned to the transformer TR1-1

13. Clear the selection and select **TR1-1**.

14. Right-click on the **Power** connector and select **Create Power Circuit.**

15. In the System Tools panel, in the Panel list, select **DP1**. The system displays as shown in Figure 12–45.

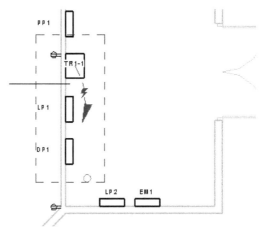

Figure 12–45

16. Release the selection.

17. Save the project.

Task 5 - Create a wiring plan.

1. Duplicate (with Detailing) the Electrical>Lighting>Floor Plans>**01 Lighting Plan** view and name it **01 Wiring Plan**.

2. Zoom into the area near the electrical room but the nearby classroom should also be displayed.

3. Hover the cursor over one of the lights in the classroom and press <Tab> to highlight the circuit. Click to select it, as shown in Figure 12–46.

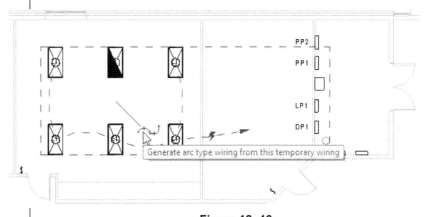

Figure 12–46

4. In the *Modify | Electrical Circuits* tab>Convert to Wire panel, click (Arc Wire). Alternatively, click on the Generate arc type wiring control in the drawing, as shown in Figure 12–46.

5. Wire displaying schematic routing of the circuit is automatically drawn. Adjust the wire arcs manually by pulling the add, remove, and move vertex controls, as shown in Figure 12–47.

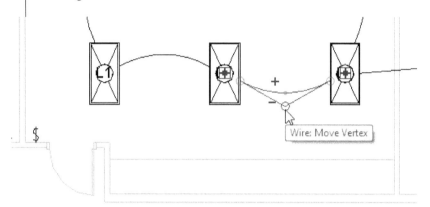

Figure 12–47

The fixture that remains in place is in the linked file.

6. Move a fixture and observe that the wire stays connected adjusting to the new fixture location. Wires are view specific.

7. Undo the move.

8. Continue adding the schematic wiring throughout the north wing of the building. Add additional circuits, if required.

9. If you have time you can also create Switch Systems for the same wing.

10. Save the project.

12.4 Setting Up Panel Schedules

Panel schedules are used to concisely present information about panels and the components connected to them through their corresponding circuits. They also list the load values of these circuits, as shown in Figure 12–48. The Autodesk Revit software creates panel schedules and automatically update them as the panel's circuit change.

Branch Panel: LP1

Location: ELECTRICAL 2500A	Volts: 480/277 Wye	A.I.C. Rating:
Supply From:	Phases: 3	Mains Type:
Mounting: Surface	Wires: 4	Mains Rating: 100 A
Enclosure: Type 3R		MCB Rating: 400 A

Notes:

CKT	Circuit Description	Trip	Poles	A	B	C	Poles	Trip	Circuit Description	CKT
1	Lighting - Dwelling Unit CLASSROOM 1509	20 A	1	496 VA 496 VA			1	20 A	Lighting - Dwelling Unit CLASSROOM 1507	2
3	Lighting - Dwelling Unit CLASSROOM 1505	20 A	1		496 VA 496 VA		1	20 A	Lighting - Dwelling Unit CLASSROOM 1503	4
5	Lighting - Dwelling Unit CLASSROOM 1501	20 A	1			496 VA 496 VA	1	20 A	Lighting - Dwelling Unit CLASSROOM 1508	6
7	Lighting - Dwelling Unit CLASSROOM 1506	20 A	1	496 VA 496 VA			1	20 A	Lighting - Dwelling Unit CLASSROOM 1504	8
9	Lighting - Dwelling Unit CLASSROOM 1502	20 A	1		496 VA 496 VA		1	20 A	Lighting - Dwelling Unit CLASSROOM 1500	10
11	Lighting - Dwelling Unit CLASSROOM 2009	20 A	1			496 VA 496 VA	1	20 A	Lighting - Dwelling Unit CLASSROOM 2007	12
13	Lighting - Dwelling Unit CLASSROOM 2005	20 A	1	496 VA 496 VA			1	20 A	Lighting - Dwelling Unit CLASSROOM 2003	14
15	Lighting - Dwelling Unit CLASSROOM 2001	20 A	1		496 VA 496 VA		1	20 A	Lighting - Dwelling Unit CLASSROOM 2008	16
17	Lighting - Dwelling Unit CLASSROOM 2006	20 A	1			496 VA 496 VA	1	20 A	Lighting - Dwelling Unit CLASSROOM 2004	18
19	Lighting - Dwelling Unit CLASSROOM 2002	20 A	1	496 VA 496 VA			1	20 A	Lighting - Dwelling Unit CLASSROOM 2000	20
21	Lighting - Dwelling Unit CLASSROOM 5009	20 A	1		496 VA 496 VA		1	20 A	Lighting - Dwelling Unit CLASSROOM 5008	22
23	Lighting - Dwelling Unit CLASSROOM 5004	20 A	1			496 VA 496 VA	1	20 A	Lighting - Dwelling Unit CLASSROOM 5003	24
25	Lighting - Dwelling Unit CLASSROOM 5000	20 A	1	496 VA 496 VA			1	20 A	Lighting - Dwelling Unit CLASSROOM 5010	26
27	Lighting - Dwelling Unit CLASSROOM 5007	20 A	1		496 VA 496 VA		1	20 A	Lighting - Dwelling Unit CLASSROOM 5006	28
29	Lighting - Dwelling Unit CLASSROOM 5002	20 A	1			496 VA 496 VA	1	20 A	Lighting - Dwelling Unit CLASSROOM 5001	30
31	Lighting - Dwelling Unit CLASSROOM 4509	20 A	1	496 VA 496 VA			1	20 A	Lighting - Dwelling Unit CLASSROOM 4508	32
33	Lighting - Dwelling Unit CLASSROOM 4504	20 A	1		496 VA 496 VA		1	20 A	Lighting - Dwelling Unit CLASSROOM 4503	34
35	Lighting - Dwelling Unit CLASSROOM 4500	20 A	1			496 VA 496 VA	1	20 A	Lighting - Dwelling Unit CLASSROOM 4510	36
37	Lighting - Dwelling Unit CLASSROOM 4507	20 A	1	496 VA 496 VA			1	20 A	Lighting - Dwelling Unit CLASSROOM 4506	38
39	Lighting - Dwelling Unit CLASSROOM 4502	20 A	1		496 VA 496 VA		1	20 A	Lighting - Dwelling Unit CLASSROOM 4501	40
41	Spare	0 A	1			0 VA				42
	Total Load:			6944 VA	6944 VA	5952 VA				
	Total Amps:			25 A	25 A	21 A				

Legend:

Load Classification	Connected Load	Demand Factor	Estimated Demand	Panel Totals	
Lighting	3840 VA	100.00%	3840 VA		
Lighting - Dwelling Unit	16000 VA	47.19%	7550 VA		
				Total Conn. Load:	19840 VA
				Total Est. Demand:	11390 VA
				Total Conn.:	24 A
				Total Est. Demand:	14 A

Figure 12–48

Creating Panel Schedules

Panel schedules can be created for each panel in the model, and it can be created anytime before or after circuits are created for the panel. Once created, panel schedules are listed in the Project Browser, in the **Panel Schedule** node, as shown in Figure 12–49.

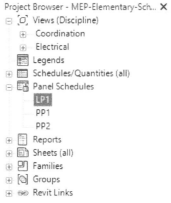

Figure 12–49

How To: Create a Panel Schedule

1. Select the panel for which you want to create the panel schedule.
2. In the *Modify | Electrical Equipment* tab>Electrical panel, expand (Create Panel Schedule) and click either (Use Default Template or (Choose a Template).

   A new panel schedule is created. Its view opens, and is listed in the Project Browser.

- Panel schedules can be placed on sheets for construction documentation.

- Panel Schedule Templates specify the formating and information displayed in the schedule. They can be created and edited. In the *Manage* tab>Settings panel, expand (Panel Schedules Templates) and click (Manage Templates) or (Edit at Template).

If a panel schedule has already been created for the selected equipment, the command is grayed out.

Modifying Panel Schedules

Circuits in a panel schedule can be rearranged, locked, grouped, or renamed. You can also balance loads across phases and add spares to the panel. While viewing, you can edit circuits, electrical equipment, and project information from the properties.

How To: Modify a Panel Schedule

1. In the panel schedule view, select the particular circuit(s) or empty slot(s) that you want to modify.

2. In the *Modify | Panel Schedule* tab, click the particular command that you want to conduct:

Icon	Command	Function
	Change Template	Opens a dialog box where you can choose from a list of available templates.
	Rebalance Loads	Rearranges the panels circuits to redistribute the loads evenly across each phase.
	Renumber Indexes	In the current panel, renumber the circuit naming index.
	Move Up, Down, Across, To	Moves the selected circuit up, down, across, or to a new slot on the circuit panel without disturbing the other circuit locations.
	Assign/Remove Spare/Space	Assigns a slot as either a spare or a space (and are automatically locked), or removes a spare or space from a slot.
	Lock/Unlock	Locks or unlocks circuits, spares, or spaces in a specific slot location.
	Group/Ungroup	Groups single-pole circuits/spares together to act as a multi-pole circuit (or ungroups them).
	Update Names	Updates the names of the circuits on panel schedules.
	Edit Font	Opens the Edit Font dialog box where you can select a font and modify the font size, style, and color.
	Horizontally Align and Vertically Align	Select the alignment of the text in the selected cells

Practice 12c | Set Up Panel Schedules

Practice Objective

- View and create panel schedules.

In this practice, you will view an existing electrical panel schedule, shown in Figure 12–50. You will also create a new panel schedule and add a power system that connects to that panel.

Branch Panel: LP1

Location: ELECTRICAL 2500A		Volts: 480/277 Wye	
Supply From:		Phases: 3	
Mounting: Surface		Wires: 4	
Enclosure: Type 3R			

Notes:

CKT	Circuit Description	Trip	Poles	A		B		C		Pole
1	Lighting - Dwelling Unit CLASSROOM 1509	20 A	1	400 VA	400 VA					1
3	Lighting - Dwelling Unit CLASSROOM 1505	20 A	1			400 VA	400 VA			1
5	Lighting - Dwelling Unit CLASSROOM 1501	20 A	1					400 VA	400 VA	1
7	Lighting - Dwelling Unit CLASSROOM 1506	20 A	1	400 VA	400 VA					1
9	Lighting - Dwelling Unit CLASSROOM 1502	20 A	1			400 VA	400 VA			1
11	Lighting - Dwelling Unit CLASSROOM 2009	20 A	1					400 VA	496 VA	1
13	Lighting - Dwelling Unit CLASSROOM 2005	20 A	1	496 VA	496 VA					1
15	Lighting - Dwelling Unit CLASSROOM 2001	20 A	1			496 VA	496 VA			1
17	Lighting - Dwelling Unit CLASSROOM 2006	20 A	1					496 VA	496 VA	1

Figure 12–50

Task 1 - Viewing and creating panel schedules.

1. In the practice files *Electrical* folder, open **Panel-School-MEP.rvt**.

2. In the Project Browser, expand the **Panel Schedules** node and double-click on the **LP1** schedule to open it.

3. Select circuit **39**, and note its description **Lighting - Dwelling Unit CLASSROOM 4502**.

4. In the *Modify Panel Schedule* tab>Circuits panel, click ⬚ (Move Across). It switches place with circuit **40** on the right (**Lighting - Dwelling Unit CLASSROOM 4501**).

5. Continue to move it up, down, or across, and then **Lock** it and try to move others near it. The locked one will not move.

6. Select an empty circuit in the panel schedule.

7. Click ⌒ (Assign Spare) and a Spare is inserted into that circuit. Note that it is automatically **Locked**, but you can unlock it and move it if required.

8. Close Panel Schedule **LP1**.

Task 2 - Create a panel schedule.

1. Open the Electrical>Power>**01 Electrical Room** view.

2. Select electrical panel **LP2**.

3. In the *Modify | Electrical Equipment* tab>Electrical panel, expand 🔲 (Create Panel Schedules) and click 🔲 (Use Default Template).

4. The Panel Schedule **LP2** is created and automatically opened, as shown in Figure 12–51. It is also listed in the Panel Schedules node in the Project Browser. There are no values assigned to the schedule.

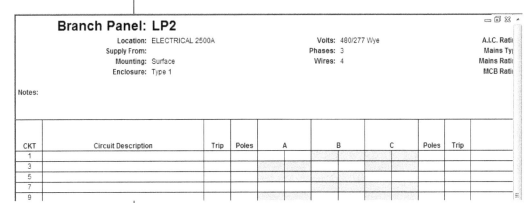

Figure 12–51

5. Open the Electrical>Power>**01 Power Plan** view.

6. Select one of the Ceiling Occupancy Sensors, as shown in Figure 12–52.

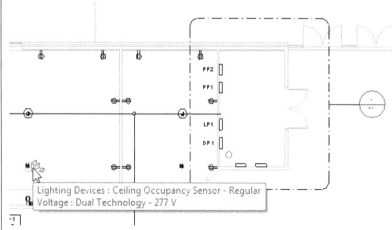

Figure 12–52

7. Right-click and select **Select All Instances>Visible in View**.

8. In the *Modify | Lighting Devices* tab>Create Systems panel, click ⟨11⟩ (Power).

9. In the *Modify | Electrical Circuits* tab>System Tools panel, expand the Panel list and select **LP2**.

10. Open the Panel Schedule **LP2**. Note that the items are added to the *Circuit Description*, as shown in Figure 12–53.

CKT	Circuit Description	Trip	Poles	A
1	Other Room 1509, 1507, 1505, 1503, 1501, 2501, ...	20 A	1	0 VA
3				
5				
7				
9				
11				

Figure 12–53

11. Save the project.

12.5 Adding Cable Trays and Conduit

Cable tray and conduit, as shown in Figure 12–54, hold electrical wiring either for power or data. The wiring that connects electrical equipment, devices, and lighting fixtures is schematic. Cable tray and conduit are not directly connected to the components in the same way that ducts and pipes are.

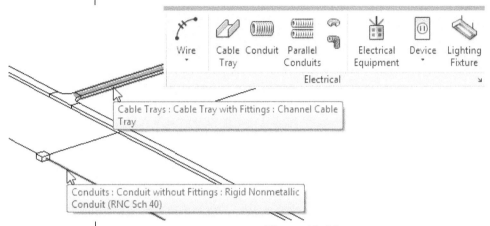

Figure 12–54

- The commands to create and place cable trays, conduits, and their appropriate fittings, are located in the *Systems* tab>Electrical panel, as shown in Figure 12–54.

- Cable trays, conduits, and fittings can be placed in any view, including plan, elevation, and 3D.

How To: Add Cable Tray or Conduit

1. In the *Systems* tab>Electrical panel, click (Cable Tray) or (Conduit).
2. In Type Selector, select a type to insert. You can select a type that includes fittings, or a type that does not include fittings.
3. In the Options Bar, for Cable Tray, set the *Width*, *Height*, *Middle Elevation* (as shown in Figure 12–55), tagging options, and *Bend Radius*.

Figure 12–55

For Conduit, set the *Diameter*, *Middle Elevation* (as shown in Figure 12–56), and tagging options.

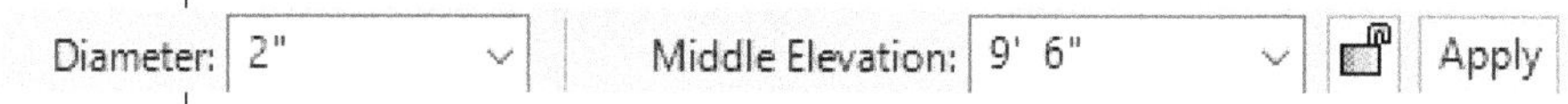

Diameter: 2"   Middle Elevation: 9' 6"   Apply

Figure 12–56

- Using ⬛ (Lock/unlock Specified Elevation) enables the locked segment elevations to maintain their current elevation. However, they cannot connect to segments on different elevations.
- To draw a vertical segment, specify a new *Offset* value in the Options Bar and click **Apply**.

4. In the *Modify | Place Cable Tray (Conduit)* tab>Tag panel, toggle ⬡① (Tag on Placement) off or on as needed.
5. Set the appropriate Placement Tools.
6. In the drawing, click at the required location to begin the cable tray or conduit run.
7. Move to a second location and click to place the other end point of the cable tray or conduit. Continue to click at other points to create additional cable tray segments starting from the last end point. Fittings are automatically added where needed.

8. Click ⬚ (Modify) to end and exit the command.

- In the *Modify | Place Cable Tray (Conduit)* tab>Placement Tools panel, click ⬚ (Automatically Connect) if you want a cable tray or conduit to connect to a lower segment and put in all of the right fittings as shown in the background in Figure 12–57. Toggle it off if you want to draw a tray that remains at the original elevation as shown in the foreground in Figure 12–57.

*When you snap to a connector, if **Automatically Connect** is not on, any changes in height and size are applied with the appropriate fittings.*

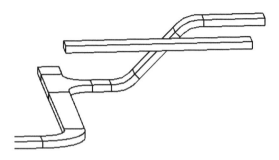

Figure 12–57

- To connect a conduit to a cable tray, start the conduit segment on a cable tray, regardless of elevation.

- For conduit, the **Placement Tools** option, ⌒ (Ignore Slope to Connect) draws conduit directly from a higher point to a lower point without any fittings, as shown on the right in Figure 12–58. If the option is off, then the conduit does not slope but bends down at the point of connection, as shown on the left in Figure 12–58.

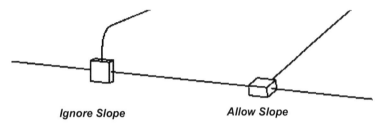

Ignore Slope   *Allow Slope*

Figure 12–58

Cable Tray and Conduit With and Without Fittings

The process of placing cable tray and conduit is the same whether you select a type with fittings (separate elbows and tees) or a type without fittings (in the field the elements are bent to create curves and bends). In both cases, the software adds fitting components, but the one with fittings includes options to create tees and crosses, as shown on the left in Figure 12–59. The type without fittings does not, as shown on the right in Figure 12–59.

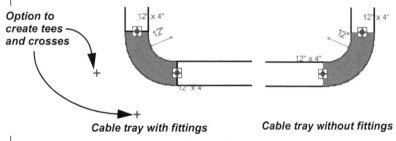

Option to create tees and crosses

Cable tray with fittings   *Cable tray without fittings*

Figure 12–59

- The without fittings type also displays as a continuous element without lines between the straight segments and the fittings. It can use the special Conduit Runs or Cable Tray Runs schedules to schedule each run for a real-life length of conduit that is going to be used at the site.

Cable Tray and Conduit Placement Options

⚙	**Justification Settings**	Opens the Justification Setting dialog box where you can specify the default settings for the **Horizontal Justification**, **Horizontal Offset**, and **Vertical Justification**.
⇉	**Inherit Elevation**	An on/off toggle. If the tool is toggled on and you start drawing a cable tray/conduit by snapping to an existing element, the new cable tray/conduit takes on the elevation of the existing one regardless of what is specified, as shown in Figure 12–60.
⬜	**Inherit Size**	An on/off toggle. If the tool is toggled on and you start drawing a cable tray/conduit by snapping to an existing element, the new cable tray/conduit takes on the size of the existing one regardless of what is specified, as shown in Figure 12–60.

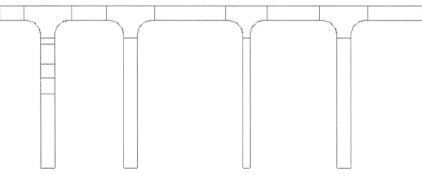

Offset lower　　*Inherit Elevation*　　*Size smaller*　　*Inherit Size*

Figure 12–60

Creating Parallel Conduit Runs

The **Parallel Conduits** tool facilitates the creation of conduit runs parallel to an existing run, as shown in Figure 12–61. This saves time because only one run needs to be laid out, and the tool generates the parallel runs for you.

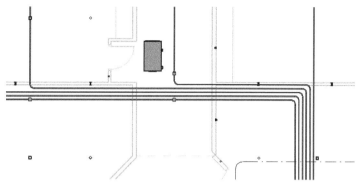

Figure 12–61

- Parallel conduit can be created in plan, section, elevation, and 3D views.

How To: Create Parallel Conduit Runs

1. Create the initial single run of conduit as required.

2. In the *Systems* tab>Electrical panel, click (Parallel Conduits).

3. In the *Modify | Place Parallel Conduits* tab>Parallel Conduits panel, set the options as required (see below).

4. Hover the cursor over the existing conduit and press <Tab> to select the existing run.

   - If you do not press <Tab>, the parallel conduit is only created for the single piece of existing conduit.

5. When the preview displays as required, click to create the parallel runs.

   - The preview and resulting parallel conduit varies depending on which side of the existing run you hover the cursor.

Parallel Conduit Creation Options

	Bend Radius	Parallel runs use the same bend radius as the original.
	Concentric Bend Radius	The bend radius of the parallel runs varies in order to remain concentric to the original run. This option results in concentric bend radii only when used with parallel conduit types without fittings. For conduit types with fittings, it gives the same result as the Same Bend Radius option.
n/a	**Horizontal Number**	The total number of parallel conduit runs in the horizontal direction.
n/a	**Horizontal Offset**	The distance between parallel conduit runs in the horizontal direction.
n/a	**Vertical Number**	The total number of parallel conduit runs in the vertical direction.
n/a	**Vertical Offset**	The distance between parallel conduit runs in the vertical direction.

- In section and elevation views, horizontal refers to parallel to the view (visually up, down, left or right from the original conduit). Vertical creates parallel conduit runs perpendicular to the view, in the direction of the user.

Modifying Cable Tray and Conduit

Cable tray and conduit can be modified using a variety of standard modifying tools. You can also change type, modify the justification, and (in the case of conduits) ignore slope to connect.

You can modify cable tray and conduit using universal methods by making changes in Properties, in the Options bar, and by using temporary dimensions, controls, and connectors. Modify tools, such as **Move**, **Rotate**, **Trim/Extend**, and **Align** enable you to place the elements in the correct locations.

Often a change using these tools automatically applies the correct fittings. For example, in Figure 12–62, the *Edit End Offset* control is changed from **12'-0"** on the left to **10'-0"** on the right and the appropriate cable tray fittings are automatically placed to facilitate the change in elevation.

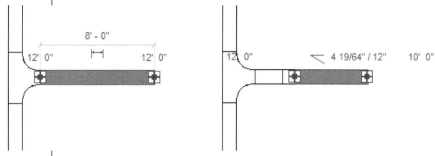

Figure 12–62

How To: Change the Type of Cable Tray and Conduit Runs

1. Select the cable tray or conduit run. Ensure that you filter out everything except related elements and fittings.

2. In the *Modify | Multi-Select* tab>Edit panel, click ⊞ (Change Type).

3. In the Type Selector, select a new type of conduit or cable tray. This changes the cable tray or conduit and also any related fittings. For example, as shown in Figure 12–63, a solid bottom cable tray is changed to a ladder cable tray.

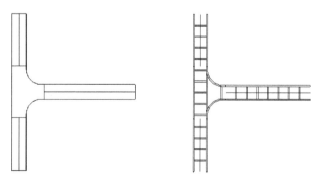

Figure 12–63

Modifying the Justification

If a cable tray or conduit run has different sizes along its run, you can modify the justification of the cable tray or conduit, as shown in Figure 12–64.

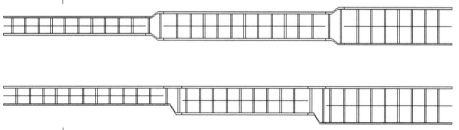

Figure 12–64

- While you can justify conduit, it is not typically required.

How To: Modify Cable Tray Justifications

1. Select the cable tray run.

2. In the *Modify | Multi-Select* tab>Edit Panel, click 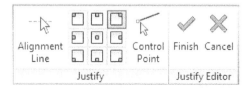 (Justify).
3. To specify the point on the cable tray you want to justify around, in the *Justification Editor* tab>Justify panel, click

   (Control Point) to cycle between the end point references. The alignment location displays as an arrow, as shown in Figure 12–65.

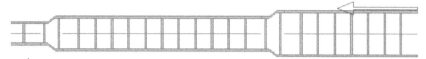

Figure 12–65

4. To indicate the required alignment, either click one of the nine alignment buttons in the Justify panel, or in a 3D view, use

   (Alignment Line) to select the required dashed line, as shown in Figure 12–66.

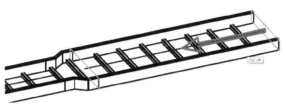

Figure 12–66

5. In the Justification Editor, click ✔ (Finish).

Adding Fittings

Revit MEP software automatically adds fittings to cable tray and conduit segments during their creation. It is also possible to manually add cable tray and conduit fittings to any existing segment or segment run. You can also use the controls on the fittings to modify the type, as shown in Figure 12–67.

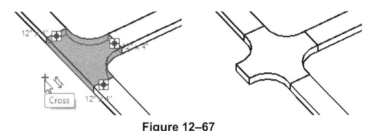

Figure 12–67

- Only Cable Tray and Conduit types with fittings display **+** to turn elbows into tees and tees into crosses.

How To: Manually Add a Cable Tray or Conduit Fitting to a Plan View

1. Open the view in which you are going to place the fitting.
2. In the *Systems* tab>Electrical panel, click either ⬭ (Cable Tray Fitting) or ⬭ (Conduit Fitting).
3. In the Type Selector, select the appropriate type you want to place.
4. In Properties, verify that the *Level* and *Offset* values are set as required.
5. Click in the view where you want to place the fitting.
6. Click ⬭ (Modify) to end and exit the command.

12.6 Testing Electrical Layouts

As you are working with electrical circuits, cable trays, and conduits, the **Show Disconnects** (shown in Figure 12–68) and **Check Circuits** tools can help you find areas that might need to be corrected.

These tools along with schedules based on spaces and lighting fixture properties can be used to help you perform lighting analysis.

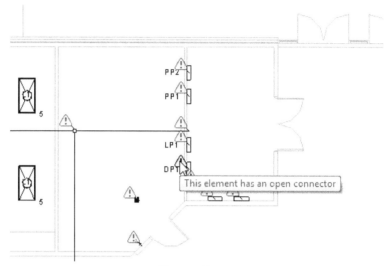

Figure 12–68

Often, these warnings are corrected as you continue working in a circuit and complete the full connection. However, some need to be corrected before the circuit works as required.

Hint: Displaying Only the MEP Analysis Panels

If you are using a copy of Autodesk Revit that has not been optimized for MEP, it is helpful to toggle off the Structural Analysis tools so that you can see the full MEP analysis panels. Expand the *File* tab and click **Options**. In the Options dialog box, in the User Interface panel, in *Tools and analysis*, clear **Structure analysis and tools**, as shown in Figure 12–69.

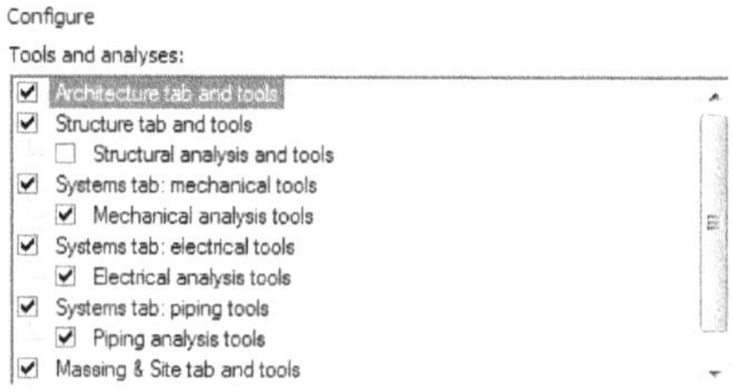

Configure
Tools and analyses:
- ☑ Architecture tab and tools
- ☑ Structure tab and tools
  - ☐ Structural analysis and tools
- ☑ Systems tab: mechanical tools
  - ☑ Mechanical analysis tools
- ☑ Systems tab: electrical tools
  - ☑ Electrical analysis tools
- ☑ Systems tab: piping tools
  - ☑ Piping analysis tools
- ☑ Massing & Site tab and tools

Figure 12–69

How To: Use the Show Disconnects Tool

1. In the *Analyze* tab>Check Systems panel, click  (Show Disconnects).
2. In the Show Disconnects Options dialog box, select the types of systems you want to display, as shown in Figure 12–70. Click **OK**.

Figure 12–70

3. The disconnects display ⚠ (Warning).
   - The disconnects continue to display until you either correct the situation or run **Show Disconnects** again and clear all of the selections.
4. Hover the cursor over the warning icon to display a tooltip with the warning. You can also click on the icon to open the Warning dialog box, shown in Figure 12–71.

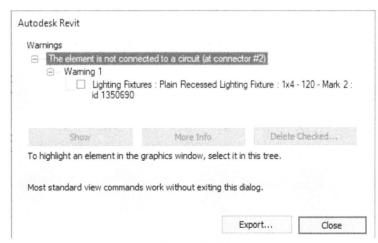

Figure 12–71

How To: Use the Check Circuits Tool

1. In the *Analyze* tab>Check Systems panel, click (Check Circuits) to toggle it on.
2. The (Warning) icon displays wherever there is an issue. Click on one of the icons to open the Warning alert box, shown in Figure 12–72.

Warning
Circuit is not assigned to a panel

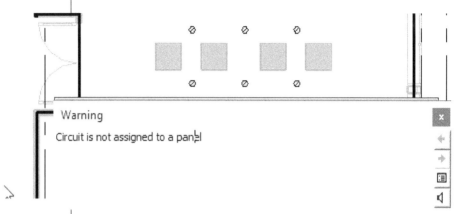

Figure 12–72

- For icons that have more than one warning, in the Warning alert box, click (Next Warning) and (Previous Warning) to search through the list.

- Click (Expand Warning Dialog) to open the dialog box, shown in Figure 12–73. You can expand each node in the box and select elements to display or delete.

*If there are a lot of warnings to review, you can click **Export...** and save an HTML report*

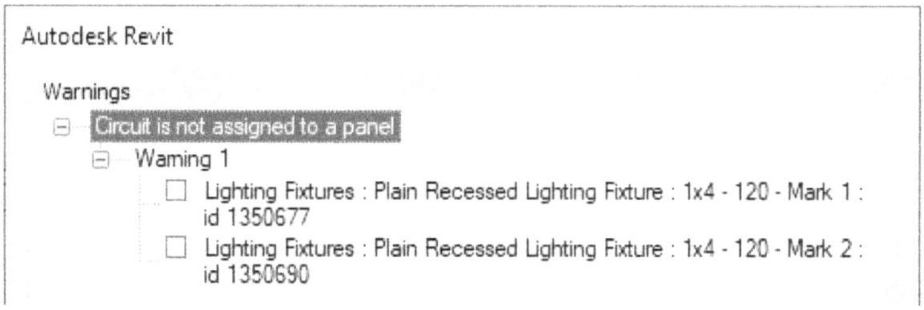

Autodesk Revit
Warnings
Circuit is not assigned to a panel
Warning 1
Lighting Fixtures : Plain Recessed Lighting Fixture : 1x4 - 120 - Mark 1 : id 1350677
Lighting Fixtures : Plain Recessed Lighting Fixture : 1x4 - 120 - Mark 2 : id 1350690

Figure 12–73

Hint: Color Fill Legends for Analysis

An additional way to analyze information about lighting and power is to create a color fill legend. Electrical color fills are typically created from spaces and can be set for parameters such as the Average Estimated Illumination or Specified Lighting Load for the spaces.

How To: Place a Color Fill Legend

1. Set the appropriate *Color Scheme* in the Properties of the view.
2. In the *Annotate* tab>Color Fill panel, click (Color Fill Legend) to place the appropriate legend.

Practice 12d | Add Conduit

Practice Objective

- Add conduit to a lighting plan.

In this practice, you will add conduit and fittings to a project, as shown in Figure 12–74.

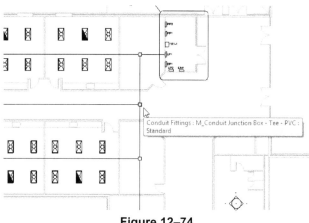

Figure 12–74

1. In the practice files *Electrical* folder, open **Conduit-School-MEP.rvt**.

2. In the *Systems* tab>Electrical panel title bar, click ⌐ (Electrical Settings).

3. In the Electrical Settings dialog box, select **Angles**.

4. In the **Angles** pane, select **Use specific angles** and clear the **22.50** and **11.25** check marks, as shown in Figure 12–75.

This limits the angles that you can draw, which is typically used to match factory fittings.

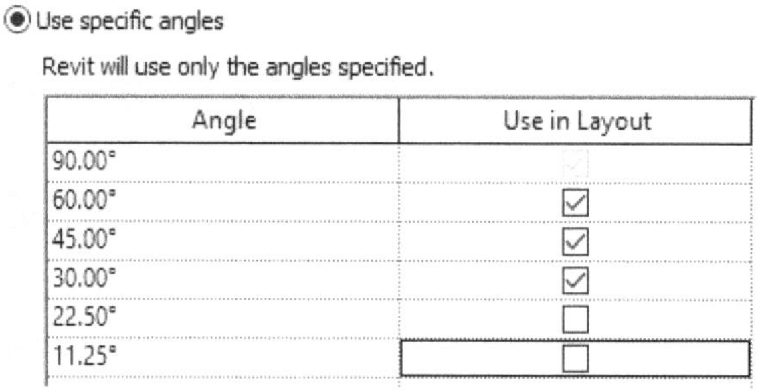

⦿ Use specific angles

Revit will use only the angles specified.

Angle	Use in Layout
90.00°	☑
60.00°	☑
45.00°	☑
30.00°	☑
22.50°	☐
11.25°	☐

Figure 12–75

5. Click **OK** to close the dialog box.

6. Open the Electrical>Lighting>Floor Plans>**01 Lighting Plan** view, if it is not already open.

7. Zoom into the electrical room area so that some portion of the classroom wing is also displayed.

8. In the *Systems* tab>Electrical panel, click 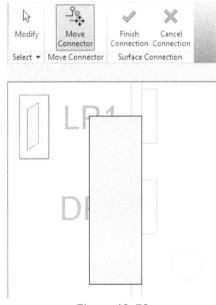 (Conduit).

9. In the Type Selector, select **Conduit with Fittings - Electrical Metallic Tubing (EMT)**.

10. In the Options Bar, verify that the *Diameter* is set to **2"** and the *Middle Elevation* is set to **9'-6"**.

11. In the Electrical Room, select the panel **LP1**. The program zooms in on the connector and the *Surface Connection* tab displays in the Ribbon, as shown in Figure 12–76.

Figure 12–76

12. Click (Finish Connection).

13. Draw the conduit down the length of the north wing.

14. Press <Esc> once to release the end of the conduit, but remain in the **Conduit** command. Draw another line of conduit vertically and then horizontally across the bottom of the other classroom in the south wing, as shown in Figure 12–77.

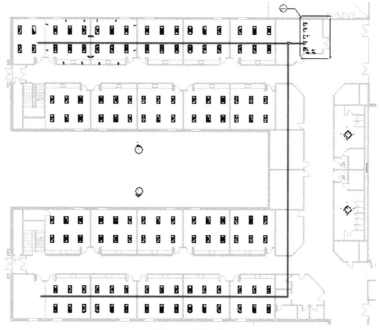

Figure 12–77

15. Draw additional lines of conduit from the vertical line down each of the hallways and the other classrooms.

16. Click **Modify** to end the command.

17. Zoom in so that you can see where the junction boxes are automatically placed, as shown in Figure 12–78.

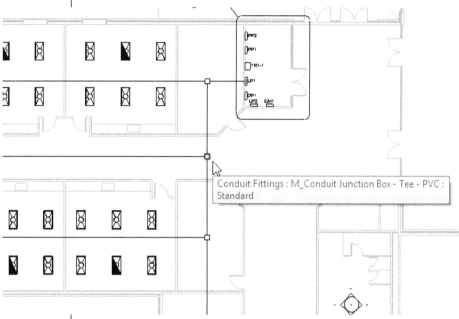

Conduit Fittings : M_Conduit Junction Box - Tee - PVC : Standard

Figure 12–78

18. Pan over to the end of one of the runs.

19. In the *Systems* tab>Electrical panel, click (Conduit Fitting).

20. In the Type Selector, select **Conduit Junction Box - Cross - Aluminum - Standard**.

21. Place the junction box at the end of the conduit segment you just created. Select the endpoint of the conduit so that the junction box takes on the height and size of the conduit.

22. Add other junction boxes as required along the lines of conduit. Snap to the conduit (Nearest) to place it correctly.

23. Save and close the project.

Chapter Review Questions

1. Which of the following is NOT a type of system that can be created in the Autodesk Revit MEP software?

   a. Power

   b. Communications

   c. Low Voltage

   d. Lighting

2. Which of the following are electrical devices that can be added to a project? (Select all that apply.)

   a. Lighting switches

   b. Communication

   c. Electrical Panels

   d. Data

3. What happens to hosted, face-based lighting fixtures in an Autodesk Revit MEP project if the ceiling (as shown in Figure 12–79) is deleted and then a new one is added at a different height in the architectural linked model?

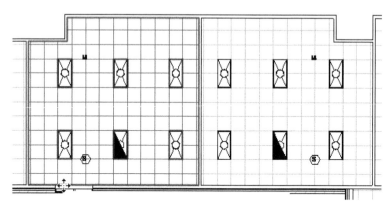

Figure 12–79

   a. The hosted lighting fixtures are deleted.

   b. A warning displays that you need a coordination review.

   c. A warning displays that the hosting element no longer exists in the linked model.

   d. Nothing happens, but in the 3D view, the light fixtures are not connected to the ceiling.

4. What must you do to change the type of a cable tray or conduit run, as shown in Figure 12–80?

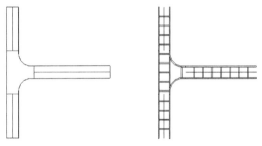

Figure 12–80

a. Redraw the run using the correct type.

b. Select one element in the run and change it in the Type Selector.

c. Select all of the elements in the run and change it in the Type Selector.

d. Select all the elements in the run and use **Change Type**.

5. Can a panel schedule, such as that shown in Figure 12–81, be modified once a circuit has been added to it?

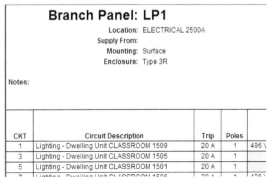

Figure 12–81

a. Yes

b. No

6. How do you move a spare circuit in a panel schedule?

a. Select it and use the **Move** tool in the *Modify* tab.

b. Select it and use **Move Up**, **Move Down**, or **Move Across**.

c. Unlock it and use the **Move** tools in the Circuits panel.

d. Move the circuit in the plan view. The panel schedule updates accordingly.

Command Summary

Button	Command	Location
Electrical Devices and Components		
	Communication	• **Ribbon:** *Systems* tab>Electrical panel>expand Device
	Data	• **Ribbon:** *Systems* tab>Electrical panel>expand Device
	Electrical Equipment	• **Ribbon:** *Systems* tab>Electrical panel
	Electrical Fixture	• **Ribbon:** *Systems* tab>Electrical panel>expand Device
	Fire Alarm	• **Ribbon:** *Systems* tab>Electrical panel>expand Device
	Lighting (switch)	• **Ribbon:** *Systems* tab>Electrical panel>expand Device
	Lighting Fixture	• **Ribbon:** *Systems* tab>Electrical panel
	Nurse Call	• **Ribbon:** *Systems* tab>Electrical panel>expand Device
	Security	• **Ribbon:** *Systems* tab>Electrical panel>expand Device
	Telephone	• **Ribbon:** *Systems* tab>Electrical panel>expand Device
Electrical Circuits		
	Add to Circuit	• **Ribbon:** *Edit Circuit* tab>Edit Circuit panel
	Create Panel Schedule	• **Ribbon:** *Modify | Electrical Equipment* tab>Electrical panel
	Edit Circuit	• **Ribbon:** *Modify | Electrical Circuits* tab>System Tools panel
	Edit Path (Circuits)	• **Ribbon:** *Modify | Electrical Circuits* tab>System Tools panel
	Edit a Template	• **Ribbon:** *Manage* tab>Settings panel expand **Panel Schedule Templates**
	Manage Templates	• **Ribbon:** *Manage* tab>Settings panel expand **Panel Schedule Templates**

	Power	• **Ribbon:** *Modify	Lighting Fixtures* tab or *Modify Electrical Equipment* tab> Create Systems panel
	Remove from Circuit	• **Ribbon:** *Edit Circuit* tab>Edit Circuit panel
	Select Panel	• **Ribbon:** *Modify	Electrical Circuits* tab>System Tools panel

Cable Tray and Conduit

	Automatically Connect	• **Ribbon:** *Modify	Place Cable Tray* or *Place Conduit* tab>Placement Tools panel
	Cable Tray	• **Ribbon:** *Systems* tab>Electrical panel
	Cable Tray Fitting	• **Ribbon:** *Systems* tab>Electrical panel
	Conduit	• **Ribbon:** *Systems* tab>Electrical panel
	Conduit Fitting	• **Ribbon:** *Systems* tab>Electrical panel
	Ignore Slope to Connect (Conduit only)	• **Ribbon:** *Modify	Place Conduit* tab> Placement Tools panel
	Inherit Elevation	• **Ribbon:** *Modify	Place Cable Tray* or *Place Conduit* tab>Placement Tools panel
	Inherit Size	• **Ribbon:** *Modify	Place Cable Tray* or *Place Conduit* tab>Placement Tools panel
	Justification	• **Ribbon:** *Modify	Place Cable Tray* or *Place Conduit* tab>Placement Tools panel
	Parallel Conduits	• **Ribbon:** *Systems* tab>Electrical panel

Creating Construction Documents

The accurate creation of construction documents in the Autodesk® Revit® software ensures that the design is correctly communicated to downstream users. Construction documents are created primarily in special views called sheets. Selecting title blocks, assigning title block information, placing views, and printing the sheets are essential steps in the construction documentation process.

Learning Objectives in This Chapter

- Add sheets with title blocks and views of a project.
- Enter the title block information for individual sheets and for an entire project.
- Place and organize views on sheets.
- Print sheets using the default Print dialog box.

13.1 Setting Up Sheets

While you are modeling a project, the foundations of the working drawings are already in progress. Any view (such as a floor plan, section, callout, or schedule) can be placed on a sheet, as shown in Figure 13–1.

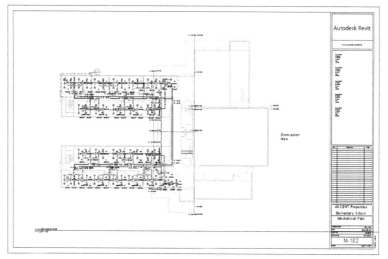

Figure 13–1

- Company templates can be created with standard sheets using the company (or project) title block and related views already placed on the sheet.

- The sheet size is based on the selected title block family.

- Sheets are listed in the *Sheets* area in the Project Browser.

- Most information on sheets is included in the views. You can add general notes and other non-model elements directly to the sheet, though it is better to add them using drafting views or legends, as these can be placed on multiple sheets.

How To: Set Up Sheets

1. In the Project Browser, right-click on the *Sheets* area header and select **New Sheet...** or in the *View* tab>Sheet

   Composition panel, click (Sheet).

2. In the New Sheet dialog box, select a title block from the list, as shown in Figure 13–2. Alternatively, if there is a list of placeholder sheets, select one or more from the list.

*Click **Load...** to load a sheet from the library.*

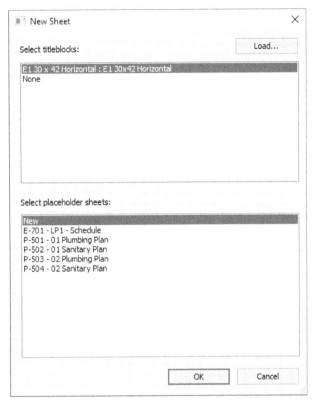

Hold <Ctrl> to select multiple placeholder sheets.

Figure 13–2

3. Click **OK**. A new sheet is created using the preferred title block.
4. Fill out the information in the title block as needed.
5. Add views to the sheet.

- When you create sheets, the next sheet is incremented numerically.

- Double-click on the sheet name to change the name and number in the Sheet Title dialog box.

- When you change the *Sheet Name* and/or *Number* in the title block, it automatically changes the name and number of the sheet in the Project Browser.

- The plot stamp on the side of the sheet automatically updates according to the current date and time. The format of the display uses the regional settings of your computer.

- The Scale is automatically entered when a view is inserted onto a sheet. If a sheet has multiple views with different scales, the scale displays **As Indicated.**

Sheet (Title Block) Properties

Each new sheet includes a title block. You can change the title block information in Properties, as shown in Figure 13–3, or by selecting any blue label you want to edit (Sheet Name, Sheet Number, Drawn by, etc.), as shown in Figure 13–4.

Figure 13–3   Figure 13–4

Properties that apply to all sheets can be entered in the Project Information dialog box (as shown in Figure 13–5). In the *Manage* tab>Settings panel, click 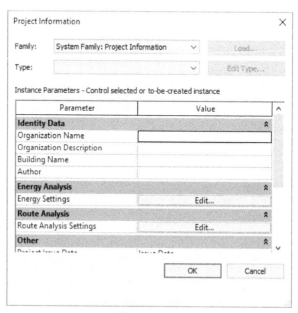 (Project Information).

Figure 13–5

13.2 Placing and Modifying Views on Sheets

The process of adding views to a sheet is simple. Drag and drop a view from the Project Browser onto the sheet. The new view on the sheet is displayed at the scale specified in the original view. The view title displays the name, number, and scale of the view, as shown in Figure 13–6.

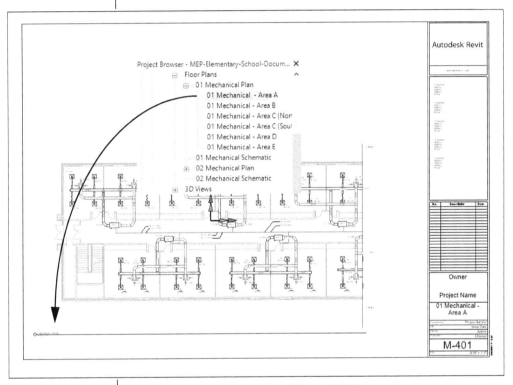

Figure 13–6

How To: Place Views on Sheets

Alignment lines from existing views display to help you place additional views.

1. Set up the view as you want it to display on the sheet, including the scale and visibility of elements.
2. Create or open the sheet where you want to place the view.
3. Select the view in the Project Browser, and drag and drop it onto the sheet.
4. The center of the view is attached to the cursor. Click to place it on the sheet.

Placing Views on Sheets

- Views can only be placed on a sheet once. However, you can duplicate the view and place that copy on a sheet.

- Views on a sheet are associative. They automatically update to reflect changes to the project.

- Each view on a sheet is listed under the sheet name in the Project Browser, as shown in Figure 13–7.

  - Similar to other views on a sheet, panel schedules are listed under the sheet's views.

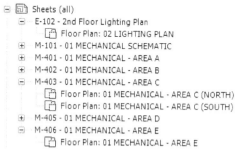

Figure 13–7

- You can also use two other methods to place views on sheets:

  - In the Project Browser, right-click on the sheet name and select **Add View...**
  - In the *View* tab>Sheet Composition panel, click

    (Place View).

This method lists only those views which have not yet been placed on a sheet.

Then, in the Views dialog box (shown in Figure 13–8), select the view you want to use and click **Add View to Sheet.**

Figure 13–8

- To remove a view from a sheet, select it and press <Delete>. Alternatively, in the Project Browser, expand the individual sheet information to show the views, right-click on the view name and select **Remove From Sheet**.

Hint: Setting Up the Project Browser

To view and change the Project Browser's types, select the top level node of the Project Browser (which is set to *Views (all)* by default) and select the type you want to use from the Type Selector. For example, you can set the Browser to only display views that are not on sheets, as shown in Figure 13–9.

Figure 13–9

Moving Views and View Titles

You can also use the
Move *command or the*
arrow keys to move a
view.

- To move a view on a sheet, select the viewport and drag it to a new location. The view title moves with the view.

- To move only the view title, select the title and drag it to the new location.

- To modify the length of the line under the title name, select the viewport and drag the controls, as shown in Figure 13–10. Hint: If you are trying to grab the control near the view title bubble and name, use <Tab> to cycle the selection options.

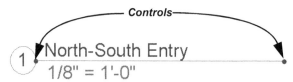

Figure 13–10

- To change the title of a view on a sheet without changing its name in the Project Browser, in the *Identity Data* area in Properties, type a new title for the *Title on Sheet* parameter, as shown in Figure 13–11.

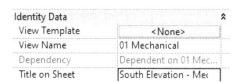

Figure 13–11

Rotating Views

- When creating a vertical sheet, you can rotate the view on the sheet by 90 degrees. Select the view and set the direction of rotation in the Rotation on Sheet drop-down list in the Options Bar, as shown in Figure 13–12.

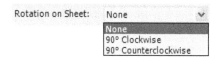

Figure 13–12

- To rotate a view to an angle other than 90 degrees, open the view, toggle on and select the crop region and use the **Rotate** command to change the angle.

Working Inside Views

To make small changes to a view while working on a sheet:

- Double-click *inside* the view to activate it.
- Double-click *outside* the view to deactivate it.

Only elements in the viewport are available for modification. The rest of the sheet is grayed out, as shown in Figure 13–13.

Only use this method for small changes. Significant changes should be made directly in the view.

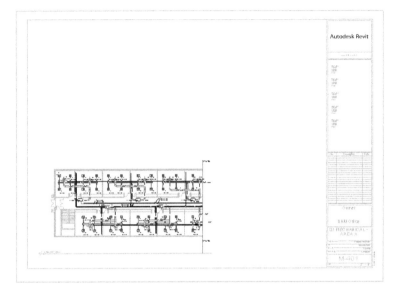

Figure 13–13

- You can activate and deactivate views by right-clicking on the edge of the view or by using the tools found on the *Modify | Viewports* and *Views* tab>Sheet Composition panel.

- Changes you make to elements when a view is activated also display in the original view.

- If you are unsure which sheet a view is on, right-click on the view in the Project Browser and select **Open Sheet**. This item is grayed out if the view has not been placed on a sheet and is not available for schedules and legends which can be placed on more than one sheet.

Resizing Views on Sheets

Each view displays the extents of the model or the elements contained in the crop region. If the view does not fit on a sheet (as shown in Figure 13–14), you might need to crop the view or move the elevation markers closer to the building.

If the extents of the view change dramatically based on a scale change or a crop region, it is easier to delete the view on the sheet and drag it over again.

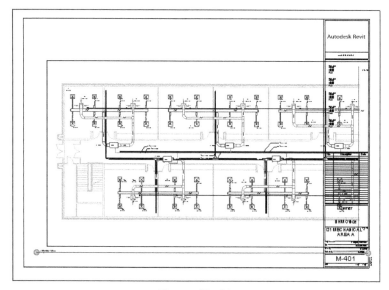

Figure 13–14

Create Similar Views on Sheets

After placing a view onto a sheet, you can add additional views to the sheet. You can select one view at a time to add.

- With the view selected on the sheet, from the *Modify | Panel Schedule Graphics* tab>Create panel, click ⌗ (Create Similar).
- From the Views dialog box, select a view and click **Add View to Sheet**, as shown in Figure 13–15.

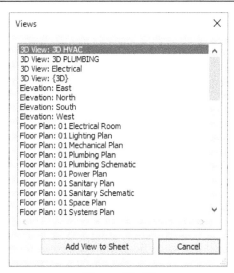

Figure 13–15

- For information about laying out views on sheets using guide grids, see *Section A.6 Guide Grids and Sheets.*

- For information about working with revisions in views and on sheets, see *Section A.7 Revision Tracking.*

Hint: Add an Image to a Sheet

Company logos and renderings saved to image files (such as .JPG and .PNG) can be added directly on a sheet or in a view.

1. In the *Insert* tab>Import panel, click  (Image).
2. In the Import Image dialog box, select and open the image file. The extents of the image display, as shown in Figure 13–16.

Figure 13–16

3. Place the image where you want it.
4. The image is displayed. Pick one of the grips and extend it to modify the size of the image.

• In Properties, you can adjust the height and width and also set the *Draw Layer* to either **Background** or **Foreground**, as shown in Figure 13–17.

Dimensions	☆
Width	1' 5 185/256"
Height	1' 1 41/64"
Horizontal Scale	1.000000
Vertical Scale	1.000000
Lock Proportions	☑
Other	☆
Draw Layer	Background

Figure 13–17

• You can select more than one image at a time and move them as a group to the background or foreground.

• In the *Modify | Raster Images* tab (as shown in Figure 13–18), you can access the Arrange options and Manage Images.

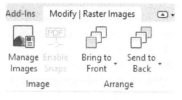

Figure 13–18

Practice 13a | Create Construction Documents

Practice Objectives

- Set up project properties.
- Create sheets individually.
- Modify views to prepare them to be placed on sheets.
- Place views on sheets.

In this practice, you will complete the project information, add new sheets and use existing sheets. You will fill in title block information and then add views to sheets, such as the Lighting Plan sheet shown in Figure 13–19. Complete as many sheets as you have time for.

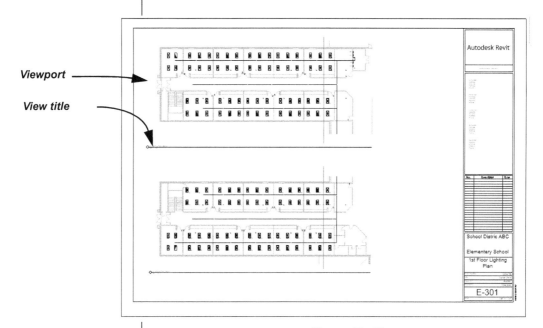

Viewport

View title

Figure 13–19

Task 1 - Complete the project information.

1. In the practice files *Documents* folder, open
   Documents-School-MEP.rvt.

2. In the *Manage* tab>Settings panel, click 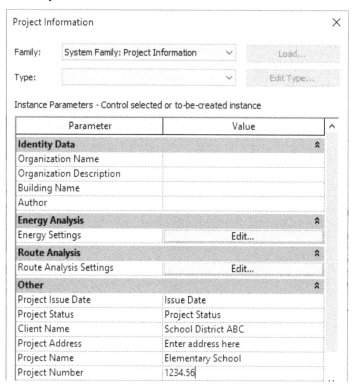 (Project
   Information).

3. In the Project Properties dialog box, add the following values,
   as shown in Figure 13–20.
   - *Client Name:* **School District ABC**
   - *Project Name:* **Elementary School**
   - *Project Number:* **1234.56**

These values are added automatically to any sheet you create.

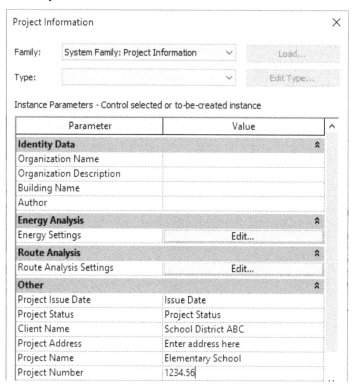

Parameter	Value
Identity Data	
Organization Name	
Organization Description	
Building Name	
Author	
Energy Analysis	
Energy Settings	Edit...
Route Analysis	
Route Analysis Settings	Edit...
Other	
Project Issue Date	Issue Date
Project Status	Project Status
Client Name	School District ABC
Project Address	Enter address here
Project Name	Elementary School
Project Number	1234.56

Figure 13–20

4. Click **OK**.

5. In the Project Browser, expand the *Sheets (all)* area and
   open **M-101 - 01 Mechanical Schematic**. There is already a
   view placed on the sheet.

6. Zoom in on the title block and review the contents. The Project Parameters that you added are automatically applied to the sheet, as shown in Figure 13–21.

*The Scale is automatically entered when a view is inserted onto a sheet. If a sheet has multiple scales, the scale reads **As Indicated**.*

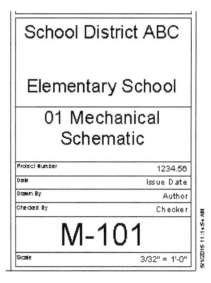

School District ABC

Elementary School

01 Mechanical Schematic

Project Number	1234.56
Date	Issue Date
Drawn By	Author
Checked By	Checker

M-101

| Scale | 3/32" = 1'-0" |

Figure 13–21

7. Set *Drawn by* to your initials. Leave the *Checked by* and *Issue Date* parameters as is.

8. Open another sheet. The project parameter values are repeated but note that the *Drawn By* value is not added because it is a parameter that is set per sheet.

9. Review the other existing Mechanical sheets and save the project.

Task 2 - Add sheets.

1. In the *View* tab>Sheet Composition panel, click (Sheet).

2. In the New Sheet dialog box, select the title block **E1 30 x42 Horizontal** and click **OK**.

3. In the Project Browser, select the new sheet, right-click, and select **Rename**.

4. In the Sheet Title dialog box, set *Number* as **C-101**, *Name* as **Cover Sheet**, and click **OK**. The title block updates as shown in Figure 13–22.

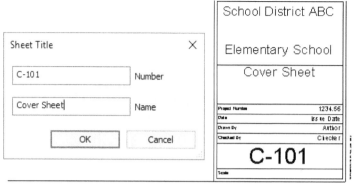

Figure 13–22

5. In the Project Browser, right-click on *Sheets (all)* and select **New Sheet...**.

6. Using the same title block, create the following sheets:
   - E-301 - 1st Floor Lighting Plan
   - E-302 - 2nd Floor Lighting Plan
   - E-303 - Power Panel Plan Detail
   - P-509 - Plumbing 3D

You can change the sheet number and name in the title block or by renaming it in the Project Browser.

7. In the Project Browser, in the *Sheets (all)* area, note that these new sheets, the other sheets that you created, and the M-# sheets that were already created for you are displayed.

8. Save the project.

Task 3 - Set up and add views to sheets.

1. In the Project Browser, in the **Electrical>Lighting>Floor Plans**, right-click on the **01 Lighting Plan** view and using **Duplicate as Dependent**, create two copies of dependent views. Name them **01 Lighting Plan - North** and **01 Lighting Plan - South**.

2. Open the **01 Lighting Plan - North** view, zoom out to see the crop region (toggle it on, if needed), and resize it to fit the north classroom wing, as shown in Figure 13–23.

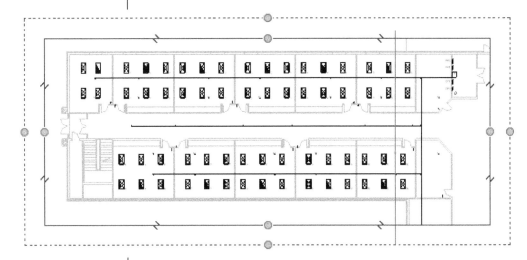

Figure 13–23

3. Toggle the crop region off.

4. Repeat the steps with the **01 Lighting Plan - South** view.

5. Open the sheet **E-301 - 1st Floor Lighting Plan** and drag and drop the **1st Floor Lighting Plan North** and **South** views you just created onto it.

6. Open the **E-303 - Power Panel Plan Detail** sheet and drag and drop the **Power Panel Callout** view onto it.

7. On the sheet, double-click on the **Power Panel Callout** to activate the view.

8. Open Visibility Graphics and expand **Site**. Uncheck **Internal Origins**.

9. Double-click anywhere outside the active view to deactivate it.

You must first select the viewport on the sheet, then click on the view title to adjust it.

10. Select the **Power Panel Callout** view on the sheet and use the controls to adjust the view title so it fits under the callout, as shown in Figure 13–24. Hint: Use <Tab> to select the grip and not the view title bubble or name.

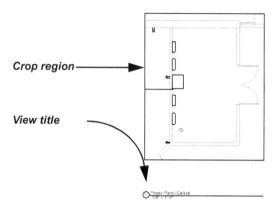

Crop region

View title

Figure 13–24

11. Switch to the **01 Power Plan** view. Zoom in on the callout marker by the power panels. Notice that it has now been automatically assigned a detail and sheet number, as shown in Figure 13–25.

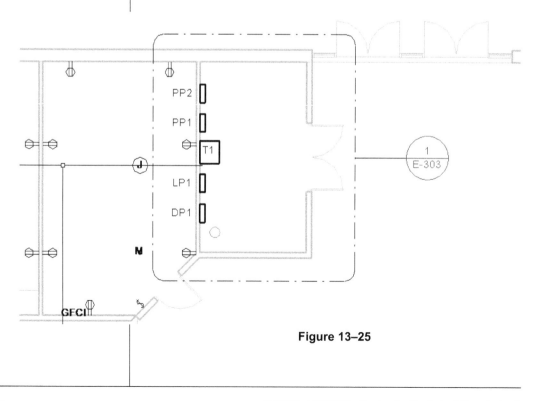

Figure 13–25

12. Repeat the process of adding views and schedules to sheets using the views and schedules you have available.

- Modify crop regions and hide unnecessary elements in the views. Toggle off crop regions after you have modified them.
- Verify the scale of a view in Properties before placing it on a sheet.
- Use alignment lines to help place multiple views on one sheet.
- Change the view title if needed, to more accurately describe what is on the sheet.
- To make minor changes to a view once it is on a sheet, right-click on the view and select **Activate View.** To return to the sheet, right-click on the view and select **Deactivate View**.
- To make larger changes to a view on a sheet, return to the original view.
- If you modify the size of a view that is already placed on a sheet, delete the view from the sheet and replace it with the updated view.

13. Save the project.

13.3 Printing Sheets

With the **Print** command, you can print individual sheets or a list of selected sheets. You can also print an individual view or a portion of a view for check prints or presentations. To open the Print dialog box (shown in Figure 13–26), in the *File* tab, click

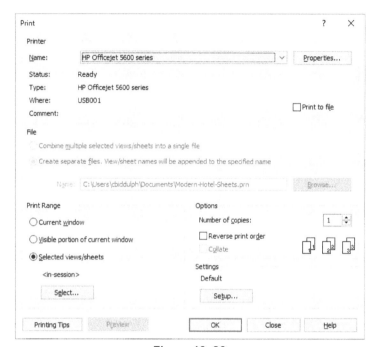 (Print).

Figure 13–26

Printing Options

The Print dialog box is divided into the following areas: *Printer*, *File*, *Print Range, Options*, and *Settings*. Modify them as needed to produce the plot you want.

- **Printing Tips**: Opens Autodesk WikiHelp online, in which you can find help with troubleshooting printing issues.

- **Preview**: Opens a preview of the print output so that you can see what is going to be printed.

Printer

Select from the list of available printers, as shown in Figure 13–27. Click **Properties...** to adjust the properties of the selected printer. The options vary according to the printer. Select the **Print to file** option to print to a file rather than directly to a printer. You can create .PLT or .PRN files.

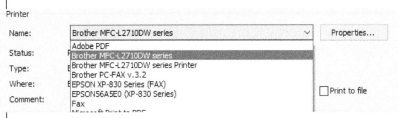

Figure 13–27

- You must have a .PDF print driver installed on your system to print to PDF.

File

The *File* area is only available if the **Print to file** option has been selected in the *Printer* area or if you are printing to an electronic-only type of printer. You can create one file or multiple files depending on the type of printer you are using, as shown in Figure 13–28. Click **Browse...** to select the file location and name.

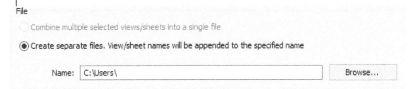

Figure 13–28

Print Range

The *Print Range* area enables you to print individual views/sheets or sets of views/sheets, as shown in Figure 13–29.

Figure 13–29

- **Current window**: Prints the entire current sheet or view you have open.

- **Visible portion of current window**: Prints only what is displayed in the current sheet or view.

- **Selected views/sheets**: Prints multiple views or sheets. Click **Select...** to open the View/Sheet Set dialog box to choose what to include in the print set. You can save these sets by name so that you can more easily print the same group again.

Options

If your printer supports multiple copies, you can specify the number in the *Options* area, as shown in Figure 13–30. You can also reverse the print order or collate your prints. These options are also available in the printer properties.

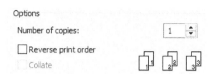

Figure 13–30

Settings

Click **Setup**... to open the Print Setup dialog box, as shown in Figure 13–31. Here, you can specify the *Orientation* and *Zoom* settings, among others. You can also save these settings by name.

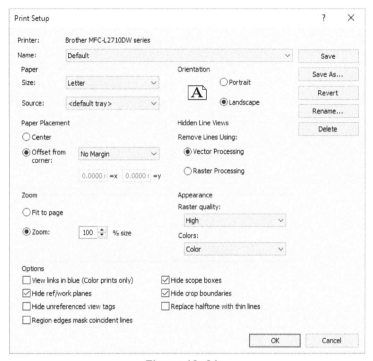

Figure 13–31

- In the *Options* area, specify the types of elements you want to print or not print. Unless specified, all of the elements in a view or sheet print.

- Sheets should always be printed at **Zoom** set to **100%** size unless you are creating a quick markup set that does not need to be exact.

Chapter Review Questions

1. How do you specify the size of a sheet?

    a. In the Sheet Properties, specify the **Sheet Size**.

    b. In the Options Bar, specify the **Sheet Size**.

    c. In the New Sheet dialog box, select a title block to control the Sheet Size.

    d. In the Sheet view, right-click and select **Sheet Size**.

2. How is the title block information filled in as shown in Figure 13–32? (Select all that apply.)

Figure 13–32

    a. Select the title block and select the label that you want to change.

    b. Select the title block and modify it in Properties.

    c. Right-click on the Sheet in the Project Browser and select **Information**.

    d. Some of the information is filled in automatically.

3. On how many sheets can a floor plan view be placed?

    a. 1

    b. 2-5

    c. 6+

    d. As many as you want.

4. Which of the following is the best method to use if the size of a view is too large for a sheet, as shown in Figure 13–33?

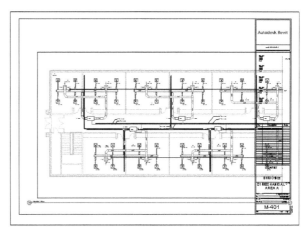

Figure 13–33

a. Delete the view, change the scale in the view and place the view back on the sheet.

b. Activate the view and change the View Scale.

5. How do you set up a view on a sheet that only displays part of a floor plan, as shown in Figure 13–34?

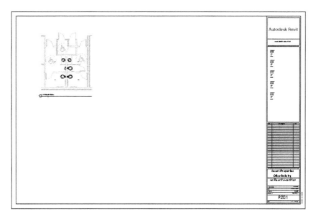

Figure 13–34

a. Drag and drop the view to the sheet and use the crop region to modify it.

b. Activate the view and rescale it.

c. Create a callout view displaying the part that you want to use and place the callout view on the sheet.

d. Open the view in the Project Browser and change the View Scale.

Command Summary

Button	Command	Location
	Activate View	• **Ribbon:** *(select the view) Modify | Viewports* tab>Viewport panel • **Double-click:** *(in viewport)* • **Right-click:** *(on view)* Activate View
	Deactivate View	• **Ribbon:** *View* tab>Sheet Composition panel>expand Viewports • **Double-click:** *(on sheet)* • **Right-click:** *(on view)* Deactivate View
	Place View	• **Ribbon:** *View* tab>Sheet Composition panel
	Print	• **File tab**
	Sheet	• **Ribbon:** *View* tab>Sheet Composition panel

Chapter

14

Annotating Construction Documents

When you create construction documents, annotations are required to show the design intent. Annotations such as dimensions and text can be added to views at any time during the creation of a project. Detail lines and symbols can also be added to views as you create the working drawing sheets, while legends can be created to provide a place to document any symbols that are used in a project.

Learning Objectives in This Chapter

- Add dimensions to the model as a part of the working drawings.
- Add text to a view and use leaders to create notes pointing to a specific part of the model.
- Create text types using different fonts and sizes to suit your company standards.
- Draw detail lines to further enhance the documentation view.
- Add view-specific annotation symbols for added clarity.
- Create legend views and populate them with symbols of elements in the project.

14.1 Working with Dimensions

You can create permanent dimensions using aligned, linear, angular, radial, diameter, and arc length dimensions. These can be individual or a string of dimensions, as shown in Figure 14–1. With aligned dimensions, you can also dimension entire walls with openings, grid lines, and/or intersecting walls.

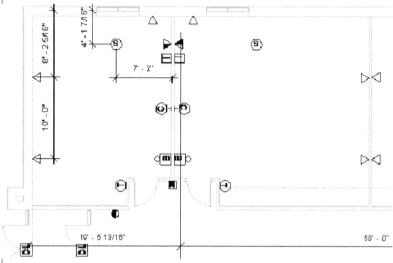

Figure 14–1

- Dimensions referencing model elements must be added to the model in a view. You can dimension on sheets, but only to items added directly on the sheets.

- Dimensions are available in the *Annotate* tab>Dimension panel, as shown in Figure 14–2, and the *Modify* tab>Measure panel.

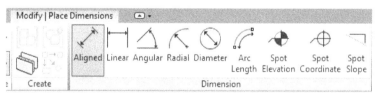

Figure 14–2

How To: Add Aligned Dimensions with Options

1. Start the ✎ (Aligned) command or type **DI**.
2. In the Type Selector, select a dimension style.

✎ *(Aligned) is also located in the Quick Access Toolbar.*

3. In the Options Bar, select the location line of the wall to dimension from, as shown in Figure 14–3.

- This option can be changed as you add dimensions.

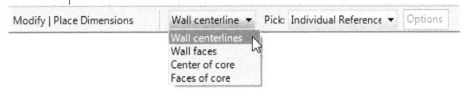

Figure 14–3

- Most MEP fixtures have alignment lines along their centerline. You can also dimension to individual parts of components, as shown in Figure 14–4.

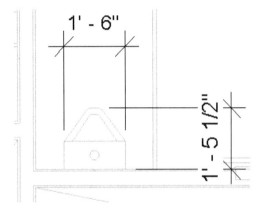

Figure 14–4

4. In the Options Bar, select your preference from the Pick drop-down list:

- **Individual References**: Select the elements in order (as shown in Figure 14–5) and then click in empty space to position the dimension string.

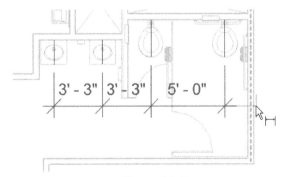

Figure 14–5

- **Entire Walls**: (Walls only) Select the wall you want to dimension.

How To: Add Other Types of Dimensions

*When the **Dimension** command is active, the dimension methods are also accessible in the Modify | Place Dimensions tab> Dimension panel.*

1. In the *Annotate* tab>Dimension panel, select a dimension method.

	Aligned	Most commonly used dimension type. Select individual elements or entire walls to dimension.
	Linear	Used when you need to specify certain points on elements.
	Angular	Used to dimension the angle between two elements.
	Radial	Used to dimension the radius of circular elements.
	Diameter	Used to dimension the diameter of circular elements.
	Arc Length	Used to dimension the length of the arc of circular elements.

2. In the Type Selector, select the dimension type.
3. Follow the prompts for the selected method.

Modifying Dimensions

When you move elements that are dimensioned, the dimensions automatically update. You can also modify dimensions by selecting a dimension or dimension string and making changes, as shown in Figure 14–6.

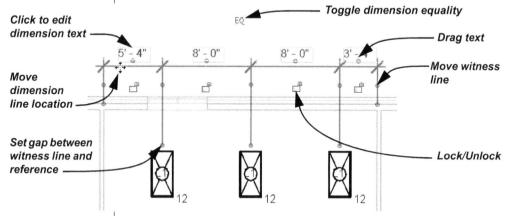

Figure 14–6

- To move the dimension text, select the **Drag text** control under the text and drag it to a new location. It automatically creates a leader from the dimension line if you drag it away. The style of the leader (arc or line) depends on the dimension style.

- To move the dimension line (the line parallel to the element being dimensioned), simply drag the line to a new location or select the dimension and drag the ⁙ (Drag to new position) control.

- To change the gap between the witness line and the element being dimensioned, drag the control at the end of the witness line.

- To move the witness line (the line perpendicular to the element being dimensioned) to a different element or face of a wall, use the **Move Witness Line** control in the middle of the witness line. While moving the witness line, you can hover your cursor over an element or component and press <Tab> repeatedly to cycle through the various options. You can also drag this control to move the witness line to a different element, or right-click on the control and select **Move Witness Line**.

Adding and Deleting Dimensions in a String

- To add a witness line to a string of dimensions, select the dimension and, in the *Modify | Dimensions* tab>Witness Lines panel, click ⊢⁒ (Edit Witness Lines). Select the element(s) you want to add to the dimension, as shown in Figure 14–7. Click in an empty space in the view to finish.

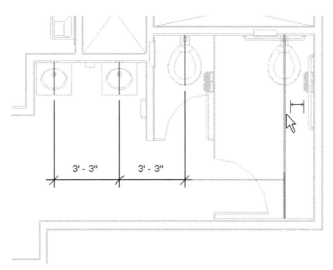

Figure 14–7

- To delete a witness line, drag the **Move Witness Line** control to a nearby witness line element. Alternatively, you can hover the cursor over the control, right-click, and select **Delete Witness Line**.

- To delete one dimension in a string and break the string into two separate dimensions, select the string, hover your cursor over the dimension that you want to delete, and press <Tab>. When it highlights (as shown in Figure 14–8), pick it and press <Delete>. The selected dimension is deleted and the dimension string is separated into two elements, as shown in Figure 14–9.

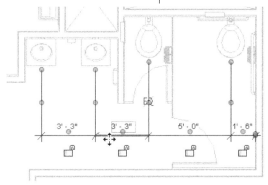

Figure 14–8

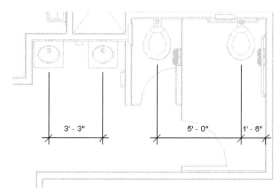

Figure 14–9

Modifying the Dimension Text

Because the Autodesk® Revit® software is parametric, changing the dimension text without changing the elements dimensioned would cause problems throughout the project. These issues could cause problems beyond the model if you use the project model to estimate materials or work with other disciplines.

You can append the text with prefixes and suffixes (as shown in Figure 14–10), which can help you in renovation projects.

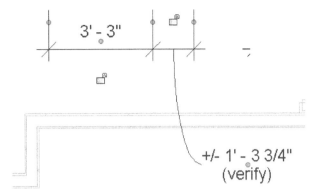

Figure 14–10

Double-click on the dimension text to open the Dimension Text dialog box, as shown in Figure 14–11, and make modifications as needed.

Figure 14–11

Setting Constraints

The three types of constraints that work with dimensions are locks and equal settings, as shown in Figure 14–12, as well as labels.

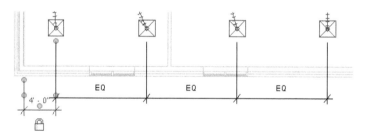

Figure 14–12

Locking Dimensions

When you lock a dimension, the value is set and you cannot make a change between it and the referenced elements. If it is unlocked, you can move it and change its value.

Note that when you use this and move an element, any elements that are locked to the dimension also move.

Setting Dimensions Equal

For a string of dimensions, select the **EQ** symbol to constrain the elements to be at an equal distance apart. This actually moves the elements that are dimensioned.

- The equality text display can be changed in Properties, as shown in Figure 14–13. The style for each of the display types is set in the dimension type.

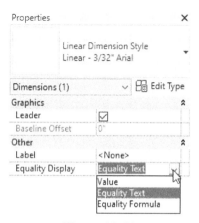

Figure 14–13

Labeling Dimensions

If you have a distance that needs to be repeated multiple times, such as the *Wall to AT* label shown in Figure 14–14, or one where you want to use a formula based on another dimension, you can create and apply a global parameter, also called a label, to the dimension.

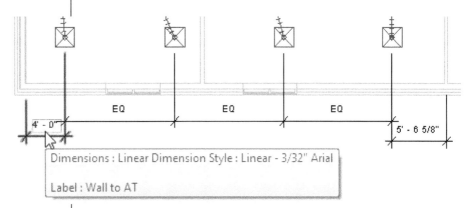

Figure 14–14

* To apply an existing label to a dimension, select the dimension and in the *Modify | Dimension* tab>Label Dimension panel, select the label in the drop-down list, as shown in Figure 14–15.

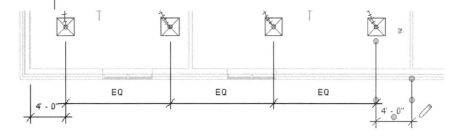

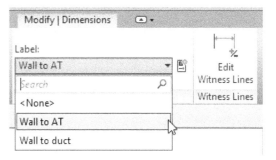

Figure 14–15

How To: Create a Label

1. Select a dimension.
2. In the *Modify | Dimension* tab>Label Dimension panel, click

   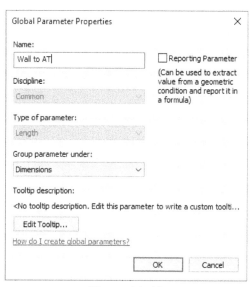 (Create Parameter).
3. In the Global Parameter Properties dialog box, type in a *Name* (as shown in Figure 14–16) and click **OK**.

Figure 14–16

4. The label is applied to the dimension.

How To: Edit the Label Information

1. Select a labeled dimension.

2. Click ✎ (Global Parameters), as shown in Figure 14–17.

3. In the Global Parameters dialog box, in the *Value* column, enter the new distance, as shown in Figure 14–18.

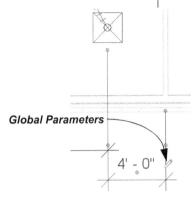

Global Parameters

Figure 14–17

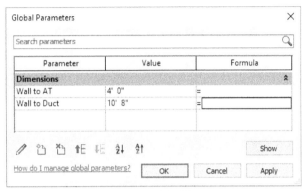

Figure 14–18

4. Click **OK**. The selected dimension and any other dimensions using the same label are updated.

- You can also edit, create, and delete Global Parameters in this dialog box.

Working with Constraints

To find out which elements have constraints applied to them, in the View Control Bar, click ⊟ (Reveal Constraints). Constraints display as shown in Figure 14–19.

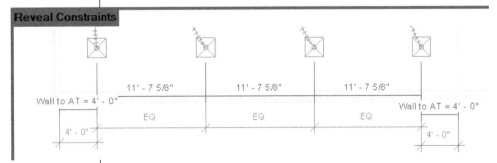

Figure 14–19

- If you try to move the element beyond the appropriate constrains, a Warning dialog box displays, as shown in Figure 14–20.

Figure 14–20

- If you delete dimensions that are constrained, a Warning dialog box displays, as shown in Figure 14–21. Click **OK** to retain the constraint or **Unconstrain** to remove the constraint.

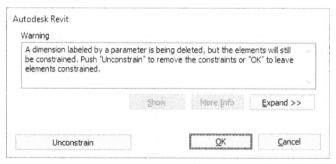

Figure 14–21

Practice 14a | Work with Dimensions - Mechanical

Practice Objectives

- Add a string of dimensions.
- Modify the dimension string.

In this practice, you will add and modify dimensions for a mechanical floor plan view.

1. In the practice files *Annotating* folder, open **Annotation-School-MEP.rvt**.

2. Open the Mechanical>HVAC>Floor Plans>**01 Mechanical Plan** view and zoom in on the upper left corner of the north wing.

3. In the *Annotate* tab>Dimension panel, click ✣ (Aligned).

4. In the Options Bar, verify that the **Wall centerlines** is selected.

5. Dimension the first four duct branches (not the diffusers or the flex duct), starting from the left side wall, as shown in Figure 14–22.

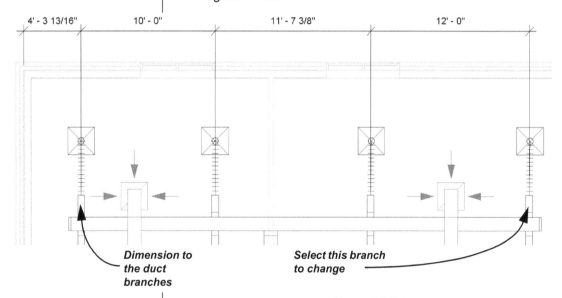

Figure 14–22

6. Click **Modify**.

7. Select the far right duct branch, as shown in Figure 14–22.

8. The corresponding dimension text turns blue. Select the dimension and change its value from **12'** to **10'**. The duct branch and the flex ductwork move accordingly, but the air terminal maintains its original position, as shown in Figure 14–23.

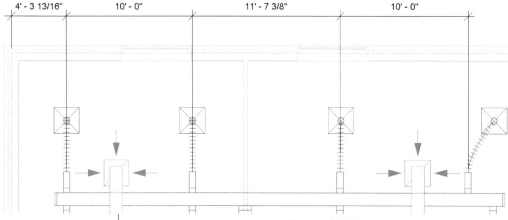

Figure 14–23

9. Click **Modify** and select the dimension line.

10. In the *Modify | Dimensions* tab>Witness Lines panel, click ⊢ (Edit Witness Lines).

11. Select the end of the main duct to add a fifth dimension to the string of dimensions, as shown in Figure 14–24. Click in an empty space in the view away from any objects to finish the command.

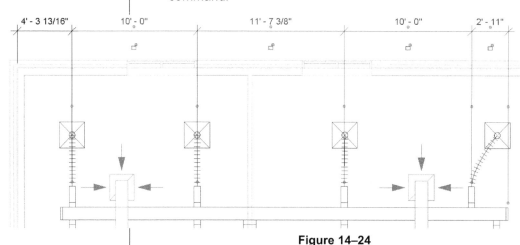

Figure 14–24

12. Click **Modify**.

13. Save and close the project.

Practice 14b | Work with Dimensions - Electrical

Practice Objectives

- Add a string of dimensions.
- Modify the dimension string.

In this practice, you will add and modify dimensions.

1. In the practice files *Annotating* folder, open **Annotation-School-MEP.rvt**.

2. Open the Electrical>Power>Floor Plans>**01 Power Plan** view and zoom in on the upper left corner of the north wing.

3. In the *Annotate* tab>Dimension panel, click ⚹ (Aligned).

4. In the Options Bar, verify that the **Wall centerlines** is selected.

5. Dimension the location of the receptacles in the first two classrooms starting from the left side wall and including the other walls, as shown in Figure 14–25.

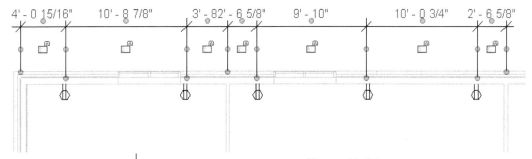

Figure 14–25

6. Select the **Move Witness Line** control on the far left as shown in Figure 14–26.

7. Drag the control and press <Tab> so that the dimension moves to the inside face of the wall, as shown in Figure 14–27.

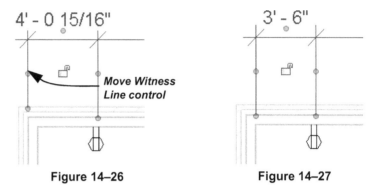

Figure 14–26   Figure 14–27

8. Repeat the process and move the witness lines at the center of the interior walls to the left side of the walls.

9. In the *Modify | Dimensions* tab>Witness Lines panel, click

   (Edit Witness Lines).

10. Add another dimension to the right side of both interior walls. (Press <Tab> to select the outer edge rather than the default alignment of center.), as shown for the second wall in Figure 14–28. Click in an empty space in the view away from any objects to finish the command.

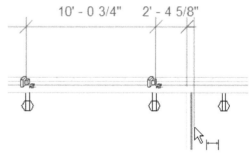

Figure 14–28

11. Use the **Drag Text** control to move some of the text so you can read each number.

12. Click **Modify**.

13. Select one of the receptacles. The corresponding dimension text turns blue. Select the dimension and change its value, as shown in Figure 14–29. The receptacle moves.

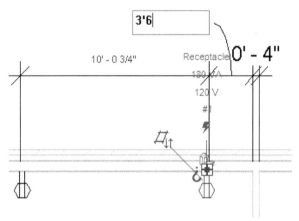

Figure 14–29

14. Make any other changes to the dimensions that you may want.

15. Save and close the project.

Practice 14c	# Work with Dimensions - Plumbing

Practice Objectives

- Add a string of dimensions.
- Modify the dimension string.

In this practice, you will add and modify dimensions.

1. In the practice files *Annotating* folder, open
    Annotation-School-MEP.rvt.

2. Open the Plumbing>Plumbing>Floor Plans>**01 Plumbing
    Plan** view and zoom in on one of the restrooms near the gym.

3. In the *Annotate* tab>Dimension panel, click ✎ (Aligned).

4. In the Options Bar, verify that the **Wall centerlines** is
    selected.

5. Dimension the location of the plumbing fixtures as shown in
    Figure 14–30.

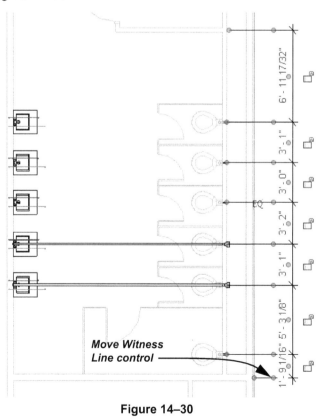

Figure 14–30

6. Zoom in on the handicap stall.

7. Select the **Move Witness Line** control on the dimension that touches the wall.

8. Drag the control and press <Tab> so that the dimension moves to the inside face of the wall, as shown in Figure 14–31.

9. Click **Modify** and select the water closet

10. The corresponding dimension text turns blue. Select the dimension text and change its value to **2'-0"**. The fixture moves but the piping retains its original position, as shown in Figure 14–31.

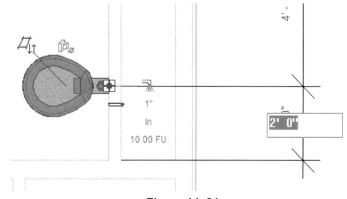

Figure 14–31

11. Undo the changes. Note that it is not advisable to modify the location of fixtures once you have added piping.

12. Save and close the project.

14.2 Working with Text

The **Text** command enables you to add notes to views or sheets, such as the view shown in Figure 14–32. The same command is used to create text with or without leaders.

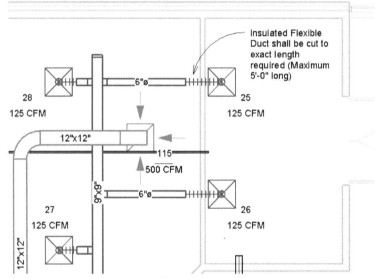

1. All ductwork shown on plans shall be concealed above ceiling or in walls unless noted otherwise.
2. All duct dimensions are in inches and are inside clear.
3. All branch duct runouts to diffusers shall be full connection size of diffuser, unless noted otherwise.

Figure 14–32

The text height is automatically set by the text type in conjunction with the scale of the view (as shown in Figure 14–33, using the same size text type at two different scales). Text types display at the specified height, both in the views and on the sheet.

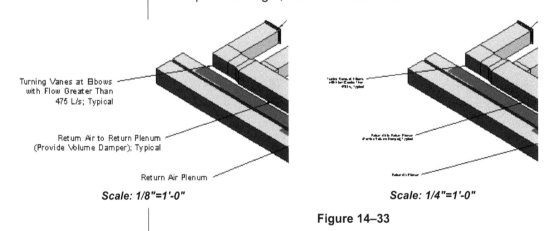

Turning Vanes at Elbows
with Flow Greater Than
475 L/s; Typical

Return Air to Return Plenum
(Provide Volume Damper); Typical

Return Air Plenum

Scale: 1/8"=1'-0"

Scale: 1/4"=1'-0"

Figure 14–33

How To: Add Text

1. In the Quick Access Toolbar or *Annotate* tab>Text panel, click **A** (Text).

The text type sets the font and height of the text.

2. In the Type Selector, set the text type.
3. In the *Modify | Place Text* tab>Leader panel, select the method you want to use: A (No Leader), ←A (One Segment), ⟋A (Two Segments), or ⟋A (Curved).
4. In the Alignment panel, set the overall justification for the text and leader, as shown in Figure 14–34.

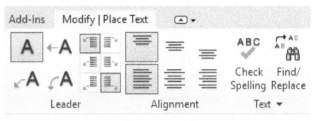

Figure 14–34

Use alignment lines to help you align the text with other text elements.

5. Select the location for the leader and text.
   - If **No leader** is selected, select the start point for the text and begin typing.
   - If using a leader, the first point places the arrow and you then select points for the leader. The text starts at the last leader point.
   - To set a word wrapping distance, click and drag the circle grip controls to set the start and end points of the text.
6. Type the needed text. In the *Edit Text* tab, specify additional options for the font and paragraph, as shown in Figure 14–35.

Figure 14–35

7. In the Edit Text tab>Edit Text panel, click ☒ (Close) or click outside the text box to complete the text element.
   - Pressing <Enter> after a line of text starts a new line of text in the same text window.

How To: Add Text Symbols

1. Start the **Text** command and click to place the text.
2. As you are typing text and need to insert a symbol, right-click and select **Symbols** from the shortcut menu. Select from the list of commonly used symbols, as shown in Figure 14–36.

Figure 14–36

3. If the symbol you need is not listed, click **Other**.
4. In the Character Map dialog box, click on a symbol and click **Select**, as shown in Figure 14–37.

Figure 14–37

5. Click **Copy** to copy the character to the clipboard and paste it into the text box.

- The Font in the Character Map should match the font used by the text type. You do not want to use a different font for symbols.

Editing Text

Editing text notes takes place at two levels:

- Modifying the text note, which includes the **Leader** and **Paragraph** styles.
- Editing the text, which includes changes to individual letters, word, and paragraphs in the text note.

Modifying the Text Note

Click once on the text note to modify the text box and leaders using controls, as shown in Figure 14–38, or using the tools in the *Modify | Text Notes* tab.

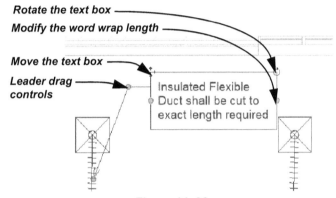

Figure 14–38

How To: Add a Leader to Text Notes

1. Select the text note.
2. In the *Modify | Text Notes* tab>Leader panel, select the direction and justification for the new leader, as shown in Figure 14–39.
3. The leader is applied, as shown in Figure 14–40. Use the drag controls to place the arrow as needed.

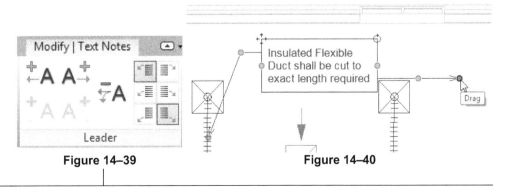

Figure 14–39   **Figure 14–40**

- You can remove leaders by clicking ⲧA (Remove Last Leader).

Editing the Text

The *Edit Text* tab enables you to make various customizations. These include modifying the font of selected words as well as creating bulleted and numbered lists, as shown in Figure 14–41.

General Notes
1. Notify designer of intention to start construction at least 10 days prior to start of site work.
2. Installer shall provide the following:
   - 24-hour notice of start of construction
   - Inspection of bottom of bed or covering required by state inspector
   - All environmental management inspection sheets must be emailed to designer's office within 24 hours of inspection.

Figure 14–41

- You can **Cut**, **Copy**, and **Paste** text using the clipboard. For example, you can copy text from a document and then paste it into the text editor in Revit.

- To help you see the text better as you are modifying it, in the *Edit Text* tab, expand the Edit Text panel, and select one or both of the options, as shown in Figure 14–42.

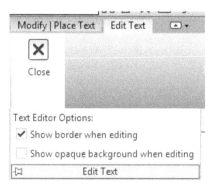

Figure 14–42

How To: Modify the Font

1. Select Individual letters or words.
2. Click on the font modification you want to include:

B (Bold)	X_2 (Subscript)
I (Italic)	X^2 (Superscript)
U̲ (Underline)	aÂ (All Caps)

- When pasting text from a document outside of Autodesk Revit, font modifications (e.g, Bold, Italic, etc.) are retained.

How To: Create Lists

1. In Edit Text mode, place the cursor in the line where you want to add to a list.
2. In the *Edit Text* tab>Paragraph panel, click the type of list you want to create:

(Bullets)	(Uppercase Letters)
(Numbers)	(Lowercase Letters)

3. As you type, press <Enter> and the next line in the list is incremented.
4. To include sub-lists, at the beginning of the next line, click

   (Increase Indent). This indents the line and applies the next level of lists, as shown in Figure 14–43.

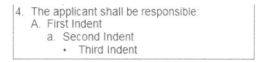

Figure 14–43

- You can change the type of list after you have applied the first increment. For example, you might want to use a list of bullets instead of letters, as shown in Figure 14–44.

5. Click (Decrease Indent) to return to the previous list style.
- Press <Shift>+<Enter> to create a blank line in a numbered list.

The indent distance is set up by the Text Type Tab Size.

- To create columns or other separate text boxes that build on a numbering system (as shown in Figure 14–44), create the second text box and list. Then, place the cursor on one of the lines and in the Paragraph panel, click ⫶⩲ (Increment List Value) until the list matches the next number in the sequence.

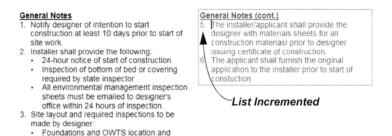

Figure 14–44

6. Click ⫶⩵ (Decrement List Value) to move back a number.

Spell Checking

The Spelling dialog box displays any misspelled words in context and provides several options for changing them, as shown in Figure 14–45.

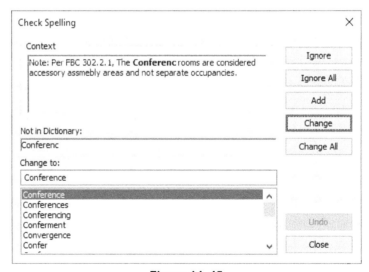

Figure 14–45

- To spell check all text in a view, in the *Annotate* tab>Text panel, click ^{ABC}✓ (Spelling) or press <F7>. As with other spell checkers, you can **Ignore**, **Add**, or **Change** the word.

- You can also check the spelling in selected text. With text selected, in the *Modify | Text Notes* tab>Tools panel, click ^{ABC}✓ (Check Spelling).

Creating Text Types

If you need new text types with a different text size or font (such as for a title or hand-lettering), you can create new ones, as shown in Figure 14–46. It is recommended that you create these in a project template so they are available in future projects.

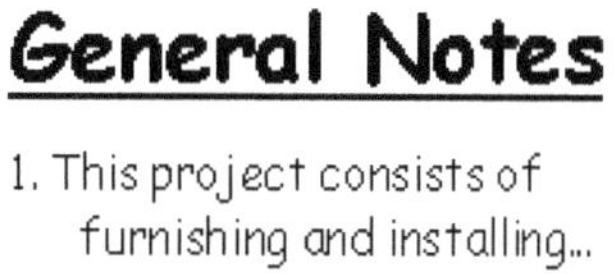

General Notes

1. This project consists of
   furnishing and installing...

Figure 14–46

- You can copy and paste text types from one project to another or use **Transfer Project Standards**.

How To: Create Text Types

1. In the *Annotate* tab>Text panel, click ⌄ (Text Types).
2. In the Type Properties dialog box, click **Duplicate**.
3. In the Name dialog box, type a new name and click **OK**.

4. Modify the text parameters, as needed. The parameters are shown in Figure 14–47.

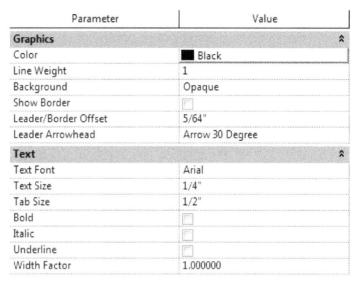

Parameter	Value
Graphics	☆
Color	■ Black
Line Weight	1
Background	Opaque
Show Border	☐
Leader/Border Offset	5/64"
Leader Arrowhead	Arrow 30 Degree
Text	☆
Text Font	Arial
Text Size	1/4"
Tab Size	1/2"
Bold	☐
Italic	☐
Underline	☐
Width Factor	1.000000

Figure 14–47

- The **Background** parameter can be set to **Opaque** or **Transparent**. An opaque background includes a masking region that hides lines or elements behind the text.

- In the *Text* area, the **Width Factor** parameter controls the width of the lettering, but does not affect the height. A width factor greater than **1** spreads the text out and a width factor less than **1** compresses it.

- The **Show Border** parameter, when selected, includes a rectangle around the text.

5. Click **OK** to close the Type Properties dialog box.

14.3 Adding Detail Lines and Symbols

While annotating views for construction documents, you might need to add detail lines and symbols to clarify the design intent or show information, such as the life safety plan exit information, as shown in Figure 14–48.

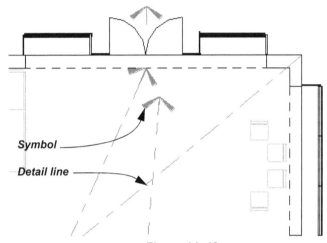

Figure 14–48

- Detail lines and symbols are view-specific, which means that they only display in the view in which they were created.

How To: Draw a Detail Line

1. In the *Annotation* tab>Detail panel, click ⬚ (Detail Line).
2. In the *Modify | Place Detail Lines* tab>Line Style panel, select the type of line you want to use, as shown in Figure 14–49.

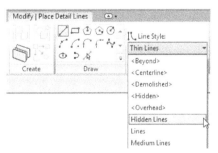

Figure 14–49

3. Use the tools in the Draw panel to create the detail lines.

Using Symbols

Many of the annotations used in working drawings are frequently repeated. Several of them have been saved as symbols in the Autodesk Revit software, such as the North Arrow, Center Line, and Graphic Scale annotations as shown in Figure 14–50. Symbols are 2D elements that only display in one view, while components can be in 3D and display in many views.

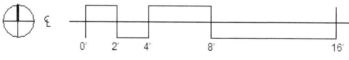

Figure 14–50

- You can also create or load custom annotation symbols.

How To: Place a Symbol

1. In the *Annotate* tab>Symbol panel, click ⊕ (Symbol).
2. In the Type Selector, select the symbol you want to use.
3. In the *Modify | Place Symbol* tab>Mode panel, click

   ⬇ (Load Family) if you want to load other symbols.
4. In the Options Bar, as shown in Figure 14–51, set the *Number of Leaders* and select **Rotate after placement** if you want to rotate the symbol as you insert it.

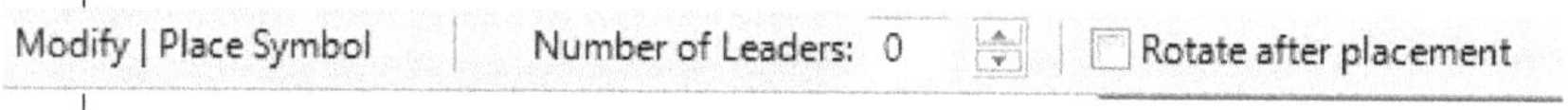

Modify | Place Symbol   Number of Leaders: 0   ⬍   ☐ Rotate after placement

Figure 14–51

5. Place the symbol in the view. Rotate it if you selected the **Rotate after placement** option. If you specified leaders, use the controls to move them into place.

- For information about adding tags to dependent views, see *Section A.8 Annotating Dependent Views*.

Practice 14d

Annotate Construction Documents - All Disciplines

Practice Objective

- Add a bulleted list of general notes to a sheet.

In this practice, you will open a sheet and add general notes to it using the text command.

1. In the practice files *Annotating* folder, open **Annotation-School-MEP.rvt**.

2. Open the sheet **C-101 - Cover Sheet**.

3. Open a text editor such as Microsoft Word or Notepad.

4. Within the text editor software, open either **General Notes.docx** or **General Notes.txt** from the practice files *Annotating* folder.

5. Copy the entire contents of the file to the clipboard (select all <Ctrl>+<A> and copy <Ctrl>+<C>).

6. In Autodesk Revit, start the **Text** command.

7. Verify that no leader is selected, set the text type to **3/32"**
Arial, and draw a text box similar to the one shown in
Figure 14–52.

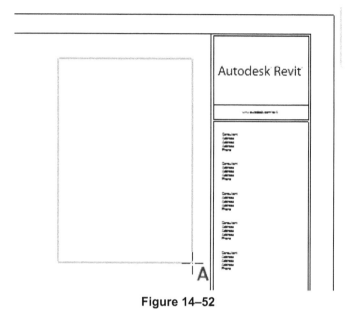

Figure 14–52

8. In the Edit Text dialog box>Clipboard panel, click 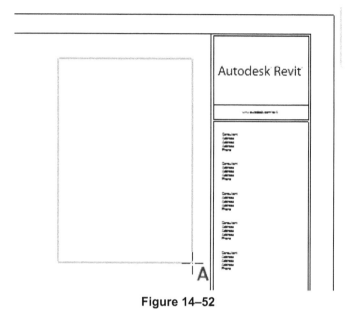 (Paste).

9. Remain in Edit Text mode and zoom in on the text box. Note
that there are numbered and lettered lists in the text but that
they are not quite correct.

10. Select all of the text and in the *Edit Text* tab>Paragraph panel, click ☰ (List: Numbers).

- The paragraphs are recognized and numbered, but the existing numbers and letters are still there. You will need to delete the existing numbering and modify the indents.

11. Select the lettered paragraphs and, in the *Edit Text* tab> Paragraph panel, click ☰ (Increase Indent), then click ☰ (List: Lowercase letters). This changes that list to a lettered list.

12. Zoom in and remove the additional numbers and letters, as shown in Figure 14–53.

1. General
   a. Existing ductwork and piping are shown only where necessary to establish relationship or connection points with new work. Not all existing ducts, pipes, and equipment are shown.
   b. For existing services at project site, verify exact size and location. Verify required clearances of equipment to new and existing material and electrical equipment.
   c. Raise, lower, remove, relocate or replace with new and reconnect to existing all piping and ductwork as required to maintain existing areas in operation during construction.
2. HVAC
   a. Examine architectural drawings to ensure that all ducts crossing fire and/or smoke separations are equipped with fire and/or smoke dampers. Notify the architect where additional dampers are required.
   b. Provide reheat coil transitions and transitions to smoke and/or fire dampers as required.
   c. Locate ceiling air outlets according to the architectural reflected ceiling plans. Confirm ceiling types shown on architectural drawings and install ceiling type supply and return or exhaust outlets to suit.
   d. All duct sizes show are inside clear dimensions.
3. Plumbing and Piping
   a. Verify exact invert elevation of points of connection to existing service prior to installation of new branch, mains or service relocation.
   b. Provide a valved drain at the low point in each piping system.
   c. Vent all high points in heating water and chilled water piping as specified.
   d. Provide condensate drip trap assemblies at the ends of steam mains, branches, and at all low points in the steam lines.
4. Electrical
   a. The electrical works shall comply with all the provisions in the Electrical Code and with consideration on the rules and regulations of local power company.
   b. Unless otherwise specified, wiring shall be done with PVC pipe.
   c. Electric meters installed by the power utility company are supplied and installed by the power utility company.
   d. The Electrical Code provides that only professional engineers can sign the electrical plans.
   e. Samples of materials to be used shall be submitted to the construction engineering office for approval before execution of the work.

Figure 14–53

13. At the beginning of the list, add the text **General Notes**. Make it bold and underlined, as shown in Figure 14–54.

14. Place the cursor at the end sentence of the **1. General** section. Hold <Shift> and press <Enter>. A new line is created without disrupting the numbering sequence.

15. Repeat this at the end of the discipline sections, as shown in Figure 14–54.

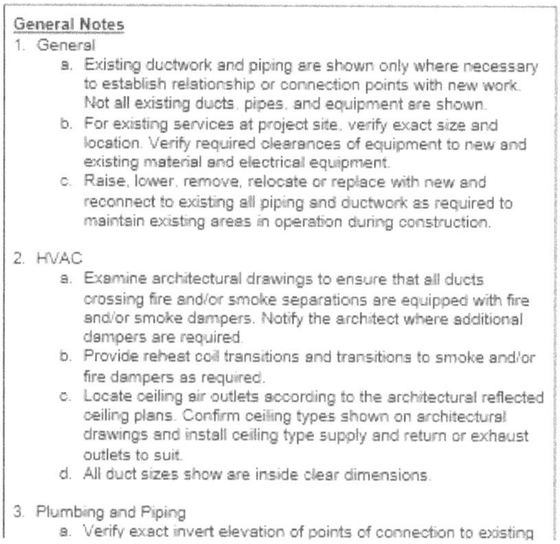

General Notes
1. General
   a. Existing ductwork and piping are shown only where necessary to establish relationship or connection points with new work. Not all existing ducts, pipes, and equipment are shown.
   b. For existing services at project site, verify exact size and location. Verify required clearances of equipment to new and existing material and electrical equipment.
   c. Raise, lower, remove, relocate or replace with new and reconnect to existing all piping and ductwork as required to maintain existing areas in operation during construction.

2. HVAC
   a. Examine architectural drawings to ensure that all ducts crossing fire and/or smoke separations are equipped with fire and/or smoke dampers. Notify the architect where additional dampers are required.
   b. Provide reheat coil transitions and transitions to smoke and/or fire dampers as required.
   c. Locate ceiling air outlets according to the architectural reflected ceiling plans. Confirm ceiling types shown on architectural drawings and install ceiling type supply and return or exhaust outlets to suit.
   d. All duct sizes show are inside clear dimensions.

3. Plumbing and Piping
   a. Verify exact invert elevation of points of connection to existing

Figure 14–54

16. Use the controls if required to relocate or resize the text note.

17. Zoom out to see the full sheet.

18. Save the project and continue to the next practice related to your discipline.

Practice 14e | Annotate Construction Documents - Mechanical

Practice Objective

- Add text with two segment leaders.

In this practice, you will annotate duct systems in a 3D view.

1. In the practice files *Annotating* folder, open **Annotation-School-MEP.rvt**.

2. Open the Mechanical>HVAC>3D Views>**Typical Classroom HVAC Systems** view.

3. In the *Annotate* tab>Text panel, click **A** (Text).

4. In the Type Selector, select **Text: 3/32" Arial**.

5. In the *Modify | Place Text* tab>Leader panel, click ⌐A (2 Segments).

6. Select a point touching one of the supply air ducts and then two other points to define the leader. Type **Supply Air Ducts**, as shown in Figure 14–55, and click an empty space in the view to finish the text note.

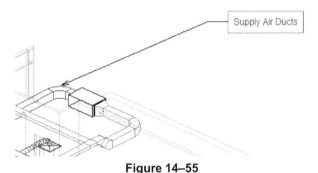

Figure 14–55

7. You are still in the **Text** command. Continue to add the leaders and text shown in Figure 14–56.

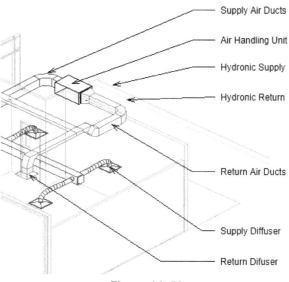

Supply Air Ducts

Air Handling Unit

Hydronic Supply

Hydronic Return

Return Air Ducts

Supply Diffuser

Return Difuser

Figure 14–56

Practice 14f | Annotate Construction Documents - Electrical

Practice Objectives

- Add detail lines.
- Duplicate a text style and add text.

In this practice, you will create an area within the electrical room and add text to denote that the area needs to stay clear.

1. In the practice files *Annotating* folder, open **Annotation-School-MEP.rvt**.
2. Open the Electrical>Power>Floor Plans>**01 Power Plan** view and zoom in on the Electrical Distribution Room in the upper right corner.
3. In the *Annotate* tab>Detail panel, click ⌐ (Detail Line).
4. In the *Modify | Place Detail Lines* tab>Line Style panel, set the *Line Style* to **MEP Hidden**.
5. Draw a rectangle from the upper left corner of the room to the lower right corner of the room, approximately **15' x 6'**, as shown in Figure 14–57.

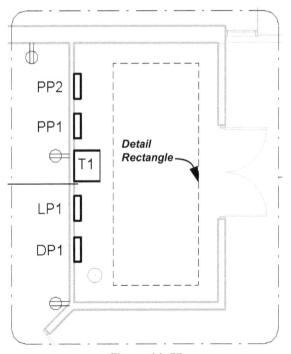

Figure 14–57

6. In the *Annotate* tab>Text panel, click **A** (Text).

7. In the Type Selector, select **Text: 3/32" Arial**.

8. In Properties, click **Edit Type**. In the Type Properties dialog box, click **Duplicate**. Type **3/64" Arial - Red** for the name and click **OK**.

9. Set the following properties:
   - *Color*: **Red**
   - *Text Font*: **Arial**
   - *Text Size*: **3/64"**
   - Select **Italic**.

10. Click **OK** to save and close the Type Properties dialog box.

11. Using the **3/64" Arial - Red** text type, add the following text inside the rectangular detail lines: **Keep this area clear for access to Electrical Panels**, as shown in Figure 14–58.

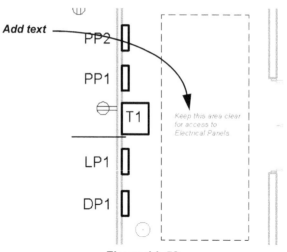

Figure 14–58

12. Save and close the project.

Practice 14g | Annotate Construction Documents - Plumbing

Practice Objective

- Add text with two segment leaders.

In this practice, you will annotate plumbing systems in a 3D view.

1. In the practice files *Annotating* folder, open **Annotation-School-MEP.rvt**.

2. Open the Mechanical>Plumbing>3D Views>**Typical Classroom Plumbing Systems** view.

3. In the *Annotate* tab>Text panel, click **A** (Text).

4. In the Type Selector, select **Text: 3/32" Arial**.

5. In the *Modify | Place Text* tab>Leader panel, click ⟋**A** (2 Segments).

6. Select a point touching one of the hot water lines and then two other points to define the leader. Type **Domestic Hot Water**, as shown in Figure 14–59, and click in an empty space in the view to finish the text note.

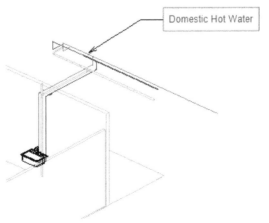

Figure 14–59

7. You are still in the **Text** command. Add the leaders and text shown in Figure 14–60.

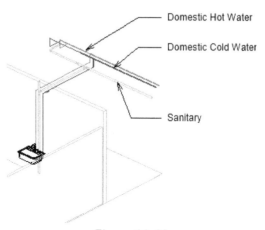

Figure 14–60

8. Save and close the project.

14.4 Creating Legends

A legend is a separate view that can be placed on multiple sheets. Legends can be used to hold installation notes that need to be placed on a sheet with each floor plan, key plans, or any 2D items that need to be repeated. You can also create and list the annotations, line styles, and symbols that are used in your project, and provide explanatory notes next to the symbol, as shown in Figure 14–61. Additionally, legends can provide a list of materials, or elevations of window types used in the project.

*The elements in this figure are inserted using the **Symbol** command rather than the **Legend Component** or **Detail Component** command.*

Electrical Legend	
Dimmer Switch	
3-Way Switch	
Key Operated Switch	
Manual Pull Fire Alarm	

Figure 14–61

- You use ⌐ (Detail Line) and **A** (Text) to create the table and explanatory notes. Once you have a legend view, you can use commands, such as (Legend Component), (Detail Component), and (Symbol), to place elements in the view.

- Unlike other views, legend views can be attached to more than one sheet.

- You can set a legend's scale in the View Status Bar.

- Elements in legends can be dimensioned.

How To: Create a Legend

1. In the *View* tab>Create panel, expand 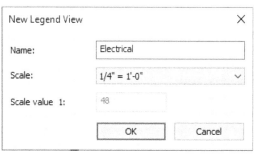 (Legends) and click (Legend) or in the Project Browser, right-click on the *Legends* area title and select **Legend**.
2. In the New Legend View dialog box, enter a name and select a scale for the legend, as shown in Figure 14–62, and click **OK**.

New Legend View		✕
Name:	Electrical	
Scale:	1/4" = 1'-0"	⌄
Scale value 1:	48	
	OK	Cancel

Figure 14–62

3. Place the components in the view first, and then sketch the outline of the table when you know the sizes. Use **Ref Planes** to line up the components.

How To: Use Legend Components

1. In the *Annotate* tab>Detail panel, expand (Component) and click (Legend Component).
2. In the Options Bar, select the *Family* type that you want to use, as shown in Figure 14–63.

- This list contains all of the elements in the project that can be used in a legend.

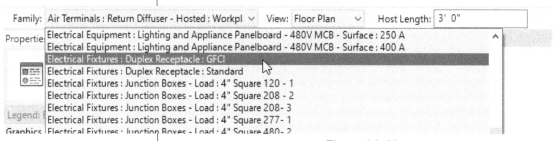

Figure 14–63

- Select the *View* of the element that you want to use. Place the component anywhere in the view.

  - Note that legend components are not counted in schedules and material takeoffs.

3. In the *Annotate* tab>Symbol panel, click (Symbol) to add a symbol (such as those shown in Figure 14–64), then add text and detail lines to complete the legend.

Figure 14–64

- Elements that are full size, such as plumbing fixtures, electrical equipment, or air terminals, come in at their full size.

- Legends are views that can be placed on multiple sheets. You can use Copy to the Clipboard and Paste to copy legends from sheet to sheet.

Practice 14h

Create a Key Plan - All Disciplines

Practice Objective

- Create a key plan, then place it on a sheet.

In this practice, you will create a key plan of the building and add it to the cover sheet.

1. In the practice files *Annotating* folder, open **Annotation-School-MEP.rvt**.

2. In the *View* tab>Create panel, expand ▦ (Legends) and click ▦ (Legend) to create a new Legend view.

3. In the New Legend View dialog box, change the *Name* to **Key Plan** and set the *Scale* to **1"=100'-0"**, then click **OK**.

4. Open the Coordination>All>Floor Plans>**Site** view.

5. In the *Annotate* tab>Detail panel, click ▨ (Detail Line). In the Line Style panel, select **Outline**.

6. In the Draw panel, click ╱ (Line).

7. From the Options Bar, select **Chain**.

8. Trace over the outer edges of the building, following the outline shown in Figure 14–65. It does not have to be exactly on the edges of the building.

Click ▤ (Thin Lines) so the line width displays.

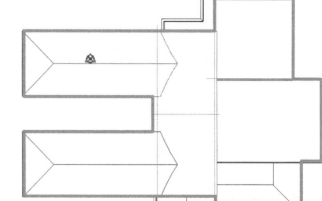

Figure 14–65

9. Click **Modify**.

10. Select all of the new detail lines.

11. In the *Modify | Lines* tab>Clipboard panel, click ✄ (Cut to Clipboard).

12. Return to the Key Plan view and press <Ctrl>+<V> to paste from the clipboard. Click to place the elements and then in the *Modify | Detail Groups* tab>Edit Pasted panel, click ✅ (Finish).

13. Select all of the lines (they will be very thick if Thin Lines is not on). In the *Modify | Lines* panel>Line Style panel, change the *Line Style* to **Wide Lines**.

14. Use the modify tools to clean up the edges and add text, as shown in Figure 14–66.

Figure 14–66

15. In the *Annotate* tab>Symbol panel, click ✛ (Symbol).

16. In the Type Selector search path, start typing **North**. Select **North Arrow 2** and place it near the word Key Plan.

17. Drag and drop the Key Plan legend to sheet **C-101 - Cover Sheet** and place it above the Revision Table in the title block.

18. With the legend still selected, in the Type Selector, select **Viewport: No Title** so there is no title below the key plan, as shown in Figure 14–67.

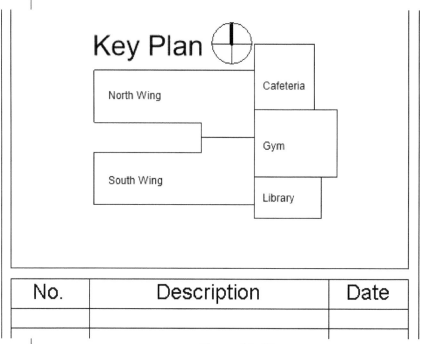

Figure 14–67

19. Zoom out to display the full sheet.

20. Save the project and continue to the next practice related to your discipline.

Practice 14i	# Create Legends - Mechanical

Practice Objectives

- Create legends using legend components and text.
- Add the legend to a sheet.

In this practice, you will create a legend using legend components, text, and detail lines, then add it to the cover sheet.

Task 1 - Add a mechanical legend.

1. In the practice files *Annotating* folder, open **Annotation-School-MEP.rvt**.

2. In the *View* tab>Create panel, expand 🖾 (Legends) and click 🖾 (Legend) to create a new Legend view.

3. Name the legend **Mechanical Legend**, set the *Scale* to **1/4"=1'-0"**, and click **OK**.

4. In the *Annotate* tab>Detail panel, expand ▱ (Component) and click ⬓ (Legend Component).

5. Add the following symbols from the *Family* list with the *View* set to **Floor Plan**:

   - **Air Terminals: Return Diffuser - Hosted: Workplane-based Return Diffuser**
   - **Air Terminals: Supply Diffuser - Perforated - Round Neck - Ceiling Mounted: 24x24x10 In Neck**
   - **Air Terminals: Supply Diffuser - Sidewall: 24 x 12**

6. Add lines and text, as shown in Figure 14–68.

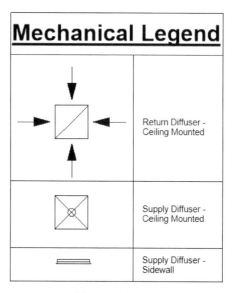

Figure 14–68

Task 2 - Add legend to cover sheet.

1. Open the **C-101- Cover Sheet** view.

2. Drag and drop the mechanical legend onto the sheet.

3. Save and close the project.

Practice 14j

Create Legends - Electrical

Practice Objectives

- Create legends using legend components and text.
- Add the legend to a sheet.

In this practice, you will create a legend using legend components, text, and detail lines, then add it to the cover sheet.

Task 1 - Add an electrical legend.

1. In the practice files *Annotating* folder, open **Annotation-School-MEP.rvt**.

2. In the *View* tab>Create panel, expand 🗔 (Legends) and click 🗔 (Legend) to create a new Legend view.

3. Name the legend **Electrical Legend**, set the *Scale* to **1/4"=1'-0"**, and click **OK**.

4. In the *Annotate* tab>Detail panel, expand 🗂 (Component) and click 🗂 (Legend Component).

   - In the Options Bar, set the *View* to **Floor Plan** and *Host Length* to **1'-0"**, and place the following *Family*:
   - **Lighting Devices: Lighting Switches: Single Pole**
   - **Lighting Devices: Lighting Switches: Three way**
   - **Lighting Devices: Lighting Switches: Dimmer**
   - **Electrical Fixtures: Duplex Receptacle: Standard**
   - **Electrical Fixtures: Duplex Receptacle: GFCI**

5. Add the other switch and outlet symbols directly below the first instance, then add lines and text, as shown in Figure 14–69.

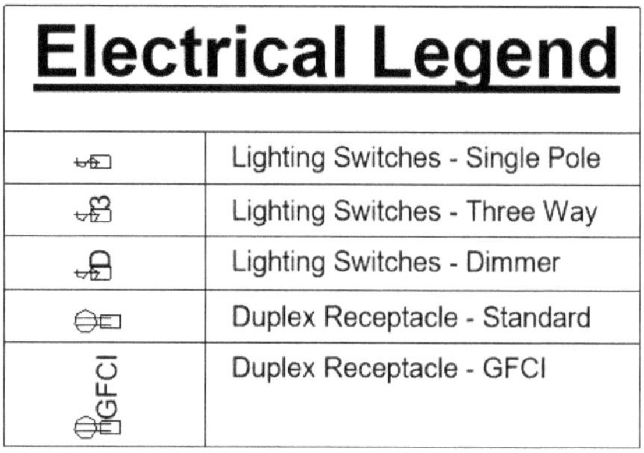

Electrical Legend

	Lighting Switches - Single Pole
	Lighting Switches - Three Way
	Lighting Switches - Dimmer
	Duplex Receptacle - Standard
GFCI	Duplex Receptacle - GFCI

Figure 14–69

Task 2 - Add legend to cover sheet.

1. Open the **C-101- Cover Sheet** view.

2. Drag and drop the electrical legend onto the sheet.

3. Save and close the project.

Practice 14k

Create Legends - Plumbing

Practice Objectives

- Create a legend using legend components and text.
- Add the legend to a sheet.

In this practice, you will create a legend using legend components, text, and detail lines, then add it to the cover sheet.

Task 1 - Add a plumbing legend.

1. In the practice files *Annotating* folder, open **Annotation-School-MEP.rvt**.

2. In the *View* tab>Create panel, expand ▦ (Legends) and click ▦ (Legend) to create a new Legend view.

3. Name the legend **Plumbing Fixture - Flush Tank** and set the *Scale* to **1/4"=1'-0"**, then click **OK**.

4. In the *Annotate* tab>Detail panel, expand ◩ (Component) and click ⬚ (Legend Component).

5. In the Options Bar, set *Family* to **Plumbing Fixtures: Water Closet - Flush Tank: Public - 1.6 gpf** and set *View* to **Elevation - Front**. Add a single instance to the current Legend view.

6. In the Options Bar, set *Family* to **Plumbing Fixtures: Water Closet - Quiet Flush Tank: Public - 1.6 gpf**, and set *View* to **Elevation - Front**. Add a single instance next to the first one, as shown in Figure 14–70. Click ⬚ (Modify) to finish.

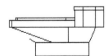

Figure 14–70

7. In the *Annotate* tab>Text panel, click **A** (Text) and label the elements, as shown in Figure 14–71.

8. Click (Detail Line) in the *Annotate* tab>Detail panel. Use the tools on the *Modify | Place Detail Lines* tab>Draw panel to add the boxes around the elements and text, as shown in Figure 14–71.

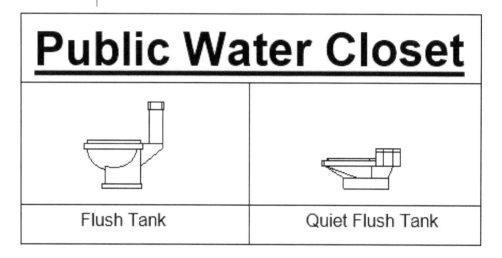

Public Water Closet

Flush Tank	Quiet Flush Tank

Figure 14–71

Task 2 - Add legend to cover sheet.

1. Open the **C-101- Cover Sheet** view.

2. Drag and drop the plumbing fixture legend onto the sheet.

3. Save and close the project.

Chapter Review Questions

1. When a fixture is moved, how do you update the dimension?
   a. Edit the dimension and move it over.
   b. Select the dimension and then click **Update** in the Options Bar.
   c. The dimension automatically updates.
   d. Delete the existing dimension and add a new one.

2. How do you create new text styles?
   a. Using the **Text Styles** command.
   b. Duplicate an existing type.
   c. They must be included in a template.
   d. Using the **Format Styles** command.

3. When you edit text, how many leaders can be added using the leader tools?
   a. One
   b. One on each end of the text.
   c. As many as you want at each end of the text.

4. A Detail Line created in one view also displays in the other view.
   a. True
   b. False

5. Which of the following describes the difference between a symbol and a component?
   a. Symbols are 3D and only display in one view. Components are 2D and display in many views.
   b. Symbols are 2D and only display in one view. Components are 3D and display in many views.
   c. Symbols are 2D and display in many views. Components are 3D and only display in one view.
   d. Symbols are 3D and display in many views. Components are 2D and only display in one view.

6. When creating a legend, which of the following elements cannot be added?
   a. Legend Components
   b. Tags
   c. Rooms
   d. Symbols

Command Summary

Button	Command	Location
Dimensions and Text		
	Aligned (Dimension)	• **Ribbon:** *Annotate* tab>Dimension panel or *Modify* tab>Measure panel, expanded drop-down list • **Quick Access Toolbar** • **Shortcut:** DI
	Angular (Dimension)	• **Ribbon:** *Annotate* tab>Dimension panel or *Modify* tab>Measure panel, expanded drop-down list
	Arc Length (Dimension)	• **Ribbon:** *Annotate* tab>Dimension panel or *Modify* tab>Measure panel, expanded drop-down list
	Diameter (Dimension)	• **Ribbon:** *Annotate* tab>Dimension panel or *Modify* tab>Measure panel, expanded drop-down list
	Linear (Dimension)	• **Ribbon:** *Annotate* tab>Dimension panel or *Modify* tab>Measure panel, expanded drop-down list
	Radial (Dimension)	• **Ribbon:** *Annotate* tab>Dimension panel or *Modify* tab>Measure panel, expanded drop-down list
A	Text	• **Ribbon:** *Annotate* tab>Text panel • **Shortcut:** TX
Detail Lines and Symbols		
	Detail Line	• **Ribbon:** *Annotate* tab>Detail panel • **Shortcut:** DL
	Symbol	• **Ribbon:** *Annotate* tab>Symbol panel
Legends		
	Legend (View)	• **Ribbon:** *View* tab>Create panel> expand Legends
	Legend Component	• **Ribbon:** *Annotate* tab>Detail panel> expand Component

Adding Tags and Schedules

Adding tags to your views helps you to identify elements such as doors, windows, or walls in the model. Tags are 2D annotation families with labels that extract information about the elements being tagged from their properties. Tags are typically added when you insert an element, but can also be added at any point in the design process. The information captured in the elements in a project is used to populate schedules, which can be added to sheets to complete the construction documents.

Learning Objectives in This Chapter

- Add tags to elements in 2D and 3D views to prepare the views to be placed on sheets.
- Load tags that are needed for projects.
- Modify schedule content, including the instance and type properties of related elements.
- Add schedules to sheets as part of the construction documents.

15.1 Adding Tags

Tags identify elements that are listed in schedules. Door and window tags are inserted automatically if you use the **Tag on Placement** option when inserting the door or window or other elements. You can also add them later to specific views as needed. Many other types of tags are available in the Autodesk® Revit® software, such as air terminal, duct, mechanical equipment and piping tags, as shown in Figure 15–1.

Additional tags are stored in the library in the Annotations folder.

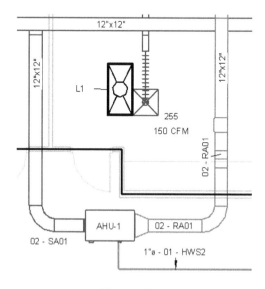

Figure 15–1

- The **Tag by Category** command works for most elements, except for a few that have separate commands.

- Tags can be letters, numbers, or a combination of the two.

You can place three types of tags, as follows:

- (Tag by Category): Tags according to the category of the element. It places door tags on doors and wall tags on walls.

- (Multi-Category Tag): Tags elements belonging to multiple categories. The tags display information from parameters that they have in common.

- (Material Tag): Tags that display the type of material. They are typically used in detailing.

How To: Add Tags

1. In the *Annotate* tab>Tag panel, click  (Tag by Category), (Multi-Category Tag), or (Material Tag) depending on the type of tag you want to place.

2. In the Options Bar, set the options as needed, as shown in Figure 15–2.

Modify | Tag   Horizontal ▾   Tags... ☑ Leader   Attached End   ▾ ↦ 1/2"

Figure 15–2

In the Load Family dialog box, if you are not routed to the Revit families folder location, click on Imperial Libraries in the Places panel.

3. Select the element you want to tag. If a tag for the selected element is not loaded, you are prompted to load it from the library.

Tag Options

- You can set tag options for leaders and tag rotation, as shown in Figure 15–3. You can also press <Spacebar> to toggle the orientation while placing or modifying the tag.

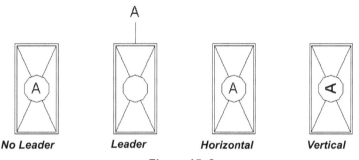

No Leader   *Leader*   *Horizontal*   *Vertical*

Figure 15–3

- Leaders can have an **Attached End** or a **Free End**, as shown in Figure 15–4. The attached end must be connected to the element being tagged.

A free end has an additional drag control where the leader touches the element.

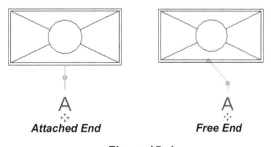

Attached End   *Free End*

Figure 15–4

- If you change between **Attached End** and **Free End**, the tag does not move and the leader does not change location.

- The **Length** option specifies the length of the leader in plotting units. It is grayed out if **Leader** is not selected or if a **Free End** leader is defined.

- If a tag is not loaded, a No Tag Loaded dialog box opens as shown in Figure 15–5. Click **Yes** to open the Load Family dialog box in which you can select the appropriate tag.

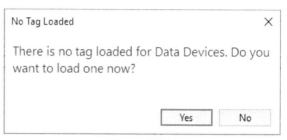

Figure 15–5

- Tags can be pinned so they stay in place if you move the element that is tagged. This is primarily used when tags have leaders, as shown in Figure 15–6.

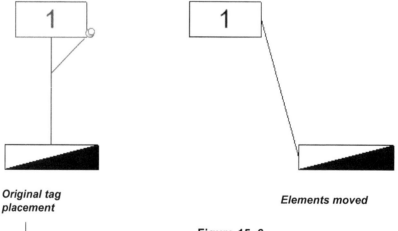

Original tag placement   *Elements moved*

Figure 15–6

How To: Add Multiple Tags

1. In the *Annotate* tab>Tag panel, click  (Tag All).
2. In the Tag All Not Tagged dialog box, shown in Figure 15–7, select the checkbox beside one or more categories to tag. Selecting the checkbox beside the Category title selects all of the tags.

*To tag only some elements, select them before starting this command. In the Tag All Not Tagged dialog box, select **Only selected objects in current view**.*

Tag All Not Tagged   ✕

Select at least one Category and Tag or Symbol Family to annotate non-annotated objects:

◉ All objects in current view

Selects all tags in the list ⟶ ◯ Only selected objects in current view

☐ Include elements from linked files

☑	Category	Loaded Tags	⌃
☑	Air Terminal Tags	Diffuser Tag	
☐	Door Tags	Door Tag	
☐	Duct Tags	Duct Size Tag	
☐	Electrical Equipment Tags	Panel Name	
☐	Electrical Fixture Tags	Electrical Device Circuit Tag	
☐	Lighting Fixture Tags	Lighting Fixture Tag : Standard	
☑	Mechanical Equipment Tags	Mechanical Equipment Tag	
☐	Pipe Tags	Pipe Size Tag	
☐	Room Tags	Room Tag	
☐	Space Tags	Space Tag	⌄

☐ Leader   Leader Length: 1/2"

Tag Orientation: Horizontal ⌄

OK	Cancel	Apply	Help

Figure 15–7

3. Set the *Leader* and *Tag Orientation* as needed.
4. Click **Apply** to apply the tags and stay in the dialog box. Click **OK** to apply the tags and close the dialog box.

- When you select a tag, the properties of that tag display. To display the properties of the tagged element, in the *Modify | <contextual>* tab>Host panel, click 🗔 (Select Host).

- Rooms can be tagged using **Tag all Not Tagged**.

How To: Load Tags

1. In the *Annotate* tab, expand the Tag panel and click

   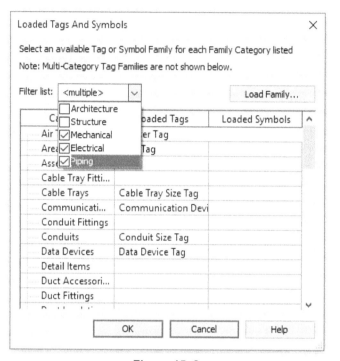 (Loaded Tags And Symbols) or, when a Tag command is active, in the Options Bar click **Tags...**

2. In the Loaded Tags And Symbols dialog box (shown in Figure 15–8), click **Load Family...**.

Loaded Tags And Symbols ✕

Select an available Tag or Symbol Family for each Family Category listed

Note: Multi-Category Tag Families are not shown below.

Filter list: <multiple> Load Family...

☐ Architecture
☐ Structure
☑ Mechanical
☑ Electrical
☑ Piping

Category	Loaded Tags	Loaded Symbols
Air T...	...er Tag	
Area...	Tag	
Asse...		
Cable Tray Fitti...		
Cable Trays	Cable Tray Size Tag	
Communicati...	Communication Devi	
Conduit Fittings		
Conduits	Conduit Size Tag	
Data Devices	Data Device Tag	
Detail Items		
Duct Accessori...		
Duct Fittings		

OK   Cancel   Help

Figure 15–8

3. In the Load Family dialog box, navigate to the appropriate *Annotations* folder, select the tag(s) needed and click **Open**.
4. The tag is added to the category in the dialog box. Click **OK**.

Instance vs. Type Based Tags

Many elements are tagged in a numbered sequence, with each instance of the element having a separate tag number. Other elements are tagged by type. Changing the information in one tag changes all instances of that element.

Both Instance and Type tags can be modified by double-clicking on the tag number, as shown in Figure 15–9.

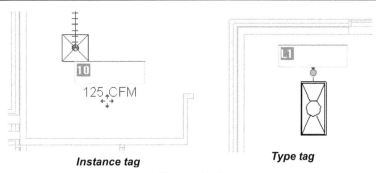

Instance tag   *Type tag*

Figure 15–9

Alternatively, you can change the tag information by selecting the element (not the tag) and changing the values in Properties for instance tags, as shown in Figure 15–10, or in Type Properties for type tags, as shown in Figure 15–11.

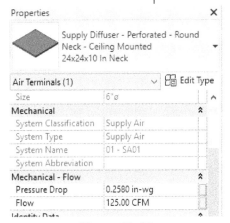

Figure 15–10

Figure 15–11

- When you change a type tag, an alert box may open to warn you that changing a type parameter affects other elements. If you want this tag to modify all other elements of this type, click **Yes**.

- If a type tag displays with a question mark, it means that no Type Mark has been assigned yet.

- When you select a tag, the properties of that tag display. To display the properties of the tagged element, in the

  Modify | <contextual> tab>Host panel, click 🔲 (Select Host).

Tagging in 3D Views

You can add tags to isometric 3D views, as shown in Figure 15–12, as long as the view is locked first.

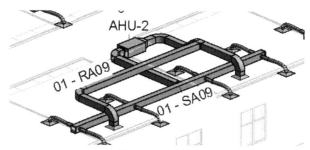

Figure 15–12

- Dimensions can be added to isometric 3D views whether they are locked or not. Proceed with caution when selecting the items to dimension to ensure that the witness lines and text orient as intended.

- Locked views can be used with perspective views. This enables you to create the view as you want it and then save it from being modified.

How To: Lock a 3D View

1. Open a 3D view and set it up as you want it to display.

2. In the View Control Bar, click on 🏠 (Unlocked 3D View) and click 🏠 (Save Orientation and Lock View).

- If you are using the default 3D view and it has not been saved, you are prompted to name and save the view first.

- You can modify the orientation of the view, by clicking on 🏠 (Locked 3D View) and click 🏠 (Unlock View). This also removes any tags you have applied.

- To return to the previous locked view, expand 🏠 (Unlocked 3D View) and click 🏠 (Restore Orientation and Lock View).

Practice 15a | Add Tags - Mechanical

Practice Objectives

- Use the Tag All Not Tagged dialog box.
- Modify tags.

In this practice, you will use the Tag All tool to add duct, pipe, and air terminal tags to a mechanical floor plan.

Task 1 - Tag all not tagged.

1. In the practice files *Schedules* folder, open **Tags-School-MEP.rvt**.

2. Open the Mechanical>HVAC>Floor Plans>**01 Mechanical Plan>01 Mechanical - AREA A** view. There are tags on the ducting and the air terminals.

3. Open the **01 Mechanical - AREA B** view. This view is missing its tags. (Type **ZF** to fit the model in the view if it is not showing.)

4. In the *Annotate* tab>Tag panel, click 🔲 (Tag All).

5. In the Tag All Not Tagged dialog box, select the following:

    - *Air Terminal Tags:* **Diffuser Tag**
    - *Duct Tags:* **Duct Size Tag**
    - *Pipe Tags:* **Pipe Size Tag**

6. Verify that the **Leader** is cleared and click **OK**.

7. If a warning dialog box displays about Elements Have Hidden Tags, click **OK**.

8. All of the air terminals, pipes, and ducts are now tagged in this view, as shown in part in Figure 15–13. Move the tags around as needed to clarify the view.

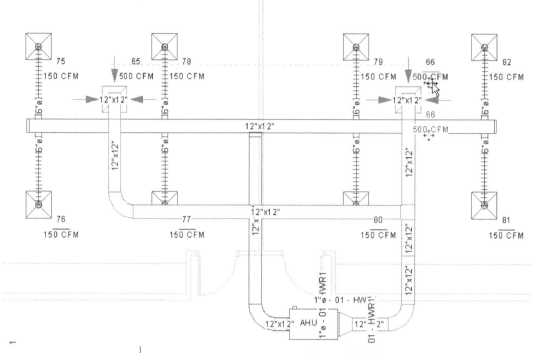

Figure 15–13

9. Select the crop region, then modify the annotation crop region (most outer line) on the right so that the extra tags do not display.

10. Hide the crop region.

Task 2 - Modify hydronic supply tags.

1. Zoom in on the hydronic supply pipe running down the middle of the north wing's hallway. There are two runs of hydronic supply pipe running from the AHU mechanical equipment so there are two tags on top of each other.

2. Select the **1"ø-01-HWR1** tag. From the Options Bar, check **Leader** and move the tag above the pipe. Do the same for the **1"ø-01-HWS1** tag.

3. Adjust the leader as needed and continue modifying the rest, similar to that shown in Figure 15–14.

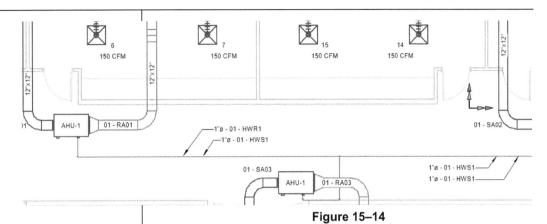

Figure 15–14

4. Save and close the project.

Practice 15b | Add Tags - Electrical

Practice Objectives

- Add tags to a model.
- Use the Tag All Not Tagged dialog box.
- Set the Type Mark parameter for tags.

In this practice, you will add lighting fixture tags and conduit tags to electrical floor plans. You will then modify the elements' type mark.

Task 1 - Add tags to an electrical floor plan.

1. In the practice files *Schedules* folder, open **Tags-School-MEP.rvt**.

2. Open the Electrical>Lighting>Floor Plans>**01 Lighting Plan** view.

3. Zoom into the classroom in the north wing's upper left corner.

4. In the *Annotate* tab>Tag panel, click 🔲 (Tag by Category).

5. In the Options Bar, select **Horizontal**, check **Leader** and **Attached End**, and set the leader length to **1/16"**. Tag the light fixtures, as shown in Figure 15–15.

*The default **Lighting Fixture Tag: Standard** is used.*

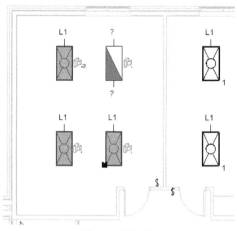

Figure 15–15

6. Tag the light fixtures again by placing the tag below each of the lights.

7. Click **Modify** and select the tags below the lights.

8. In the Type Selector, select **Lighting Fixture Circuit Tag: Standard**. The tag information changes from displaying the lighting fixture number to the circuit number. Because the lights are not connected to a circuit, they display a question mark.

9. With the tags still selected, toggle off the leader and move them to the lower right of the fixture, as shown in Figure 15–16, so that they match the tags in the room next door.

Alignment lines display when the cursor lines up with other tags.

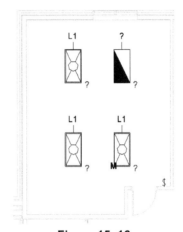

Figure 15–16

Task 2 - Modify tag information.

---

1. Click **Modify** and select the emergency recessed lighting fixture. In Properties, click (Edit Type).

2. In the Type Properties dialog box, in the *Identity Data* area, set the *Type Mark* to **E1** and click **OK**. All of the emergency lighting fixture tags update to display this information, as shown in Figure 15–17.

3. In the next room, hover the cursor over one of the light fixtures and press <Tab> until the circuit displays. Click to select the circuit.

4. In the *Modify | Electrical Circuits* tab>System Tools panel, click (Edit Circuit).

5. The 🔲 (Add to Circuit) command is active. Select the three standard light fixtures (not the emergency fixture).

6. Select the emergency fixture. When the Select Connector dialog box displays select **Connector 1: Power: Emergency** and click **OK**.

7. Click ✔ (Finish Editing Circuit). The Circuit tags now display with the circuit number, as shown in Figure 15–17.

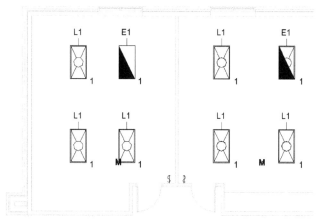

Figure 15–17

8. Save the project.

Task 3 - Load and use a conduit tag.

---

1. Open the Electrical>Power>Floor Plans>**01 Power Plan** view.

2. Zoom in on the same rooms you worked in with the lighting fixtures.

3. Using 🏷 (Tag by Category), click on the conduit that runs horizontally along the classrooms.

4. An alert box displays, warning you that no tag is loaded for Conduits. Click **Yes** to load one now.

5. In the Load Family dialog box, you should default to the Revit library. Navigate to the *Annotations>Electrical>Conduit* folder and select **Conduit Size Tag.rfa**. Click **Open**.

6. The **Tag by Category** tool is still running.

7. In the Options Bar, select **Leader,** and in the drop-down list, select **Free End**.

8. Add two tags to the conduit in the classroom, as shown in Figure 15–18.

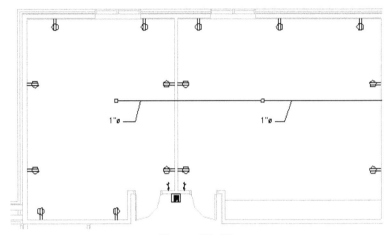

Figure 15–18

9. Click **Modify** and select the conduit in the smaller classroom.

10. In the Options Bar, change the *Diameter* to **3/4"**. The tag updates automatically, as shown in Figure 15–19.

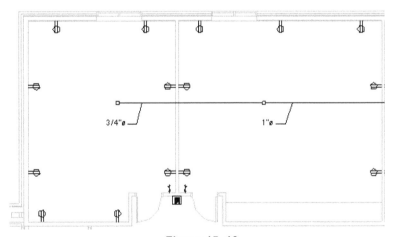

Figure 15–19

11. Type **ZF** to zoom out to fit the view.

12. Save the project.

Practice 15c | Add Tags - Plumbing

Practice Objectives

- Add tags to a model.
- Lock a 3D view to tag plumbing systems and fixtures.
- Modify the Type Mark parameter for tags.

In this practice, you will add plumbing fixture tags and rotate a 3D view and lock it into place. You will then add tags to plumbing systems and fixtures, then modify the fixtures' type mark to update the tags.

Task 1 - Add tags to a floor plan.

1. In the practice files *Schedules* folder, open **Tags-School-MEP.rvt**.

2. Open the Plumbing>Plumbing>3D Views>**3D Plumbing** view. In the Project Browser, rename it to **3D Plumbing - Domestic Water**.

3. Select the linked architectural model and type **VH** to hide it in the view.

Alternatively, you can select the restroom items and from the Modify | Multi-Select tab, select Section Box.

4. From Properties, turn on **Section Box** and use the control grips to only see the first floor bathroom, as shown in Figure 15–20.

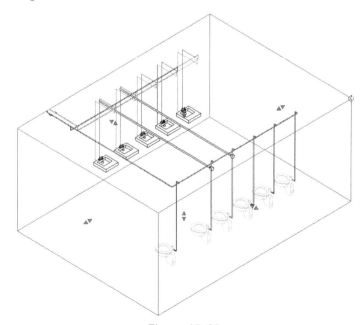

Figure 15–20

5. From the View Control Bar, click (Unlocked 3D View) and select **Save Orientation and Lock View** to lock the view in place.

6. Start the **Tag by Category** command. From the Options Bar, set the tag orientation to **Horizontal** and uncheck **Leader**. Tag the pipe.

7. While still in Tag by Category, tag one lavatory and one water closet. They both have question marks for their tags.

Task 2 - Modify plumbing fixtures to update the tags.

---

1. Modify the lavatory and water closet's **Type Mark** within Properties>**Edit Type** to update the plumbing fixture tags.

2. If you have not already, tag the rest of the lavatories and water closets. The tags for all the lavatories and water closets will be the same because the tag is pulling parameter information from the elements' type properties.

3. Adjust the view scale if needed.

4. Save and close the project.

15.2 Working with Schedules

Schedules extract information from a project and display it in table form. Each schedule is stored as a separate view and can be placed on sheets, as shown in Figure 15–21. Any changes you make to the project elements that affect the schedules are automatically updated in both views and sheets.

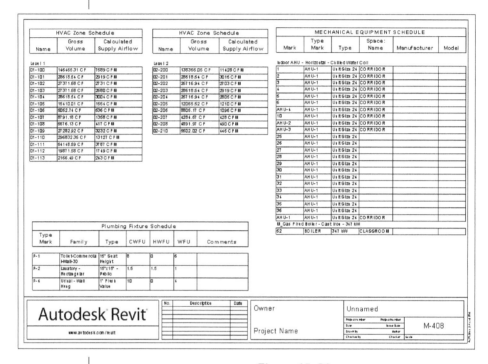

Figure 15–21

- The default MEP templates do not include any schedules. The **Construction-Default.rte**, **Residential-Default.rte**, and **Commercial-Default.rte** template files do include useful schedules.

How To: Work with Schedules

1. In the Project Browser, expand the *Schedules/Quantities* area, as shown in Figure 15–22, and double-click on the schedule you want to open.

Figure 15–22

2. Schedules are automatically filled out with the information stored in the instance and type parameters of related elements that are added to the model.
3. Fill out additional information in either the schedule or Properties.
4. From the *Modify Schedule | Quantities* tab>Appearance panel, you can select ▦ (Freeze Header) to keep the header row visible while you scroll through the schedule.
5. When selecting on a schedule's row, it will highlight in blue.
6. Drag and drop the schedule onto a sheet.

• You can zoom in to read small text in schedule views. Hold down the <Ctrl> key and scroll using the mouse wheel or press **<Ctrl>+<+>** to zoom in or **<Ctrl>+<->** to zoom out.

Modifying Schedules

Information in schedules is bi-directional:

• Make changes to elements and the schedule automatically updates.

• Make changes to information in the schedule cells and the elements automatically update.

How To: Modify Schedule Cells

1. Open the schedule view.
2. Select the cell you want to change. Some cells have drop-down lists, as shown in Figure 15–23. Others have edit fields.

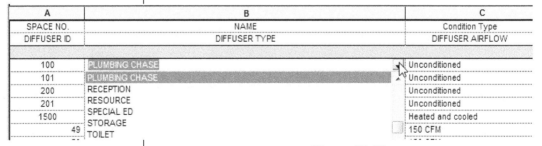

A	B	C
SPACE NO.	NAME	Condition Type
DIFFUSER ID	DIFFUSER TYPE	DIFFUSER AIRFLOW
100	PLUMBING CHASE	Unconditioned
101	PLUMBING CHASE	Unconditioned
200	RECEPTION	Unconditioned
201	RESOURCE	Unconditioned
1500	SPECIAL ED	Heated and cooled
49	STORAGE	150 CFM
	TOILET	

Figure 15–23

• If you change a Type Property in the schedule, it applies to all elements of that type. If you change an Instance Property, it only applies to that one element.
3. Add the new information. The change is reflected in the schedule, on the sheet, and in the elements of the project.

- If you change a Type Property, an alert box opens, as shown in Figure 15–24.

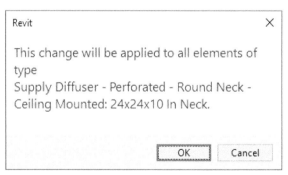

Figure 15–24

- When you select an element in a schedule, in the *Modify Schedule/Quantities* tab>Element panel, you can click (Highlight in Model). This opens a close-up view of the element with the Show Element(s) in View dialog box, as shown in Figure 15–25. Click **Show** to display more views of the element. Click **Close** to finish the command.

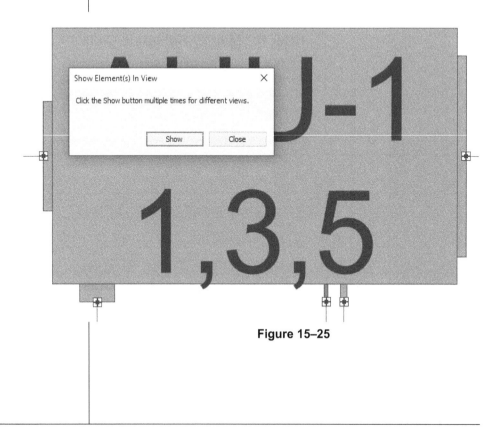

Figure 15–25

Hint: Customizing Schedules

Schedules are typically included in project templates, which are set up by the BIM Manager or other advanced users. They can be complex to create as there are many options.

- For information about creating basic schedules, see *Section A.10 Creating Building Component Schedules*.

- For information on using schedules data outside of Autodesk Revit, see *Section A.9 Importing and Exporting Schedules*.

- For more information about creating schedules, refer to the ASCENT guide *Autodesk Revit: BIM Management: Template and Family Creation*.

Modifying a Schedule on a Sheet

Once you have placed a schedule on a sheet, you can manipulate it to fit the information into the available space. Select the schedule to display the controls that enable you to modify it, as shown in Figure 15–26.

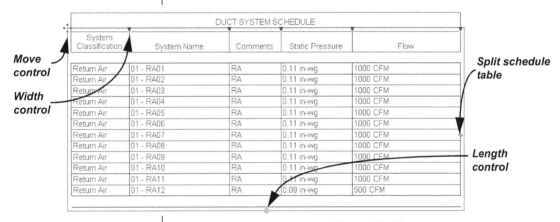

Figure 15–26

- The blue triangles modify the width of each column.

- The break mark splits the schedule into two parts.

- In a split schedule, you can use the arrows in the upper left corner to move that portion of the schedule table. The control at the bottom of the first table changes the length of the table and impacts any connected splits, as shown in Figure 15–27.

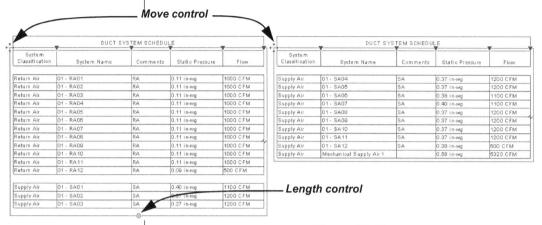

Figure 15–27

- To unsplit a schedule, drag the Move control from the side of the schedule that you want to unsplit back to the original column.

Practice 15d

Work with Schedules - Mechanical/Plumbing

Practice Objectives

- Update schedule information.
- Add a schedule to a sheet.

In this practice, you will update a schedule and place it on a sheet, as shown in Figure 15–28.

MECHANICAL EQUIPMENT SCHEDULE					
Type Mark	Mark	Space: Name	Manufacturer	Model	Comments
AHU-1	1	CORRIDOR	ME Unlimited	AHU-24-M	
AHU-1	2	CORRIDOR	ME Unlimited	AHU-24-M	
AHU-1	3	CORRIDOR	ME Unlimited	AHU-24-M	
AHU-1	4	CORRIDOR	ME Unlimited	AHU-24-M	
AHU-1	5	CORRIDOR	ME Unlimited	AHU-24-M	
AHU-1	6	CORRIDOR	ME Unlimited	AHU-24-M	
AHU-1	7	CORRIDOR	ME Unlimited	AHU-24-M	
AHU-1	8	CORRIDOR	ME Unlimited	AHU-24-M	
AHU-3	9	CORRIDOR	ME Unlimited	AHU-36-L	
AHU-1	10	CORRIDOR	ME Unlimited	AHU-24-M	
AHU-1	11	CORRIDOR	ME Unlimited	AHU-24-M	
AHU-1	12	CORRIDOR	ME Unlimited	AHU-24-M	
AHU-2	13	CORRIDOR	ME Unlimited	AHU-12-S	
HW-1	14	STORAGE	ME Unlimited	HWH-10-M	
HW-1	15	STORAGE	ME Unlimited	HWH-10-M	
HW-1	16	JNTR.	ME Unlimited	HWH-10-M	
HW-1	17	JNTR.	ME Unlimited	HWH-10-M	

Figure 15–28

Task 1 - Fill in schedules.

1. In the practice files *Schedules* folder, open **Schedules-School-MEP.rvt**.

2. Open the Plumbing>Plumbing>3D Views>**3D Plumbing** view.

3. In the Project Browser, expand **Schedules/Quantities** and open **MECHANICAL EQUIPMENT SCHEDULE**. The schedule is already populated with some information, as shown in Figure 15–29.

<MECHANICAL EQUIPMENT SCHEDULE>					
A	B	C	D	E	F
Type Mark	Mark	Space: Name	Manufacturer	Model	Comments
AHU-1	1	CORRIDOR			
AHU-1	2	CORRIDOR			
AHU-1	3	CORRIDOR			
AHU-1	4	CORRIDOR			
AHU-1	5	CORRIDOR			
AHU-1	6	CORRIDOR			
AHU-1	7	CORRIDOR			

Figure 15–29

4. Several Type Marks are empty. Click in one of the empty *Type Mark* cells. In the *Modify Schedules/Quantities* tab> Element panel, click ⬚ (Highlight in Model).

5. If a dialog box opens stating there is no open view that shows any of the highlighted elements, click **OK** to search through closed views.

6. In the view that comes up, if it is not showing the element you need to see, click **Show**. If you can see the element, click **Close** in the Show Element(s) in View dialog box.

7. Zoom out so that you can see the element (i.e., a hot water heater) in context.

8. In Properties, click ⬚ (Edit Type).

9. In the Type Properties dialog box, in the *Identity Data* area, set the *Type Mark* to **HW-1**.

10. Click **OK** to finish.

11. Return to the Mechanical Equipment Schedule (select the tab or press <Ctrl>+<Tab> to switch between open windows).

12. All of the hot water heaters in the project now have a *Type Mark* set, as shown in Figure 15–30.

<MECHANICAL EQUIPMENT SCHEDULE>					
A	B	C	D	E	F
Type Mark	Mark	Space: Name	Manufacturer	Model	Comments
AHU-1	1	CORRIDOR			
AHU-1	2	CORRIDOR			
AHU-1	3	CORRIDOR			
AHU-1	4	CORRIDOR			
AHU-1	5	CORRIDOR			
AHU-1	6	CORRIDOR			
AHU-1	7	CORRIDOR			
AHU-1	8	CORRIDOR			
AHU-1	9	CORRIDOR			
AHU-1	10	CORRIDOR			
AHU-1	11	CORRIDOR			
AHU-1	12	CORRIDOR			
HW-1	49	STORAGE			
HW-1	50	STORAGE			
HW-1	51	JNTR.			
HW-1	52	JNTR.			
AHU-1	53	CORRIDOR			

Figure 15–30

13. In the *Mark* column you can see that the numbers are out of sequence. The numbering of hot water heaters and one air handling unit (AHU-1) is incorrect, starting at 49.

14. Change the *Mark* of the incorrectly numbered AHU-1 from **53** to **13**, then adjust each of the HW-1 to follow sequence.

15. In the schedule view, change the name of the Manufacturer of one of the AHUs to **ME Unlimited**. An alert displays warning that changing this changes all of the elements of this type, as shown in Figure 15–31. Click **OK**.

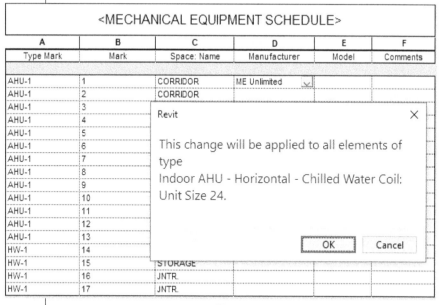

Figure 15–31

16. Open the Mechanical>HVAC>Floor Plans>**01 Mechanical Plan** view and zoom to the south wing and to the far right end of the hall in the office area.

17. Select the AHU that is connected to the Office duct system. In the Type Selector, change it to **Indoor AHU - Horizontal - Chilled Water Coil: Unit Size 12**.

18. While it is still selected, click **Edit Type** and set the *Type Mark* to **AHU-2**.

19. Switch back to the schedule view to see the change.

20. In the *Manufacturer* column, use the drop-down list to select the same *Manufacturer* for the modified AHU, as shown in Figure 15–32. Click **OK** in the dialog box notifying you of the change to any other elements of that type.

<MECHANICAL EQUIPMENT SCHEDULE>					
A	B	C	D	E	F
Type Mark	Mark	Space: Name	Manufacturer	Model	Comments
AHU-1	1	CORRIDOR	ME Unlimited		
AHU-1	2	CORRIDOR	ME Unlimited		
AHU-1	3	CORRIDOR	ME Unlimited		
AHU-1	4	CORRIDOR	ME Unlimited		
AHU-1	5	CORRIDOR	ME Unlimited		
AHU-1	6	CORRIDOR	ME Unlimited		
AHU-1	7	CORRIDOR	ME Unlimited		
AHU-1	8	CORRIDOR	ME Unlimited		
AHU-1	9	CORRIDOR	ME Unlimited		
AHU-1	10	CORRIDOR	ME Unlimited		
AHU-1	11	CORRIDOR	ME Unlimited		
AHU-1	12	CORRIDOR	ME Unlimited		
AHU-2	13	CORRIDOR	▼		
HW-1	14	STORAGE	ME Unlimited		
HW-1	15	STORAGE			
HW-1	16	JNTR.			
HW-1	17	JNTR.			

Figure 15–32

21. Fill in the other information.

22. Save the project.

Task 2 - Modify the plumbing fixture schedule.

---

1. In the Project Browser, expand **Schedules/Quantities** and open **PLUMBING FIXTURE SCHEDULE**. The schedule is already populated with some information.

2. From the *Modify Schedule | Quantities* tab>Appearance panel, select ⌗ (Freeze Header). Scroll down the schedule and note that the schedule's headers stay at the top.

3. Note that the *Elevation from Level* column shows some of the sinks/lavatories at **0'-0"**. This means they have been orphaned.

4. Click on one of them. In the *Modify Schedules | Quantities* tab>Element panel, click ⌗ (Highlight in Model).

5. Click **OK**, **Show**, or **Close** as needed.

6. Select the sink. From the *Modify | Plumbing Fixtures* tab> Work Plane panel, select [icon] (Pick Host). In the Placement panel, select [icon] (Face). Hover over the linked architectural model's sink and use the midpoint to place the sink, as shown in Figure 15–33.

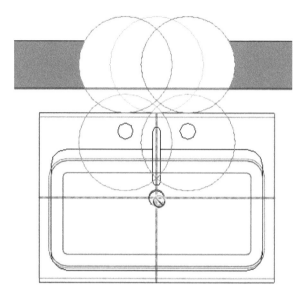

Figure 15–33

7. Switch back to the plumbing fixture schedule and notice that just the one sink updated. Each sink/lavatory and water closet would need to be rehosted to update.

8. Open the Plumbing>Plumbing>Floor Plans>**01 Plumbing Plan** view.

9. Select one sink in any classroom and right-click on it. Choose **Select All Instances>Visible in View**.

10. From Properties, change the *Schedule Level* to **Level 1**.

11. Switch back to the plumbing fixture schedule and notice that the *Elevation from Level* has changed without rehosting all of the sinks.

12. Continue to do this with the rest of the plumbing fixtures on Level 1.

Task 3 - Add schedules to a sheet.

1. In the Project Browser, right-click on Sheets (all) and select **New Sheet**. Select the E-sized title block and click **OK**.

2. In the Project Browser, right-click on the new sheet (which is bold) and select Rename. In the Sheet Title dialog box, set the *Number* to **M-801** and the *Name* to **Schedules** and click **OK**.

3. Drag and drop the **MECHANICALEQUIPMENT SCHEDULE** view onto the sheet, as shown in Figure 15–34.

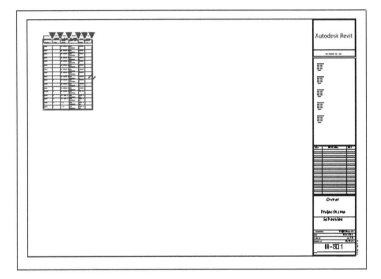

Figure 15–34

4. Zoom in and use the arrows at the top to modify the width of the columns so that the titles display correctly.

5. Click in an empty space on the sheet to finish placing the schedule.

6. Switch back to the **01 Mechanical Plan** view and select one of the Classroom AHUs.

7. In the Type Selector, change the size to **Unit Size 36**. In Type Properties add the *Model*, *Manufacturer*, and *Type Mark*.

8. Return to the Schedule sheet. The information is automatically populated.

9. Drag and drop the PLUMBING FIXTURE SCHEDULE view onto the sheet. Because it is itemized, it is too long for the schedule. Place it anyway.

10. Using the split schedule table control, split the schedule as many times as you need to and use the length control to change the length so that they fit and look appropriate, as shown in Figure 15–35.

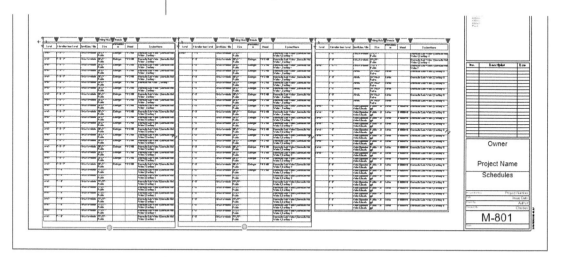

Figure 15–35

11. Save and close the project.

Practice 15e

Work with Schedules - Electrical

Practice Objectives

- Update schedule information.
- Add a schedule to a sheet.

In this practice, you will update a schedule and place it on a sheet, as shown in Figure 15–36.

Type Mark	Description	Count	Manufacturer	Model	Lamp	Lamp Wattage	Illuminance	Electrical Data
EM-1	Emergency Recessed Lighting Fixture: 2x4 - 277	22	Columbina			96 W	73 lx	Emergency 277 V/1-96 VA- 277 V/1 -32 VA
L1	Troffer Light - 2x4 Parabolic: 2'x4'(2 Lamp) - 277V	106	Vantage		T-12	80 W	54 lx	277 V/1-80 VA
L2	Troffer Light - 2x2 Parabolic: 2'x2'(2 Lamp) - 120V	8	Vantage		T-12	40 W	22 lx	120 V/1-40 V A
L3	Sconce Light - Flat Round: 60W - 120V	4	Sconces R Us		A-19	60 W	7 lx	120 V/1-60 V A
Grand total: 140								

(LIGHTING FIXTURE SCHEDULE)

Figure 15–36

Task 1 - Fill in schedules.

1. In the practice files *Schedules* folder, open **Schedules-School-MEP.rvt**.

2. Open the Electrical>Lighting>Floor Plans>**01 Lighting Plan** view.

3. In the Project Browser, expand **Schedules/Quantities**. Several schedules have been added to this project.

4. Double-click on **LIGHTING FIXTURE SCHEDULE** to open it. The schedule is already populated with some of the basic information, as shown in part in Figure 15–37.

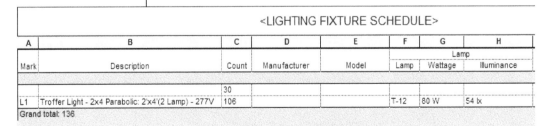

			<LIGHTING FIXTURE SCHEDULE>				
A	B	C	D	E	F	G	H
Mark	Description	Count	Manufacturer	Model	Lamp	Lamp Wattage	Illuminance
		30					
L1	Troffer Light - 2x4 Parabolic: 2'x4'(2 Lamp) - 277V	106			T-12	80 W	54 lx
Grand total: 136							

Figure 15–37

5. Click in the empty *Type Mark* cell. In the *Modify Schedules | Quantities* tab>Element panel, click ⬚ (Highlight in Model).

6. In the view that comes up, click **Close** in the Show Element(s) in View dialog box.

7. In Properties, you can see that Multiple Families are selected, as shown in Figure 15–38. More than one lighting fixture type is selected and you cannot edit the types.

Figure 15–38

Isolating the category would show all lighting fixtures.

8. In the View Control Bar, expand ✎ (Temporary Hide/Isolate) and select **Isolate Elements**.

The selected fixtures display and you can easily see that there are at least two different types of lights, as shown for the south wing of the building in Figure 15–39.

South wing

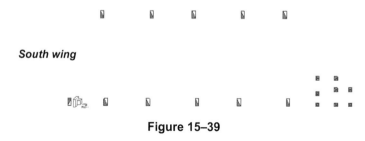

Figure 15–39

9. Click **Modify** and select one of the rectangular fixtures.

10. In Properties, you can see that it is an emergency light fixture. Click 📇 (Edit Type).

11. In the Type Properties dialog box, in the *Identity Data* area, set the *Type Mark* to **EM-1**.

12. Click **OK** to finish.

13. Return to the Lighting Fixture Schedule (select the tab or press <Ctrl>+<Tab> to switch between open windows).

All of the emergency lighting fixtures in the project now have a *Type Mark* set, as shown in Figure 15–40.

<LIGHTING FIXTURE SCHEDULE>

A	B	C	D	E	F	G	H
						Lamp	
Type Mark	Description	Count	Manufacturer	Model	Lamp	Wattage	Illuminance
	Troffer Light - 2x2 Parabolic: 2'x2'(2 Lamp) - 120V	8			T-12	40 W	22 lx
EM-1	Emergency Recessed Lighting Fixture: 2x4 - 277	22				96 W	73 lx
L1	Troffer Light - 2x4 Parabolic: 2'x4'(2 Lamp) - 277V	106			T-12	80 W	54 lx

Figure 15–40

14. There is still a lighting fixture type without a type mark. Type **L2** in the *Type Mark* column and press <Enter>. An alert displays warning that this action changes all of the elements of this type, as shown in Figure 15–41. Click **OK**.

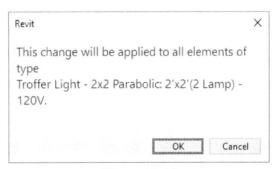

Figure 15–41

15. Switch to the **01 Lighting Plan** view.

16. Select one of the square lighting fixtures and in the Type Properties, assign a name in the *Manufacturer* column and click **OK**.

17. In the View Control Bar, reset **Temporary Hide/Isolate**.

18. Zoom into the office area, then load and add several new wall sconce fixtures. (You will need to load them from the library.)

19. Return to the lighting fixture schedule. The new sconce lights are added, as shown in Figure 15–42.

If you do not see the Lighting Fixture tool from the System tab on the ribbon, you may need to revise the tools and analyses in the User Interface within Options.

<LIGHTING FIXTURE SCHEDULE>

A	B	C	D	E	F	G	H
						Lamp	
Type Mark	Description	Count	Manufacturer	Model	Lamp	Wattage	Illuminance
	Sconce Light - Flat Round: 60W - 120V	4			A-19	60 W	7 lx
EM-1	Emergency Recessed Lighting Fixture: 2x4 - 277	22				96 W	73 lx
L1	Troffer Light - 2x4 Parabolic: 2'x4'(2 Lamp) - 277V	106			T-12	80 W	54 lx
L2	Troffer Light - 2x2 Parabolic: 2'x2'(2 Lamp) - 120V	8	Vantage		T-12	40 W	22 lx
Grand total: 140							

Figure 15–42

20. In the *Manufacturer* column, use the drop-down list to select the same *Manufacturer* for the other Troffer light.

21. Fill in some of the other information.

22. Save the project.

Task 2 - Add a schedule to a sheet.

1. In the Project Browser, right-click on **Sheets** (all) and select **New Sheet**. Select the E-sized title block and click **OK**.

2. In the Project Browser, right-click on the new sheet (which is bold) and select **Rename**. In the Sheet Title dialog box, set the *Number* to **E-801** and the *Name* to **Schedules**. Click **OK**.

3. Drag and drop the **LIGHTING FIXTURE SCHEDULE** view onto the sheet, as shown in Figure 15–43.

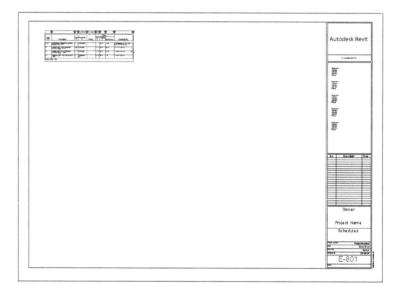

Figure 15–43

4. Zoom in and use the arrows at the top to modify the width of the columns so that the titles display correctly.

5. Click in empty space on the sheet to finish placing the schedule.

6. Save and close the project.

Chapter Review Questions

1. Which of the following elements cannot be tagged using **Tag by Category**?

   a. Spaces

   b. Ducts

   c. Plumbing Fixtures

   d. Communication Devices

2. What happens when you delete an air terminal in an Autodesk Revit model?

   a. You must delete the air terminal on the sheet.

   b. You must delete the air terminal from the schedule.

   c. The air terminal is removed from the model, but not from the schedule.

   d. The air terminal is removed from the model and the schedule.

3. In a schedule, if you change type information (such as a Type Mark) all instances of that type update with the new information.

   a. True

   b. False

Command Summary

Button	Command	Location
	Freeze Header	• **Ribbon:** *Modify Schedule	Quantities* tab>Titles & Header panel
	Highlight in Model	• **Ribbon:** *Modify Schedule	Quantities* tab>Element panel
	Material Tag	• **Ribbon:** *Annotate* tab>Tag panel
	Multi-Category	• **Ribbon:** *Annotate* tab>Tag panel
	Tag All Not Tagged	• **Ribbon:** *Annotate* tab>Tag panel
	Tag by Category	• **Ribbon:** *Annotate* tab>Tag panel • **Shortcut:** TG

Creating Details

Creating details is a critical part of the design process, as it is the step where you specify the exact information that is required to build a construction project. The elements that you can add to a model include detail components, detail lines, text, tags, symbols, and filled regions. Details can be created from views in the model, but you can also add 2D details in separate views.

Learning Objectives in This Chapter

- Create drafting views where you can add 2D details.
- Add detail components that show the typical elements in a detail.
- Annotate details using detail lines, text, tags, symbols, and patterns that define materials.

16.1 Setting Up Detail Views

Most of the work you do in the Autodesk® Revit® software is exclusively with *smart* elements that interconnect and work together in the model. However, the software does not automatically display how elements should be built to fit together. For this, you need to create detail drawings, as shown in Figure 16–1.

Details are created either in 2D drafting views, or in callouts from plan, elevation, or section views.

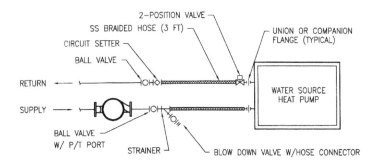

WATER SOURCE HEAT PUMP
PIPING DETAIL

Figure 16–1

How To: Create a Drafting View

1. In the *View* tab>Create panel, click 🖻 (Drafting View).
2. In the New Drafting View dialog box, enter a *Name* and set a *Scale*, as shown in Figure 16–2.

Drafting views are listed in their own section in the Project Browser.

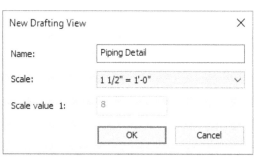

Figure 16–2

3. Click **OK**. A blank view is created with space in which you can sketch the detail.

How To: Create a Detail View from Model Elements

1. Start the **Section** or **Callout** command.
2. In the Type Selector, select the **Detail View: Detail** type.
   - The marker indicates that it is a detail, as shown for a section in Figure 16–3.

Callouts also have a Detail View Type that can be used in the same way.

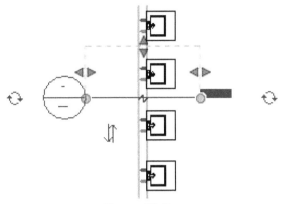

Figure 16–3

3. Place the section or a callout of the area you want to use for the detail.
4. Open the new detail.
5. Change the detail level to see more or less of the element materials.
6. Use the Detail Line tool to sketch on top of or add to the building elements.

- Because you are working with smart elements, a detail of the model is a true representation. When the building elements change, the detail changes as well, as shown in Figure 16–4.

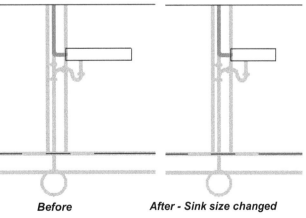

Before   *After - Sink size changed*

Figure 16–4

- You can create detail elements on top of the model and then toggle the model off so that it does not show in the detail view. In Properties, in the *Graphics* area, change *Display Model* to **Do not display**. You can also set the model to **Halftone**, as shown in Figure 16–5.

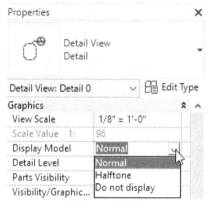

Figure 16–5

Referencing a Drafting View

Once you have created a drafting view, you can reference it in another view (such as a callout, elevation, or section view), as shown in Figure 16–6. For example, in a section view, you might want to reference an existing roof detail. You can reference drafting views, sections, elevations, and callouts.

Figure 16–6

- You can use the search feature to limit the information displayed.

How To: Reference a Drafting View

1. Open the view in which you want to place the reference.
2. Start the **Section**, **Callout**, or **Elevation** command.
3. In the *Modify | <contextual>* tab>Reference panel, select **Reference Other View**.

4. In the drop-down list, select **<New Drafting View>** or an existing drafting view.
5. Place the view marker.
6. When you place the associated drafting view on a sheet, the marker in this view updates with the appropriate information.

*   If you select **<New Drafting View>** from the drop-down list, a new view is created in the *Drafting Views (Detail)* area in the Project Browser. You can rename it as needed. The new view does not include any model elements.

*   When you create a detail based on a section, elevation, or callout, you do not need to link it to a drafting view.

*   You can change a referenced view to a different view. Select the view marker and in the ribbon, select the new view from the list.

Saving Drafting Views

To create a library of standard details, save the non-model specific drafting views to your server. They can then be imported into a project and modified to suit. They are saved as .RVT files.

Drafting views can be saved in two ways:

*   Save an individual drafting view to a new file.
*   Save all of the drafting views as a group in one new file.

How To: Save One Drafting View to a File

1. In the Project Browser, right-click on the drafting view you want to save and select **Save to New File…**, as shown in Figure 16–7.

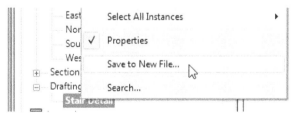

Figure 16–7

2. In the Save As dialog box, specify a name and location for the file and click **Save**.

You can save sheets, drafting views, model views (floor plans), schedules, and reports.

How To: Save a Group of Drafting Views to a File

1. In the *File* tab, expand ![Save As icon] (Save As), expand ![Library icon] (Library) and then click ![View icon] (View).
2. In the Save Views dialog box, in the *Views:* pane, expand the list and select **Show drafting views only**.
3. Select the drafting views that you want to save, as shown in Figure 16–8.

Figure 16–8

4. Click **OK**.
5. In the Save As dialog box, specify a name and location for the file and click **Save**.

How To: Use a Saved Drafting View in Another Project

1. Open the project to which you want to add the drafting view.
2. In the *Insert* tab>Import panel, expand ![Insert from File icon] (Insert from File) and click ![Insert Views from File icon] (Insert Views from File).
3. In the Open dialog box, select the project in which you saved the detail and click **Open**.
4. In the Insert Views dialog box, limit the types of views to **Show drafting views only**, as shown in Figure 16–9.

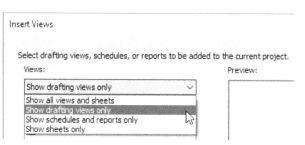

Figure 16–9

5. Select the view(s) that you want to insert and click **OK**.

Hint: Importing Details from Other CAD Software

You might already have a set of standard details created in a different CAD program, such as the AutoCAD® software. You can reuse the details in the Autodesk Revit software by importing them into a temporary project. Once you have imported the detail, it helps to clean it up and save it as a view before bringing it into your active project.

1. In a new project, create a drafting view and make it active.

2. In the *Insert* tab>Import panel, click 🖼 (Import CAD).
3. In the Import CAD dialog box, select the file to import. Most of the default values are what you need. You might want to change the *Layer/Level colors* to **Black and White**.
4. Click **Open**.

- If you want to modify the detail, select the imported data. In the *Modify | [filename]* tab>Import Instance panel, expand

  🗐 (Explode) and click 🗐 (Partial Explode) or 🗐 (Full

  Explode). Click 🗐✗ (Delete Layers) before you explode the detail. A full explode greatly increases the file size.

- Modify the detail using tools in the Modify panel. Change all the text and line styles to Autodesk Revit specific elements.

16.2 Adding Detail Components

Autodesk Revit elements typically require additional information to ensure that they are constructed correctly. To create details (such as the one shown in Figure 16–10), you add detail components, detail lines, and various annotation elements.

- Detail elements are not directly connected to the model, even if model elements display in the view.

Figure 16–10

- If you want to draw detail lines in 3D, use Model Line. Detail Line is grayed out when you are in a 3D view or perspective view.

Detail Components

Detail components are families made of 2D and annotation elements. Over 500 detail components organized by CSI format are found in the *Detail Items* folder of the library, as shown in Figure 16–11.

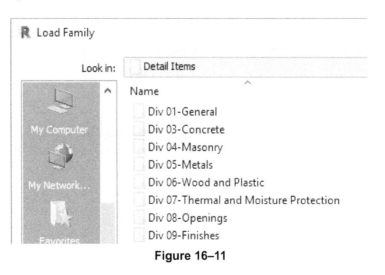

Figure 16–11

How To: Add a Detail Component

1. In the *Annotate* tab>Detail panel, expand ⬚ (Component) and click ⬚ (Detail Component).
2. In the Type Selector, select the detail component type. You can load additional types from the library.
3. Many detail components can be rotated as you insert them by pressing <Spacebar>. Alternatively, select **Rotate after placement** in the Options Bar, as shown in Figure 16–12.

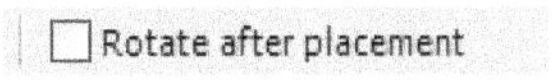

☐ Rotate after placement

Figure 16–12

4. Place the component in the view.

Adding Break Lines

The Break Line is a detail component found in the *Detail Items\ Div 01-General* folder. It consists of a rectangular area (shown highlighted in Figure 16–13) which is used to block out elements behind it. You can modify the size of the area that is covered and change the size of the cut line using the controls.

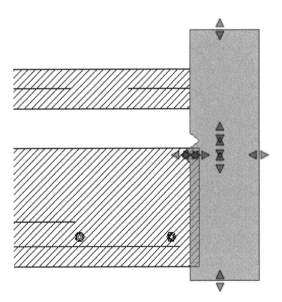

Figure 16–13

Hint: Working with the Draw Order of Details

When you select detail elements in a view, you can change the draw order of the elements in the *Modify | Detail Items* tab> Arrange panel. You can bring elements in front of other elements or place them behind elements, as shown in Figure 16–14.

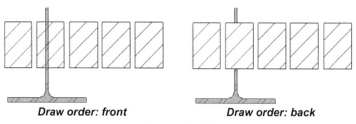

Draw order: front   Draw order: back

Figure 16–14

- ⬚ **(Bring to Front):** Places element in front of all other elements.

- ⬚ **(Send to Back):** Places element behind all other elements.

- ⬚ **(Bring Forward):** Moves element one step to the front.

- ⬚ **(Send Backward):** Moves element one step to the back.

- You can select multiple detail elements and change the draw order of all of them in one step. They keep the relative order of the original selection.

Repeating Details

Instead of having to insert a component multiple times (such as brick or concrete block), you can use ⬚ (Repeating Detail Component) and create a string of components, as shown in Figure 16–15.

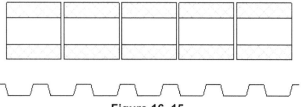

Figure 16–15

How To: Insert a Repeating Detail Component

1. In the *Annotate* tab>Detail panel, expand 🔲 (Component) and click ⠿ (Repeating Detail Component).
2. In the Type Selector, select the detail you want to use.
3. In the Draw panel, click ✎ (Line) or ⚟ (Pick Lines).
4. In the Options Bar, type a value for the *Offset*, if needed.
5. The components repeat to fit the length of the sketched or selected line, as shown in Figure 16–16. You can lock the components to the line.

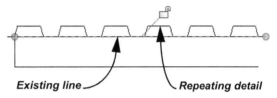

Existing line ——— *Repeating detail*

Figure 16–16

Hint: ⊗ (Insulation)

Adding batt insulation is similar to adding a repeating detail component, but instead of a series of bricks or other elements, it creates the linear batting pattern, shown in Figure 16–17.

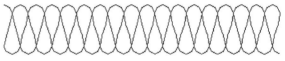

Figure 16–17

Before you place the insulation in the view, specify the *Width* and other options in the Options Bar, as shown in Figure 16–18.

Modify | Place Insulation   Width 0' 3 1/2   ☐ Chain   Offset: 0' 0"   to center ▾

Figure 16–18

16.3 Annotating Details

After you have added components and sketched detail lines, you need to add annotations to the detail view. You can place text notes and dimensions as shown in Figure 16–19, as well as symbols and tags. Filled regions are used to add hatching.

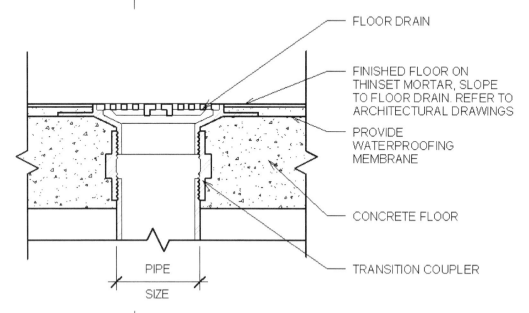

Figure 16–19

Creating Filled Regions

Many elements include material information that displays in plan and section views, while other elements need more details to be added. For example, the concrete wall shown in Figure 16–20 includes material information, while the earth to the left of the wall needs to be added using the **Filled Region** command.

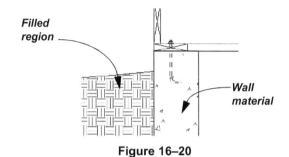

Figure 16–20

The patterns used in details are *drafting patterns*. They are scaled to the view scale and update if you modify it. You can also add full-size *model patterns*, such as a Flemish Bond brick pattern, to the surface of some elements.

How To: Add a Filled Region

1. In the *Annotate* tab>Detail panel, expand (Region) and click (Filled Region).
2. Create a closed boundary using the Draw tools.
3. In the Line Style panel, select the line style for the outside edge of the boundary. If you do not want the boundary to display, select the <Invisible lines> style.
4. In the Type Selector, select the fill type, as shown in Figure 16–21.

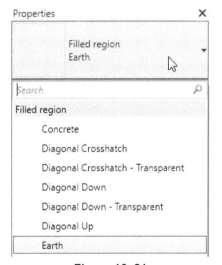

Figure 16–21

5. Click (Finish Edit Mode).

- You can modify a region by changing the fill type in the Type Selector or by editing the sketch.

- Double-click on the edge of the filled region to edit the sketch.

  If you have the Selection option set to (Select elements by face), you can select the pattern.

Adding Detail Tags

Besides adding text to a detail, you can tag detail components using 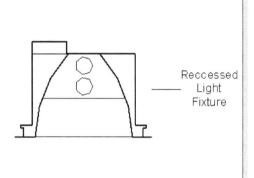 (Tag By Category). The tag name is set in the Type Parameters for that component, as shown in Figure 16–22. This means that if you have more than one copy of the component in your project, you do not have to rename it each time you place its tag.

Reccessed Light Fixture

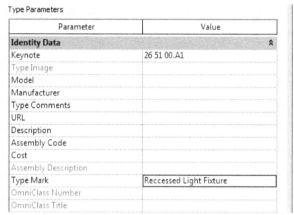

Type Parameters	
Parameter	Value
Identity Data	≽
Keynote	26 51 00.A1
Type Image	
Model	
Manufacturer	
Type Comments	
URL	
Description	
Assembly Code	
Cost	
Assembly Description	
Type Mark	Reccessed Light Fixture
OmniClass Number	
OmniClass Title	

Figure 16–22

- The **Detail Item Tag.rfa** tag is located in the *Annotations* folder in the library.

- For more information on annotating using keynotes, see *Section A.11 Keynoting and Keynote Legends*.

Hint: Multiple Dimension Options

If you are creating details that show one element with multiple dimension values, as shown in Figure 16–23, you can easily modify the dimension text.

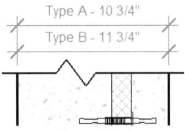

Figure 16–23

Select the dimension and then the dimension text. The Dimension Text dialog box opens. You can replace the text, as shown in Figure 16–24, or add text fields above or below, as well as a prefix or suffix.

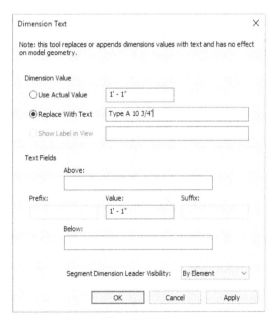

Figure 16–24

- This also works with Equality Text Labels.

Practice 16a	# Create a Fire Damper Detail

Practice Objectives

- Create a drafting view.
- Add filled regions, detail components, and annotations.

In this practice, you will create a drafting view. In the new view you will add detail lines of different weights, insulation, and filled regions. You will also add detail components, including Break Lines and text notes. Finally, you will place the detail view on a sheet (as shown in Figure 16–25) and place a reference section.

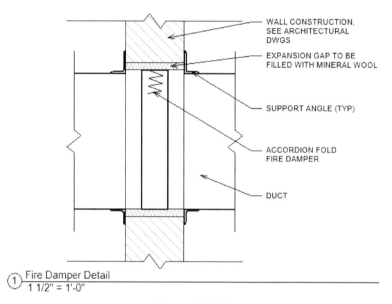

WALL CONSTRUCTION, SEE ARCHITECTURAL DWGS

EXPANSION GAP TO BE FILLED WITH MINERAL WOOL

SUPPORT ANGLE (TYP)

ACCORDION FOLD FIRE DAMPER

DUCT

① Fire Damper Detail
  1 1/2" = 1'-0"

Figure 16–25

Task 1 - Create a drafting view.

1. In the practice files *Detailing* folder, open **Detailing-School-MEP.rvt**.

2. In the *View* tab>Create panel, click 🖨 (Drafting View).

3. In the New Drafting View dialog box, set the name and scale as follows:
   - *Name*: **Fire Damper Detail**
   - *Scale*: **1-1/2"=1'-0"**

4. In the Project Browser, expand the **Coordination** node until you can see the new detail view. Select the view, as shown in Figure 16–26.

Figure 16–26

5. In Properties, change *Discipline* to **Mechanical** and *Sub-Discipline* to **HVAC**. The new view moves to that node in the Project Browser.

Task 2 - Draw detail lines.

1. In the *Annotate* tab>Detail panel, click ⬛ (Detail Line).

2. In the *Modify | Place Detail Lines* tab, set the *Line Style* to **Thin Lines** and make sure **Chain** is unchecked. Draw the two vertical lines shown in Figure 16–27.

3. Change the *Line Style* to **Wide Lines** and draw the two horizontal lines shown in Figure 16–27. These become the primary duct and wall lines.
   - If the difference in the line weights does not display clearly, zoom in and, in the Quick Access Toolbar, toggle off ⬛ (Thin Lines).

The dimensions are for information only.

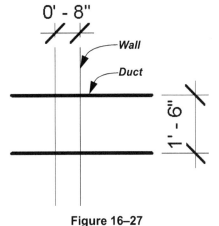

Figure 16–27

4. Continue adding and modifying detail lines to create the elements shown in Figure 16–28. Use modify commands (such as **Split** and **Offset**) and the draw tools.

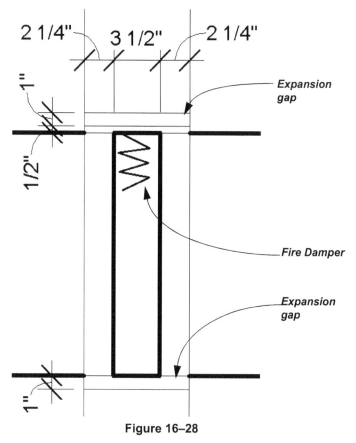

Figure 16–28

5. Save the project.

Task 3 - Add detail components.

1. In the *Annotate* tab>Detail panel, expand ▧ (Component) and select ▧ (Detail Component).

2. In the Type Selector, select **AISC Angle Shapes - Section L3X2X1/4**.

3. Place the angle on the top left, as shown in Figure 16–29.

   - Press <Spacebar> to rotate the angle before placing it.

4. Change the type **to AISC Angle Shapes - Section L2X2X1/4** and place the angle on the bottom of the duct, as shown in Figure 16–29.

5. Select the two angle components and mirror them to the other side, as shown in Figure 16–29.

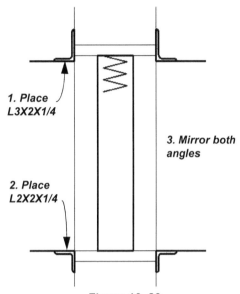

Figure 16–29

6. Add four break line components. Rotate and use the controls to modify the size until all of your excess lines are covered, as shown in Figure 16–30

The exact location and size of your break lines might vary.

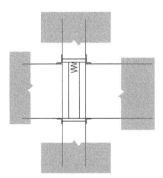

Figure 16–30

7. Save the project.

Task 4 - Add insulation and filled regions.

1. In the *Annotate* tab>Detail panel, click ⊗ (Insulation).

2. In the Options Bar, set the *Width* to **1"**.

3. Draw the insulation lines in the two expansion gaps, as shown in Figure 16–31.

4. In the *Annotate* tab>Detail panel, expand Region and click ⊡ (Filled Region).

5. In the Type Selector, select **Filled region: Diagonal Down**.

6. Draw rectangles around the wall areas as shown in Figure 16–31.

7. Click ✓ (Finish). The filled regions display.

The filled region pattern does not display until you finish the process.

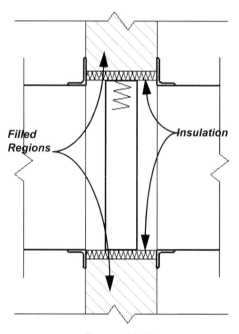

Figure 16–31

8. Save the project.

Task 5 - Add text notes.

1. In the *Annotate* tab>Text panel, click **A** (Text).

2. In the *Modify | Place Text* tab>Leader panel, select ⸜A (Two Segments) as the leader style.

3. In the Type Selector, select **Text: 3/32" Arial**.

4. Add text notes, as shown in Figure 16–32.

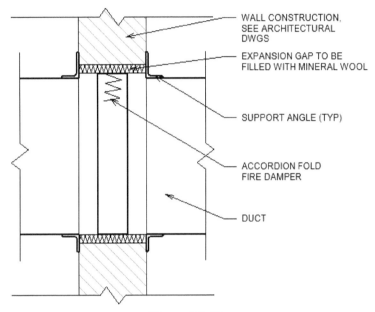

WALL CONSTRUCTION, SEE ARCHITECTURAL DWGS

EXPANSION GAP TO BE FILLED WITH MINERAL WOOL

SUPPORT ANGLE (TYP)

ACCORDION FOLD FIRE DAMPER

DUCT

Figure 16–32

5. Save the project.

Task 6 - Place the detail on a sheet and reference it in the project.

1. In the Project Browser, open the sheet **M601 - HVAC Details**.

2. In the Project Browser, drag the **Fire Damper Detail** view to the sheet.

3. Open the Mechanical>HVAC>**1 - Mech** view.

4. Zoom in on one of the duct systems.

5. In the *View* tab>Create panel, click ⌕ (Callout).

6. In the *Modify | Callout* tab>Reference panel, select **Reference Other View**.

7. Expand the drop-down list and select the new **Fire Damper Detail**, as shown in Figure 16–33.

8. Place the callout at the intersection of a duct and the wall, as shown in Figure 16–33. The information is filled out based on the location of the detail view on the sheet.

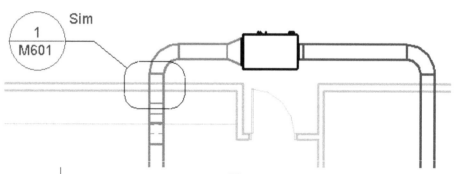

Figure 16–33

9. Save the project.

Practice 16b | Create a Meter Pedestal Detail

Practice Objective

• Create and annotate details.

In this practice, you will create a detail using detail lines and filled regions. You will then annotate the detail with text and dimensions, as shown in Figure 16–34. This practice is designed without individual steps.

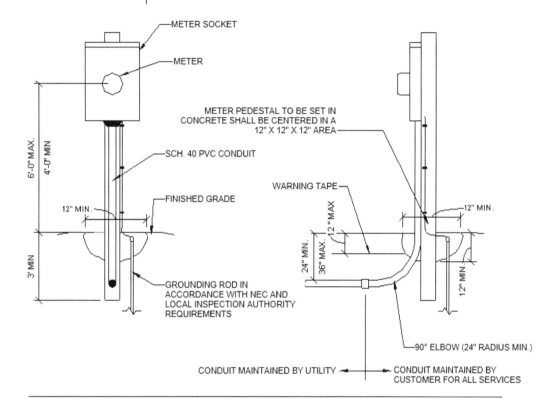

METER PEDESTAL - UG SERVICE
1 PHASE & 3 PHASE ALL VOLTAGES
SERVICE SIZE: 600 AMP MAXIMUM

Figure 16–34

Use the **Detailing-School-MEP.rvt** project as the base file for these tasks.

Practice 16c | Create a Floor Drain Detail

Practice Objective

- Create and annotate details.

In this practice, you will create a floor drain detail using detail components. You will then annotate the floor drain detail with text and a dimension, as shown in Figure 16–35. This practice is designed without individual steps.

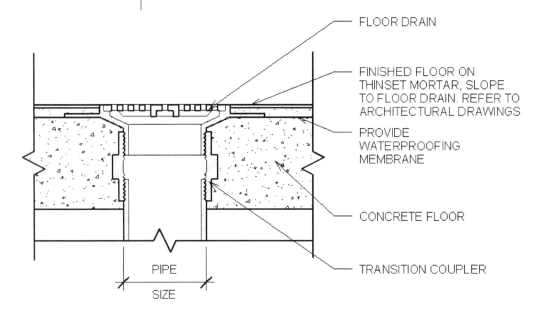

FLOOR DRAIN

FINISHED FLOOR ON THINSET MORTAR, SLOPE TO FLOOR DRAIN. REFER TO ARCHITECTURAL DRAWINGS

PROVIDE WATERPROOFING MEMBRANE

CONCRETE FLOOR

TRANSITION COUPLER

PIPE SIZE

Figure 16–35

Use the **Detailing-School-MEP.rvt** project as the base file for these tasks.

The following components and pattern are included in the practice file:

- Floor Drain - Section
- Resilient Flooring - Section
- Slab with Optional Haunch-Section
- Filled Region: Grout

Chapter Review Questions

1. Which of the following are ways in which you can create a detail? (Select all that apply.)

    a. Make a callout of a section and sketch over it.

    b. Draw all of the elements from scratch.

    c. Import a CAD detail and modify or sketch over it.

    d. Insert an existing drafting view from another file.

2. In which type of view (access shown in Figure 16–36) can you NOT add detail lines?

Figure 16–36

    a. Plans

    b. Elevations

    c. 3D views

    d. Legends

3. How are detail components different from building components?

    a. There is no difference.

    b. Detail components are made of 2D lines and annotation only, while building components are 3D.

    c. Detail components are made of building elements, but only display in detail views.

    d. Detail components are made of 2D and 3D elements.

4. Detail Lines only display in the view they were created in.

    a. True

    b. False

5. Which command do you use to add a pattern (such as concrete or earth, as shown in Figure 16–37) to part of a detail?

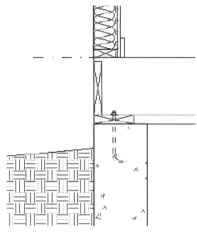

Figure 16–37

a. Region

b. Filled Region

c. Masking Region

d. Pattern Region

Command Summary

Button	Command	Location
CAD Import Tools		
	Delete Layers	• **Ribbon:** *Modify	<imported filename>* tab>Import Instance panel
	Full Explode	• **Ribbon:** *Modify	<imported filename>* tab>Import Instance panel> expand Explode
	Import CAD	• **Ribbon:** *Insert* tab>Import panel
	Partial Explode	• **Ribbon:** *Modify	<imported filename>* tab>Import Instance panel> expand Explode
Detail Tools		
	Detail Component	• **Ribbon:** *Annotate* tab>Detail panel> expand Component
	Detail Line	• **Ribbon:** *Annotate* tab>Detail panel
	Insulation	• **Ribbon:** *Annotate* tab>Detail panel
	Filled Region	• **Ribbon:** *Annotate* tab>Detail panel
	Repeating Detail Component	• **Ribbon:** *Annotate* tab>Detail panel> expand Component
View Tools		
	Bring Forward	• **Ribbon:** *Modify	Detail Items* tab> Arrange panel
	Bring to Front	• **Ribbon:** *Modify	Detail Items* tab> Arrange panel
	Drafting View	• **Ribbon:** *View* tab>Create panel
	Insert from File: Insert Views from File	• **Ribbon:** *Insert* tab>Import panel> expand Insert from File
	Send Backward	• **Ribbon:** *Modify	Detail Items* tab> Arrange panel
	Send to Back	• **Ribbon:** *Modify	Detail Items* tab> Arrange panel

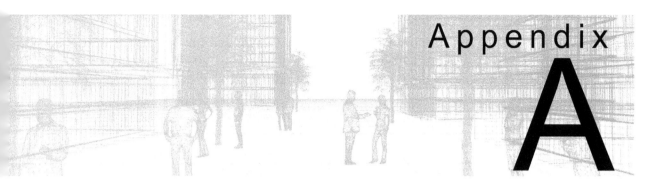

Additional Tools

There are many other tools available in the Autodesk® Revit® software that you can use when creating and using models. This appendix provides details about several tools and commands that are related to those covered in this guide.

Learning Objectives in This Appendix

- Customize building type settings for heating and cooling loads.
- Define color schemes.
- Create custom ducts and piping types.
- Modify system graphics using filters and overrides.
- Produce Pressure Loss reports.
- Use guide grids to help place views on sheets.
- Add revision clouds, tags, and information.
- Annotate dependent views with matchlines and view references.
- Import and export schedules.
- Create basic building component schedules.
- Add keynotes and keynote legends.

A.1 Building Type Settings

For even more control over Heating and Cooling Load analysis, you can customize the Building Types using the Building/Space and Type Settings dialog box, as shown in Figure A–1.

- To open the dialog box, in the *Manage* tab>Settings panel, expand (MEP Settings) and click (Building/Space and Type Settings), or in the *Analyze* tab, click in the Reports & Schedules panel title.

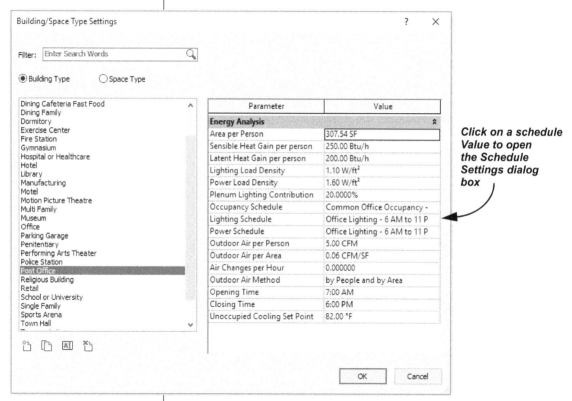

Click on a schedule Value to open the Schedule Settings dialog box

Figure A–1

- You can add, duplicate, rename and delete Building and Space Types.

- For each type of building or space you can specify energy analysis information, such as the number of people and expected heat gain per person, as well as the schedules of typical times that the building is occupied, as shown for a Warehouse in Figure A–2.

- To get to the Schedule Settings dialog box, click on a Building Type on the left, then on the right, click on Occupancy, Lighting, or Power Schedule and click within the *Value* name.

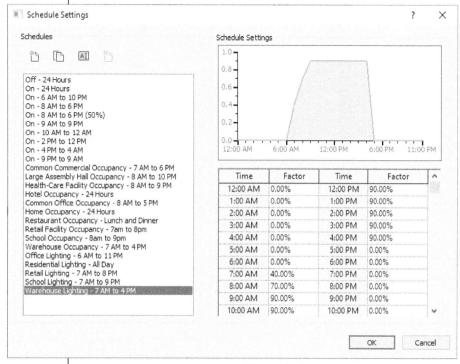

Figure A–2

- Building/Space type names are exported when you export a project to gbXML for further processing in other energy analysis programs.

A.2 Defining Color Schemes

Color Schemes are used with Space, Zones, ducts and pipes. You can define colors using many of the properties connected to the elements such as the Duct Friction Color Fill, as shown in Figure A–3.

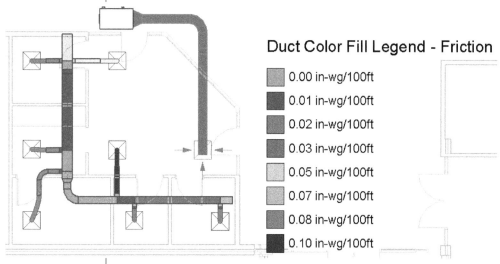

Duct Color Fill Legend - Friction

- 0.00 in-wg/100ft
- 0.01 in-wg/100ft
- 0.02 in-wg/100ft
- 0.03 in-wg/100ft
- 0.05 in-wg/100ft
- 0.07 in-wg/100ft
- 0.08 in-wg/100ft
- 0.10 in-wg/100ft

Figure A–3

How To: Define a Color Scheme

1. In Properties, click the button next to the **Color Scheme** (for Spaces and HVAC Zones) or **System Color Schemes** (for Pipes and Ducts) parameter.
   - **Color Schemes:** For spaces and HVAC zones, in the Edit Color Scheme dialog box, *Schemes* area, select a **Category**.
   - **System Color Scheme:** For pipes and ducts, in the Color Schemes dialog box, select the *Color scheme* for either the Pipes or Ducts category. Then, in the Edit Color Scheme dialog box, select a **Category** in the *Scheme* area.
2. Select an existing scheme and click ⬚ (Duplicate).
3. In the New color scheme dialog box, enter a new name and click **OK**. If the Colors Not Preserved warning displays, click **OK** again.
4. In the *Scheme Definition* area, type a name for the *Title* of the color scheme. This displays when the legend is placed in the view.

5. In the Color drop-down list, select an option, as shown in Figure A–4. The available parameters depend on the type of scheme you are creating.

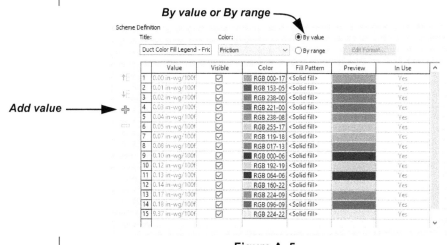

Figure A–4

6. Select the **By value** or **By range** options to set how the color scheme displays. Depending on the selection made in the Color drop-down list, **By range** might not be available.

7. If required, click ✛ (Add Value) to add more rows to the scheme, as shown in Figure A–5. Modify the visibility (*Visible* column), *Color*, and *Fill Pattern* as needed.

Figure A–5

8. In the *Options* area, select **Include elements from linked files** if you are using linked models.
9. Click **OK** to end the command.

Color Schemes By Value

If you select the **By value** option, you can modify the visibility, color, and fill pattern of the scheme. The value is assigned by the parameter data in the room or area object.

- Values are automatically updated when you add data to the parameters used in the color scheme. For example, if you create a color by space name and then add another space name in the project, it is also added to the color scheme.

- Click ↑E (Move Rows Up) and ↓E (Move Rows Down) to change the order of rows in the list.

- To remove a row, select it and click ▭ (Remove Value). This is only available if the parameter data is not being used in the room or area elements in the project.

Color Schemes By Range

If you select the **By range** option, you can modify the *At Least* variable and the *Caption*, as well as the visibility, color, and fill pattern, as shown in Figure A–6.

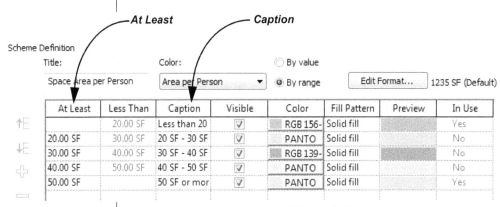

Figure A–6

- Click **Edit Format...** to modify the units display format.

- To add rows, select the row above the new row and click ✛ (Add Value). The new row increments according to the previous distances set or by double the value of the first row.

A.3 Custom Duct and Piping Types

Duct/Pipe Types and Settings

The System and Mechanical default templates are pre-loaded with duct/pipe types and routing preferences set up. You can create additional duct/pipe types and modify the routing preferences. Ducts and pipes are system families; therefore, you need to duplicate an existing family in the Type Properties, as shown in Figure A–7.

Select Edit Type for a duct or pipe

Click Edit next to Routing Preferences

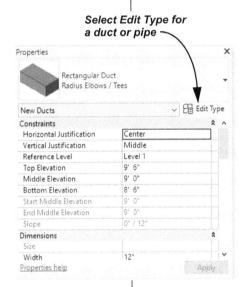
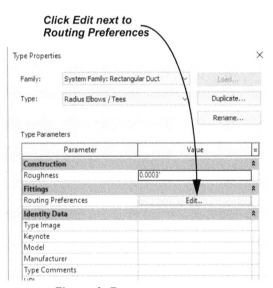

Figure A–7

Routing Preferences

The Routing Preferences dialog box enables you to specify the kind of pipe and pipe fittings to use. You can have a simple pipe type with one kind of pipe segment used for all sizes and one family for each kind of pipe fitting. Alternatively, you can set up the pipe type so that as the pipe size increases, different pipe and different fittings are used. Use ⊕ (Add Row) and ▭ (Remove Row) to create or remove rows, and the arrows to re-order items.

- Duct routing preferences are similar.

The Routing Preferences dialog box is shown in Figure A–8.

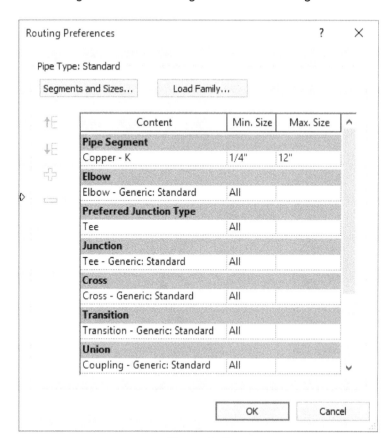

Figure A–8

- **Segments and Sizes...** enables you to create named segments with corresponding standard pipe sizes.

- **Load Family...** enables you to load additional pipe fittings if needed.

A.4 Work with System Graphics

Default system colors are set up by graphic overrides at the system family level. These can be modified to suit your company standards. Another useful graphic override is to create filters that display only the systems you want to see in a view. For example, use graphic override filters to display the sanitary piping only and not the hot and cold water piping, as shown in Figure A–9.

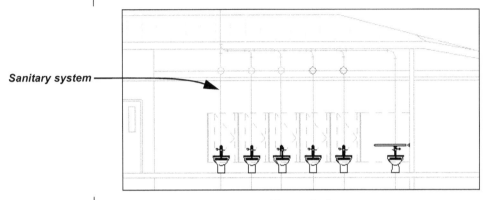

Sanitary system

Figure A–9

System Graphic Overrides

By default, in the Autodesk Revit templates, the Return Air Systems are magenta and Supply Air Systems are blue. In Figure A–10, Hydronic Supply and Return Systems also have the colors specified. System colors display in all views including 3D views.

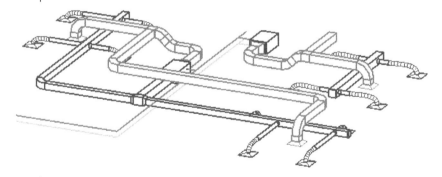

Figure A–10

- System graphic overrides are consistent across the entire project. They are not view specific.

How To: Set Up System Graphic Overrides

1. In the Project Browser, expand Families>Piping (or Duct) Systems>Piping (or Duct) System, as shown in Figure A–11.
2. Double-click on the one that you want to modify or right-click and select **Type Properties**.

To create a new system family, in the Project Browser, right-click on an existing type and duplicate it.

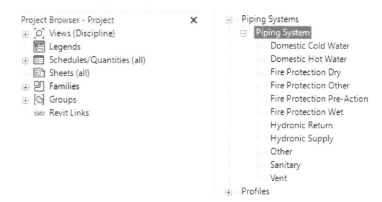

Figure A–11

3. In Type Properties, next to *Graphic Overrides*, click **Edit...**.
4. In the Line Graphics dialog box (shown in Figure A–12), make changes to the *Weight*, *Color*, and/or *Pattern*.

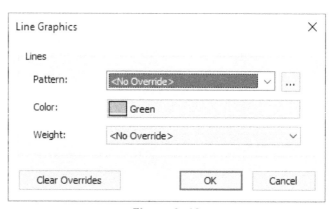

Figure A–12

5. Click **OK** twice to apply the changes.

Using Graphic Override Filters

Any view can be set to display specific systems by using filters. In the example in Figure A–13, the view on the left displays all of the systems along with extra elements such as data components. The view on the right has graphic overrides that toggle off extraneous elements and filter out all systems except duct and hydronic piping.

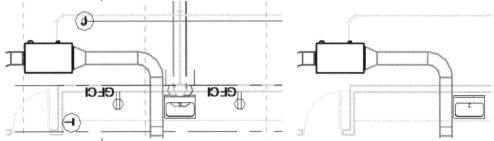

Figure A–13

How To: Apply a View Filter to Override a View

1. Open the Visibility/Graphic Overrides dialog box.
2. In the dialog box, select the *Filters* tab.
3. In the *Visibility* column, select the overrides you want to display. In Figure A–14, the Domestic Cold and Hot Water have been toggled off while the Sanitary and Vent systems display.

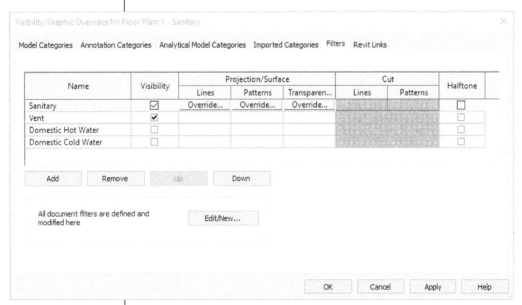

Figure A–14

---

4. To add a new filter to this view, click **Add**.
5. In the Add Filters dialog box (shown in Figure A–15), select the type of systems you want to modify and click **OK**.

The list might vary depending on the filters set up in the project.

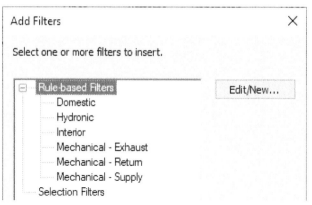

Figure A–15

- View Filters override system graphics so any colors you set in this dialog box supersede those specified in the System Type.

- If you need to change information about the filter itself, click **Edit/New...** in the Add Filters or Filters dialog box. Then, modify the *Categories* or *Filter Rules*. For example, the **Mechanical - Exhaust Filter** does not include *Air Terminals* by default so you need to select it, as shown in Figure A–16.

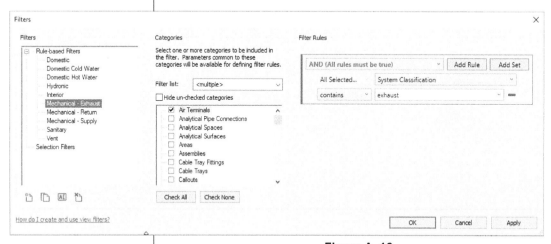

Figure A–16

A.5 Pressure Loss Reports

Pressure Loss reports are HTML files, as shown in Figure A–17, that include all of the data that can be viewed dynamically in the System Inspector. The reports can be set up to export exactly the information you need. They can be created for duct or pipe systems. The analysis for each system includes total pressure loss for the system and detailed information for various sections of duct or pipe.

System Classification	Return Air
System Type	Return Air
System Name	01 - RA01
Abbreviation	

Total Pressure Loss Calculations by Sections

Section	Element	Flow	Size	Velocity	Velocity Pressure	Length	Loss Co
	Duct	500 CFM	12"x12"	500 FPM	-	3' - 11 1/2"	-
1	Fittings	500 CFM	-	500 FPM	0.02 in-wg	-	0.17
	Air Terminal	500 CFM	-	-	-	-	-
2	Duct	1000 CFM	12"x12"	1000 FPM	-	12' - 4 15/16"	-
	Fittings	1000 CFM	-	1000 FPM	0.06 in-wg	-	0.81490!
3	Fittings	1000 CFM	-	409 FPM	0.01 in-wg	-	0
	Equipment	1000 CFM	-	-	-	-	-
4	Duct	500 CFM	12"x12"	500 FPM	-	24' - 7 1/2"	-
	Fittings	500 CFM	-	500 FPM	0.02 in-wg	-	0.34
	Air Terminal	500 CFM	-	-	-	-	-

Critical Path : 4-2-3 ; Total Pressure Loss : 0.14 in-wg

Detail Information of Straight Segment by Sections

Section	Element ID	Flow	Size	Velocity	Velocity Pressure
1	250437	500 CFM	12"x12"	500 FPM	0.02 in-wg
	250440	500 CFM	12"x12"	500 FPM	0.02 in-wg
2	250623	1000 CFM	12"x12"	1000 FPM	0.06 in-wg
	252421	1000 CFM	12"x12"	1000 FPM	0.06 in-wg
	252430	1000 CFM	12"x12"	1000 FPM	0.06 in-wg
4	250445	500 CFM	12"x12"	500 FPM	0.02 in-wg
	250446	500 CFM	12"x12"	500 FPM	0.02 in-wg
	250449	500 CFM	12"x12"	500 FPM	0.02 in-wg

Figure A–17

How To: Create a Duct/Pipe Pressure Loss Report

1. Select a system in a view. In the contextual *Modify Duct (or Pipe) Systems* tab>Duct (or Pipe) System Report panel, click

   (Duct Pressure Loss Report) or (Pipe Pressure Loss Report). These tools are also found in the *Analyze* tab> Reports & Schedules panel.

2. If you have not preselected a system in the view, the Duct (or Pipe) Pressure Loss Report - System Selector dialog box (shown in Figure A–18) enables you to select the systems that you want to include in the report.

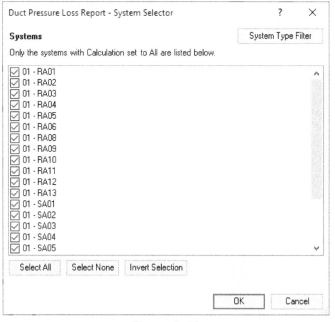

Figure A–18

- To limit the systems displayed in the System Selector, click **System Type Filter** to open the dialog box shown in Figure A–19. Select the types of systems you want to include in the report and click **OK** to return to the main dialog box.

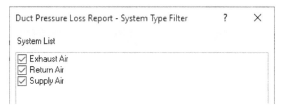

Figure A–19

- Use **Select All**, **Select None**, and **Invert Selection** to help with the selection.

3. When you have finished selecting the systems to include, click **OK**.

4. In the Duct/Pipe Pressure Loss Reports Settings dialog box, specify the type of Report Format and the Reports Fields, and other information as shown in Figure A–20.

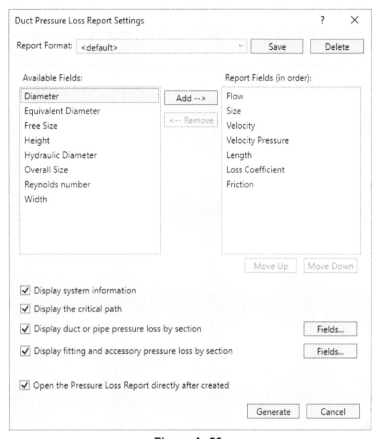

Figure A–20

5. Click **Generate**.

A.6 Guide Grids and Sheets

Guide grids, as shown in Figure A–21, help you place views on sheets. Guide grids can be set up per sheet. You can also create different types with various grid spacings.

When moving a view to a guide grid, only orthogonal datum elements (levels and grids) and reference planes snap to the guide grid.

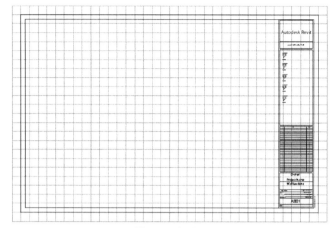

Figure A–21

- You can move guide grids and resize them using controls.

How To: Add a Guide Grid

1. When a sheet is open, in the *View* tab>Sheet Composition panel, click ⊞ (Guide Grid).
2. In the Assign Guide Grid dialog box, select from existing guide grids (as shown in Figure A–22), or create a new one.
3. The guide grid displays. You can change the size and name in Properties, as shown in Figure A–23.

Figure A–22

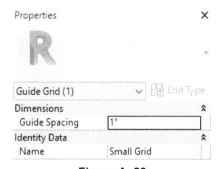

Figure A–23

A.7 Revision Tracking

When a set of working drawings has been put into production, you need to show where changes are made. Typically, these are shown on sheets using revision clouds and tags along with a revision schedule in the title block, as shown in Figure A–24. The revision information is set up in the Sheet Issues/Revisions dialog box.

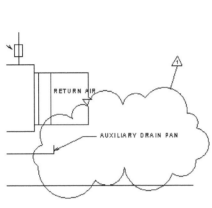

No.	Description	Date
1	Changed drain pan size	5-30-12
2	Added sensor	5-30-12

Figure A–24

- More than one revision cloud can be associated with a revision number.

- The title blocks that come with the Autodesk Revit software already have a revision schedule inserted into the title area. It is recommended that you also add a revision schedule to your company title block.

How To: Add Revision Information to the Project

1. In the *View* tab>Sheet Composition panel, click (Sheet Issues/Revisions).
2. In the Sheet Issues/Revisions dialog box, set the type of *Numbering* you want to use.
3. Click **Add** to add a new revision.

4. Specify the *Date* and *Description* for the revision, as shown in Figure A–25.

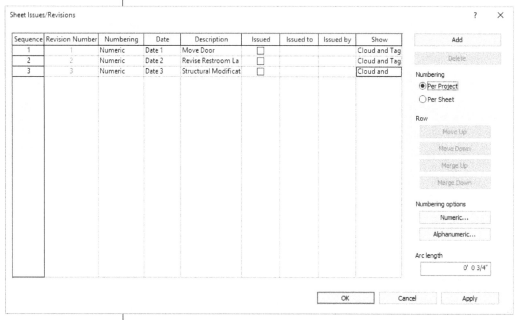

Figure A–25

- Do not modify the *Issued*, *Issued by*, or *Issued to* columns. You should wait to issue revisions until you are ready to print the sheets.

5. Click **OK** when you have finished adding revisions.

- To remove a revision, select its *Sequence* number and click **Delete**.

Revision Options

- *Numbering:* specify **Per Project** (the numbering sequence is used throughout the project) or **Per Sheet** (the number sequence is per sheet).

- *Row*: To reorganize the revisions, select a row and click **Move Up** and **Move Down**, or use **Merge Up** and **Merge Down** to combine the revisions into one.

- *Numbering Options:* Click **Numeric...** or **Alphanumeric...** to bring up the Customize Numbering Options dialog box where you can specify the numbers or letters used in the sequence as well as any prefix or suffix, as shown for the *Alphanumeric* tab in Figure A–26.

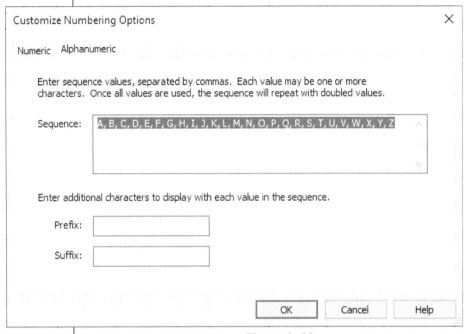

Figure A–26

- *Arc length:* Specify the length of the arcs that form the revision cloud. It is an annotation element and is scaled according to the view scale.

How To: Add Revision Clouds and Tag

1. In the *Annotate* tab>Detail panel, click (Revision Cloud).
2. In the *Modify | Create Revision Cloud Sketch* tab>Draw panel, use the draw tools to create the cloud.

3. From Properties, select which Revision type to use, as shown in Figure A–27.

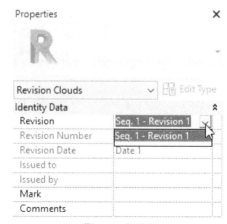

Figure A–27

4. Click ✓ (Finish Edit Mode).
5. To modify a revision cloud, select a revision cloud and, from the Options Bar or Properties, expand the Revision drop-down list and select the revision, as shown in Figure A–28.

If the revision table has not be set up, you can do this at a later date.

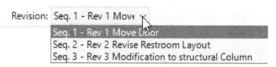

Figure A–28

6. In the *Annotate* tab>Tag panel, click ⌐① (Tag By Category).
7. Select the revision cloud to tag, as shown in Figure A–29. A tooltip containing the revision number and revision from the cloud properties displays when you hover the cursor over the revision cloud.

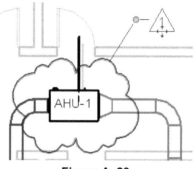

Figure A–29

- If the revision cloud tag is not loaded, load **Revision Tag.rfa** from the *Annotations* folder in the library.

- The *Revision Number* and *Date* are automatically assigned according to the specifications in the revision table.

- Double-click on the edge of revision cloud to switch to the Edit Sketch mode and modify the size or location of the revision cloud arcs.

Issuing Revisions

When you have completed the revisions and are ready to submit new documents to the field, you should first lock the revision for the record. This is called issuing the revision. An issued revision is noted in the tooltip of a revision cloud, as shown in Figure A–30.

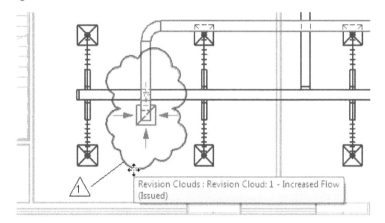

Revision Clouds : Revision Cloud: 1 - Increased Flow (Issued)

Figure A–30

How To: Issue Revisions

1. In the *View* tab>Sheet Composition panel, click ⬚ (Sheet Issues/Revisions).
2. In the Sheet Issues/Revisions dialog box, in the row for the revision that you are issuing, type a name in the *Issued to* and *Issued by* fields, as needed.
3. In the same row, select **Issued**.
4. Continue issuing any other revisions, as needed.
5. Click **OK** to finish.

- Once **Issued** is selected, you cannot modify that revision in the Revisions dialog box or by moving the revision cloud(s). The tooltip on the cloud(s) note that it is **Issued**.

- You can unlock the revision by clearing the **Issued** option. Unlocking enables you to modify the revision after it has been locked.

A.8 Annotating Dependent Views

The **Duplicate as a Dependent** command creates a copy of the view and links it to the selected view. Changes made to the original view are also made in the dependent view and vice-versa. Use dependent views when the building model is so large you need to split the building up on separate sheets, as shown in Figure A–31.

Figure A–31

- Using one overall view with several dependent views makes it easier to see changes, such as *to the scale* or *detail level*.

- Dependent views display in the Project Browser under the top-level view, as shown in Figure A–32.

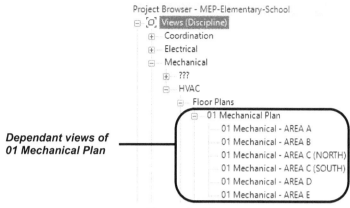

Figure A–32

How To: Duplicate Dependent Views

1. Select the view you want to use as the top-level view.
2. Right-click and select **Duplicate View>Duplicate as a Dependent**.
3. Rename the dependent views as needed.
4. Modify the crop region of the dependent view to show the specified portion of the model.

- If you want to separate a dependent view from the original view, right-click on the dependent view and select **Convert to independent view**.

Annotating Views

To clarify and annotate dependent views, use **Matchlines** and **View References**, as shown in Figure A–33.

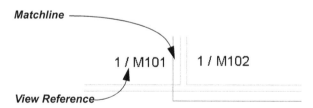

Figure A–33

- Sketch Matchlines in the primary view to specify where dependent views separate. They display in all related views and extend through all levels of the project by default.

- View References are special tags that display the sheet location of the dependent views.

How To: Add Matchlines

1. In the *View* tab>Sheet Composition panel, click

   ▢ (Matchline).
2. In the Draw panel, click ✎ (Line) and sketch the location of the matchline.
3. In the Matchline panel, click ✓ (Finish Edit Mode) when you are finished.
- To modify an existing matchline, select it and click ▧ (Edit Sketch) in the *Modify | Matchline* tab>Mode panel.

- To modify the color and linetype of Matchlines, in the *Manage* tab>Settings panel, click ▦ (Object Styles).

How To: Add View References

1. In the *View* tab>Sheet Composition panel or *Annotate* tab>Tag panel, click ▦ (View Reference).
2. In the *Modify | View Reference* tab>View Reference panel specify the *View Type* and *Target View*, as shown in Figure A–34.

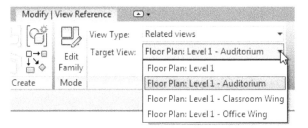

Figure A–34

3. Place the tag on the side of the matchline that corresponds to the target view.

4. Click ▷ (Modify) to clear the selection.
5. Repeat the process and place the tag on the other side of the matchline.
6. The tags display as empty dashes until the views are placed onto sheets. They then update to include the detail and sheet number, as shown in Figure A–35.

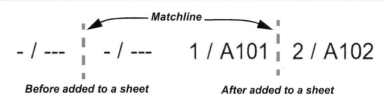

Figure A–35

- Double-click on the view reference to open the associated view.

*The **View Reference.rfa** tag is located in the Annotations folder*

- If only a label named **REF** displays when you place a view reference, it means you need to load and update the tag. In the Type Selector, select one of the view references and, in Properties, click ⊞ (Edit Type). Select the **View Reference** tag in the drop-down list, as shown in Figure A–36.

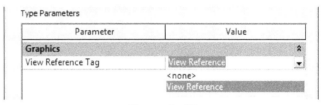

Figure A–36

A.9 Importing and Exporting Schedules

Schedules are views that can be copied into your project from other projects. Only the formatting information is copied; the information about individually scheduled items is not included. That information is automatically added by the project the schedule is copied into. You can also export the schedule information to be used in spreadsheets.

How To: Import Schedules

*If the referenced project contains many types of views, change Views: to **Show schedules and reports only**.*

1. In the *Insert* tab>Import panel, expand 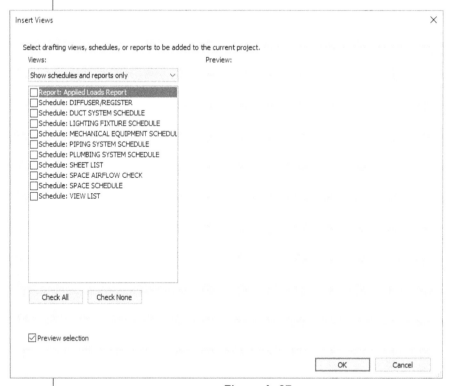 (Insert from File) and click (Insert Views from File).
2. In the Open dialog box, locate the project file containing the schedule you want to use.
3. Select the schedules you want to import, as shown in Figure A–37.

Figure A–37

4. Click **OK**.

How To: Export Schedule Information

1. Switch to the schedule view that you want to export.
2. In the *File* tab, click 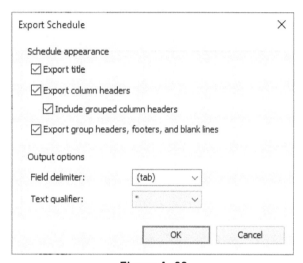 (Export)> (Reports)> (Schedule).
3. Select a location and name for the text file in the Export Schedule dialog box and click **Save**.
4. In the Export Schedule dialog box, set the options in the *Schedule appearance* and *Output options* areas that best suit your spreadsheet software, as shown in Figure A–38.

Figure A–38

5. Click **OK**. A new text file is created that you can open in a spreadsheet, as shown in Figure A–39.

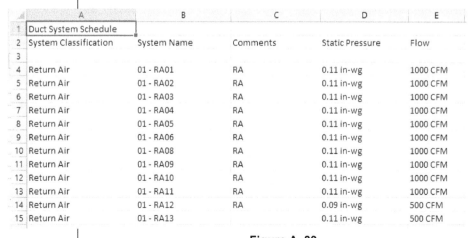

	A	B	C	D	E
1	Duct System Schedule				
2	System Classification	System Name	Comments	Static Pressure	Flow
3					
4	Return Air	01 - RA01	RA	0.11 in-wg	1000 CFM
5	Return Air	01 - RA02	RA	0.11 in-wg	1000 CFM
6	Return Air	01 - RA03	RA	0.11 in-wg	1000 CFM
7	Return Air	01 - RA04	RA	0.11 in-wg	1000 CFM
8	Return Air	01 - RA05	RA	0.11 in-wg	1000 CFM
9	Return Air	01 - RA06	RA	0.11 in-wg	1000 CFM
10	Return Air	01 - RA08	RA	0.11 in-wg	1000 CFM
11	Return Air	01 - RA09	RA	0.11 in-wg	1000 CFM
12	Return Air	01 - RA10	RA	0.11 in-wg	1000 CFM
13	Return Air	01 - RA11	RA	0.11 in-wg	1000 CFM
14	Return Air	01 - RA12	RA	0.09 in-wg	500 CFM
15	Return Air	01 - RA13		0.11 in-wg	500 CFM

Figure A–39

A.10 Creating Building Component Schedules

A Building Component schedule, as shown in Figure A–40, is a table view of the type and instance parameters of a specific element. You can specify the parameters (fields) you want to include in the schedule. All of the parameters found in the type of element you are scheduling are available to use.

Air Terminal Schedule					
Type Mark	Family	Type	Flow	Manufacturer	Model
RD-1	Return Diffuser - Hosted	Workplane-based Retur	500 CFM		
RD-2	Return Diffuser	24 x 24 Face 12 x 12 C	500 CFM		
SD-1	Supply Diffuser - Perforated - R	24x24x10 In Neck	100 CFM	Price	TBD2
SD-1	Supply Diffuser - Perforated - R	24x24x10 In Neck	123 CFM	Price	TBD2
SD-1	Supply Diffuser - Perforated - R	24x24x10 In Neck	124 CFM	Price	TBD2
SD-1	Supply Diffuser - Perforated - R	24x24x10 In Neck	125 CFM	Price	TBD2
SD-1	Supply Diffuser - Perforated - R	24x24x10 In Neck	150 CFM	Price	TBD2
SD-1	Supply Diffuser - Perforated - R	24x24x10 In Neck	760 CFM	Price	TBD2
SD-2	Supply Diffuser - Perforated - R	24x12x6 In Neck	275 CFM		
SD-3	Supply Diffuser - Perforated - R	24x24x12 In Neck	1100 CFM		

Figure A–40

How To: Create a Building Component Schedule

1. In the *View* tab>Create panel, expand ▦ (Schedules) and click ▦ (Schedule/Quantities), or in the Project Browser, right-click on the **Schedule/Quantities** node and select **New Schedule/Quantities**.
2. In the New Schedule dialog box, select a category from the list, as shown in Figure A–41.

In the Filter list drop-down list, you can specify the discipline(s) to show only the categories that you want to display.

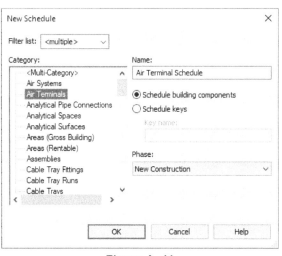

Figure A–41

3. Type a new *Name*, if the default does not suit.
4. Select **Schedule building components**.
5. Specify the *Phase*, as needed.
6. Click **OK**.
7. Fill out the information in the Schedule Properties dialog box, in the *Fields*, *Filter*, *Sorting/Grouping*, *Formatting*, and *Appearance* tabs.
8. Click **OK**. A schedule report is created in its own view.

Fields Tab

In the *Fields* tab, select from a list of available fields and organize them in the order you want them to display in the schedule, as shown in Figure A–42.

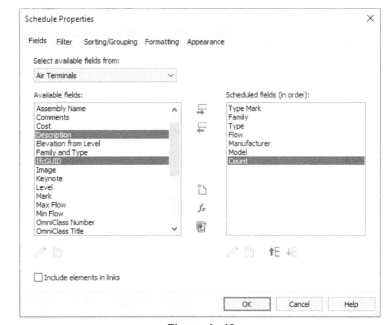

Figure A–42

How To: Fill Out the Fields Tab

1. In the *Available fields* area, select one or more fields you want to add to the schedule and click ⬅ (Add parameter(s)). The field(s) are placed in the *Scheduled fields (in order)* area.
2. Continue adding fields, as needed.

   • Click ⬅ (Remove parameter(s)) to move a field from the *Scheduled fields* area back to the *Available fields* area.

   • Use ↑E (Move parameter up) and ↓E (Move parameter down) to change the order of the scheduled fields.

You can also double-click on a field to move it from the Available fields area to the Scheduled fields area, or double-click on a field to remove it from the Scheduled fields area.

Fields Tab Options

Select available fields from	Select additional category fields for the schedule. The available list of fields depends on the original category of the schedule.
Include elements in links	Enables you to include elements from a linked file in the schedule.
(New parameter)	Adds a new field according to your specification. New fields can be placed by instance or by type.
f_x **(Add Calculated parameter)**	Creates a formula based field made up of other fields.
(Combine parameters)	Combines two or more parameters in one column. You can put any fields together even if they are used in another column.
(Edit parameter)	Enables you to edit custom fields. This is grayed out if you select a standard field.
(Delete parameter)	Deletes selected custom fields. This is grayed out if you select a standard field.

Filter Tab

You can create filters for up to eight values. All values must be satisfied for the elements to display.

In the *Filter* tab, set up filters so that only elements meeting specific criteria are included in the schedule. For example, you might only want to show information for one level, as shown in Figure A–43.

Figure A–43

- The parameter you want to use as a filter must be included in the schedule. You can hide the parameter once you have completed the schedule, if needed.

Filter by	Select the field to filter. Not all fields can be filtered.
Condition	Select the condition that must be met. This includes **equal**, **not equal**, **greater than**, and **less than**.
Value	Select the value of the element to be filtered from a drop-down list of appropriate values. For example, if you set *Filter By* to **Level**, it displays the list of levels in the project.

Sorting/ Grouping Tab

In the *Sorting/Grouping* tab, you can set how you want the information to be sorted, as shown in Figure A–44. For example, you can sort by **Mark** (number) and then by **Type**.

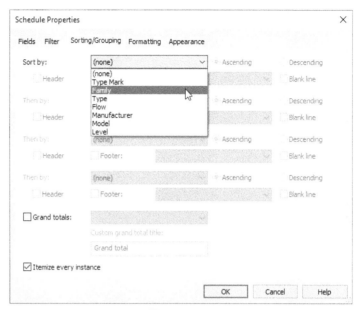

Figure A–44

Sort by	Select the field(s) you want to sort by, up to four levels.
Ascending/ Descending	Sorts fields in **Ascending** or **Descending** order.
Header/ Footer	Group similar information and separate it by a **Header** with a title and/or a **Footer** with quantity information.
Blank line	Adds a blank line between groups.
Grand totals	Select from a list of totals to display and specify a name to display in the schedule for the grand total.
Itemize every instance	If selected, displays each instance of the element in the schedule. If not selected, displays only one instance of each type.

Formatting Tab

In the *Formatting* tab, you can control how the headers of each field display, as shown in Figure A–45.

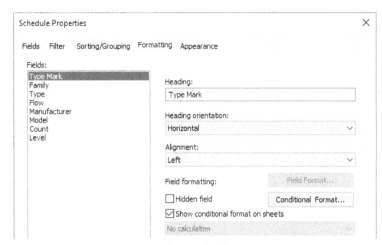

Figure A–45

Fields	Enables you to select the field for which you want to modify the formatting.
Heading	Enables you to change the heading of the field if you want it to be different from the field name. For example, replace **Mark** (a generic name) with the more specific **Door Number** in a door schedule.
Heading orientation	Enables you to set the heading on sheets to **Horizontal** or **Vertical**.
Alignment	Aligns the text in rows under the heading to be **Left**, **Right**, or **Center**.
Field Format...	Sets the units format for the length, area, volume, angle, or number field. By default, this is set to use the project settings.
Conditional Format...	Sets up the schedule to display visual feedback based on the conditions listed.
Hidden field	Enables you to hide a field. For example, you might want to use a field for sorting purposes, but not have it display in the schedule.
Show conditional format on sheets	Select if you want the color code set up in the Conditional Format dialog box to display on sheets.

Calculation options	Select the type of calculation you want to use. All values in a field are:
	• **Standard** - Calculated separately.
	• **Calculate totals** - Added together.
	• **Calculate minimum** - Reviewed and only the smallest amount is displayed.
	• **Calculate maximum** - Reviewed and only the largest amount is displayed.
	• **Calculate minimum and maximum** - Reviewed and both the smallest and largest amounts are displayed.
	• This is often used with rebar sets.

Appearance Tab

In the *Appearance* tab, you can set the text style and grid options for a schedule, as shown in Figure A–46.

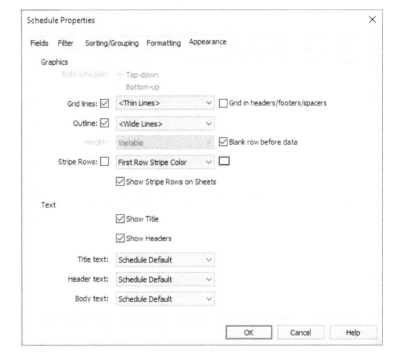

Figure A–46

Grid lines	Displays lines between each instance listed and around the outside of the schedule. Select the style of lines from the drop-down list; this controls all lines for the schedule, unless modified.
Grid in headers/ footers/spacers	Extends the vertical grid lines between the columns.
Outline	Specify a different line type for the outline of the schedule.
Blank row before data	Select this option if you want a blank row to be displayed before the data begins in the schedule.
Stripe Rows	Select this option if you want to highlight alternating rows within the schedule to help differentiate the rows in large schedules.
Show Title/Show Headers	Select these options to include the text in the schedule.
Title text/Header text/Body Text	Select the text style for the title, header, and body text.

Embedded Schedules

When working with schedules that refer to spaces or rooms, you can use embedded schedules. For example, in Figure A–47, a space schedule that is displaying the Space **Number** and **Name**, also has an embedded schedule displaying information about the air terminals in each space.

- This is most frequently used with MEP schedules but also works with any elements that you may want to group by room or space.

A	B
SPACE NO.	NAME
DIFFUSER ID	DIFFUSER TYPE
1501	CLASSROOM
29	Supply Diffuser - Perforated - Round Neck - Ceiling Mounted:
30	Supply Diffuser - Perforated - Round Neck - Ceiling Mounted:
31	Supply Diffuser - Perforated - Round Neck - Ceiling Mounted:
32	Supply Diffuser - Perforated - Round Neck - Ceiling Mounted:
1502	CLASSROOM
45	Supply Diffuser - Perforated - Round Neck - Ceiling Mounted:
46	Supply Diffuser - Perforated - Round Neck - Ceiling Mounted:
47	Supply Diffuser - Perforated - Round Neck - Ceiling Mounted:
48	Supply Diffuser - Perforated - Round Neck - Ceiling Mounted:

Figure A–47

How To: Add an Embedded Schedule

1. Create the base Space or Room schedule.
2. In the Schedule Properties dialog box, select the *Embedded Schedule* tab.
3. Select the **Embedded Schedule** option, and then select a category type from the Category list, as shown in Figure A–48.

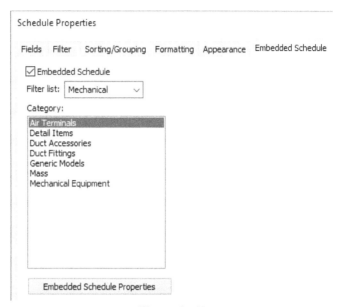

Figure A–48

4. Click **Embedded Schedule Properties**.
5. In the Schedule Properties dialog box, in the *Field* tab, add the required fields and then add filters, sorting, and formatting as required.
6. Click **OK** until the schedule displays. The fields display in sequence, directly under the base schedule columns, as shown in Figure A–49.

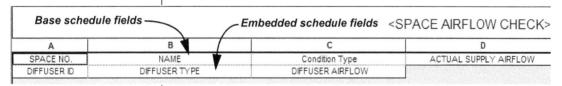

Figure A–49

Schedule Properties

Schedule views have properties including the *View Name*, *Phases* and methods of returning to the Schedule Properties dialog box, as shown in Figure A–50. In the *Other* area, select the button next to the tab that you want to open in the Schedule Properties dialog box. In the dialog box, you can switch from tab to tab and make any required changes to the overall schedule.

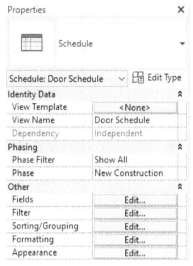

Figure A–50

A.11 Keynoting and Keynote Legends

A keynote is a special kind of tag that applies specific numbers to various elements in a detail. Keynotes can be used on all model and detail elements, as well as materials.Using keynotes requires less room on a view than standard text notes, as shown in Figure A–51. The full explanation of the note is shown in a corresponding *keynote legend* placed elsewhere in the sheet or sheet set.

By default, the Autodesk Revit software uses the CSI master format system of keynote designations.

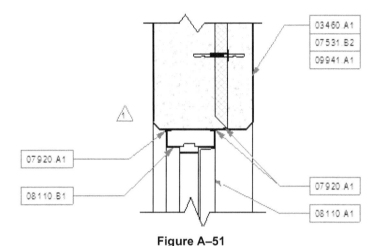

Figure A–51

- Keynote tags are found in the library in the *Annotations* folder and should be loaded into a project before you can apply them.

There are three types of keynote tags:

- **Element:** Used to tag elements, such as a door, wall, or detail components.

- **Material:** Used for the material assigned to a component or applied onto a surface.

- **User:** A keynote that must first be developed in a keynote table.

- Keynotes are stored in a keynote table (a text file), as shown in Figure A–52. Any updates made to the keynote table are reflected in the project after it is closed and then re-opened.

Figure A–52

How To: Place a Keynote

1. In the *Annotate* tab>Tag panel, expand (Keynote) and click (Element Keynote), (Material Keynote), or (User Keynote).
2. Move the cursor over the element you want to keynote and select it.
3. If an element has keynote information assigned to it, the keynote is automatically applied. If it is not assigned, the Keynotes dialog box opens, as shown in Figure A–53.

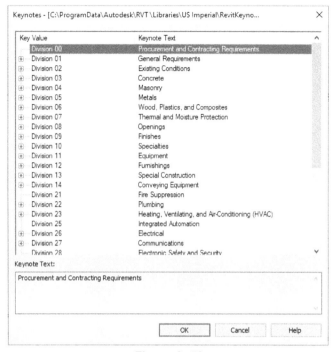

Figure A–53

4. Select the keynote you need from the list of divisions and click **OK**.

• The options for keynotes are the same as for other tags, including orientation and leaders, as shown in Figure A–54.

The keynote remembers the leader settings from the last time it was used.

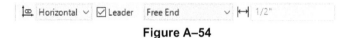

Figure A–54

Hint: Setting the Keynote Numbering Method

Keynotes can be listed by the full keynote number or by sheet, as shown in Figure A–55. Only one method can be used at a time in a project, but you can change between the two methods at any time in the project.

By Keynote   By Sheet

Figure A–55

1. In the *Annotate* tab>Tag panel, expand ⌐¹ (Keynote) and click ✎ (Keynoting Settings).
2. In the Keynoting Settings dialog box, specify the *Keynote Table* information and the *Numbering Method*, as shown in Figure A–56.

Figure A–56

- If you are using keynoting by sheet, create the Keynote Legend and in the Keynote Legend Properties, in the *Filter* tab, select **Filter by Sheet.**

Keynote Legends

A keynote legend is different from a standard legend.

A keynote legend is a table containing the information stored in the keynote that is placed on a sheet, as shown in Figure A–57. In the Autodesk Revit software, it is created in a similar way to schedules.

<Keynote Legend>	
A	**B**
Key Value	Keynote Text
11200	Water Supply and Treatment Equipment
15400	Plumbing Fixtures and Equipment
16200	Electrical Power

Figure A–57

How To: Create a Keynote Legend

1. In the *View* tab>Create panel, expand 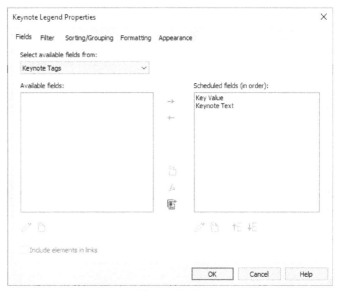 (Legends) and click (Keynote Legend).
2. Type a name in the New Keynote Legend dialog box and click **OK**.
3. The Keynote Legend Properties dialog box typically only displays two scheduled fields, which are already set up for you, as shown in Figure A–58.

Figure A–58

4. In the other tabs, set up the format of the table as required.
5. Click **OK** to create the keynote legend.
6. When you are ready to place a keynote legend, drag it from the Project Browser onto the sheet. You can manipulate it in the same way, similar to modifying other schedules.

- As you add keynotes to the project, they are added to the keynote legend.

Command Summary

Button	Command	Location
Annotations		
	Element Keynote	• **Ribbon:** *Annotate* tab>Tag panel, expand Keynote
	Material Keynote	• **Ribbon:** *Annotate* tab>Tag panel, expand Keynote
	User Keynote	• **Ribbon:** *Annotate* tab>Tag panel, expand Keynote
	Matchline	• **Ribbon:** *View* tab>Sheet Composition panel
	View Reference	• **Ribbon:** *View* tab>Sheet Composition panel or *Annotate* tab>Tag panel
MEP Tools		
	Building/Space and Type Settings	• **Ribbon:** *Manage* tab>Settings panel, expand MEP Settings. • **Ribbon:** *Analyze* tab> Reports and Schedules panel title
	Duct Pressure Loss Report	• **Ribbon:** *Analyze* tab>Reports & Schedules panel
	Pipe Pressure Loss Report	• **Ribbon:** *Analyze* tab>Reports & Schedules panel
Revisions		
	Revision Cloud	• **Ribbon:** *Annotate* tab>Detail panel
	Sheet Issues/ Revisions	• **Ribbon:** *Manage* tab>Settings panel> expand Additional Settings
Schedules		
	Insert Views from File	• **Ribbon:** *Insert* tab>expand **Insert from File**
n/a	**Schedule (Export)**	• **Ribbon:** *File* tab>expand Export> Reports>Schedule
	Schedule/ Quantities	• **Ribbon:** *View* tab>Create panel> expand Schedules • **Project Browser:** right-click on Schedule/Quantities node>New Schedule/Quantities...

Index

CPSIA information can be obtained
at www.ICGtesting.com
Printed in the USA
LVHW111253130122
708513LV00015B/134